THE BIRDS OF SUSSEX
Their Present Status

THE BIRDS OF SUSSEX

THEIR PRESENT STATUS

MICHAEL
SHRUBB

PHILLIMORE

1979

Published by
PHILLIMORE & CO. LTD.
London and Chichester
Head Office: Shopwyke Hall,
Chichester, Sussex, England

ISBN 0 85033 326 1

Printed in Great Britain by
UNWIN BROTHERS LIMITED
at The Gresham Press, Old Woking, Surrey
and bound by
THE NEWDIGATE PRESS LTD.
at Book House, Dorking, Surrey

CONTENTS

LIST OF PLATES
(Between pages 48 and 49)

Coastal Marshes
1. Thorney Deeps
2. Pagham Harbour at half tide

High Wealden Woodland
3. Darwell Wood
4. Darwell Wood: open oak woodland

Downland Woodland
5. Damp coppice near Arundel
6. Downland plantations at West Dean woods

Modern Heathland 'Management'
7. Casual burn in Ashdown Forest
8. After two years

Wet Grassland
9. Amberley Wildbrooks in winter
10. The S.O.S's. flood scheme in Glynde Levels

Gravel Pits at Chichester
11. Gravel handling plant
12. Wildfowl habitat

Changes on the Downs
13. Barley is the dominant crop
14. The Slype photographed after Second World War
15. The Slype in 1977

Lullington Heath and its Environs
16. From the south-west, April 1954
17. From the south-west, 1978
18. View south-west, April 1954
19. View south-west, 1978

LIST OF FIGURES

ACKNOWLEDGEMENTS

It is impossible to produce a book like this single-handed, and I must acknowledge the help and advice of many people in its preparation.

First I must thank my wife for many hours' meticulous and accurate help in typing, checking and proof-reading, perhaps the least exciting but one of the most necessary parts of producing work of this kind.

Then a number of leading Sussex ornithologists have provided help. Here I must first thank R. D. M. Edgar for preparing the sections on bird habitats, without which the book would be incomplete. The text figures and maps for his part were drawn by M. J. Helps, and T. W. Parmenter took and processed many of the accompanying photographs; others were supplied by D. H. Harvey and B. Darby. D. H. Harvey also read and commented on the habitat sections. Both Robert Edgar and I are most grateful for these people's help.

I am also particularly grateful to Dr. M. Hollings for carrying out a detailed analysis of the results of the Woodland Survey, the figures from which are published for the first time, and to S. W. M. Hughes and W. Merritt for much advice on species they have particularly studied or surveyed, and for allowing me to use maps and tables from their published papers. Then I must thank A. R. Kitson and R. J. Sandison for some of the original species' analysis as long ago as 1970, and John Reaney for his splendid cover design.

Finally, I must thank the Council of the Sussex Ornithological Society for unlimited access to their files, which cannot always have been convenient to other workers, and the Society's members and other bird-watchers in the county for the records they have contributed to this system and often answers to my questions. The help of all these people has been invaluable.

INTRODUCTION

THIS IS THE third book on the birds of Sussex to appear in about 40 years. Changes in the countryside and the status of our birds now occur frequently, providing a sound reason for revising county avifaunas more often than is usual. Many counties have active ornithological societies, which accumulate a great store of records and information which is unlikely to see daylight unless produced in this form. At least this is so in Sussex where, since its formation in 1962, the Sussex Ornithological Society has organised a series of population studies and encouraged the growth of ornithological activity in the county. Doing so has produced a mass of detailed information not previously available, and I feel very strongly that for so much information to remain unpublished forms a sad waste of effort and enthusiasm. In addition, I believe that this present book should complement Walpole-Bond's *History of Sussex Birds* and des Forges and Harber's *Guide to the Birds of Sussex,* since I have dealt primarily with populations, a subject of much greater concern to the present generation of ornithologists than to our predecessors. Walpole-Bond by contrast concentrated very largely on breeding biology, and des Forges and Harber on migration. Without doubt each of these works reflected the main ornithological concern of its generation.

The Period Covered and the Records Used

Since des Forges and Harber brought the available information up to date to 1961, I have dealt very largely with the years 1962 to 1976 inclusive, and for waders and wildfowl up to early 1974. With most species I have summarised the position described by des Forges and Harber to provide necessary historical background. Sometimes, however, I have gone back to Walpole-Bond or have found that the sheer volume of information available to me has led me to revise the status given in former works.

I have not thought it necessary to repeat the thorough historical research carried out by Walpole-Bond for *History of Sussex Birds,* which was brought up to date by des Forges and Harber. I have therefore adopted the latters' *Guide* as a basic definitive list of Sussex birds, and, for records up to 1961, have deviated from it only by deleting the now rejected record of Audubon's Shearwater in 1936, and including the Rufous Bushchat at the Wicks on 12 September 1951, which is included in the B.O.U.'s most recent checklist as a Kent/Sussex record. From 1962 I have used the records accepted for the Sussex Ornithological Society by D. D. Harber until 1965, and by the Society's records committee from 1966. For records coming under the scrutiny of *British Birds* Rarities Committee, the Society's rules state that they must be accepted by *British Birds* before it will use them; but this does not mean that we always accept those records sent to *British Birds* but not to us. The Society maintains an extensive filing system for records sent to it for the Sussex Bird Report. The amount of information supplied by observers to this sytem increases annually and, together with the results of systematic studies listed under ornithological activities, it has provided the main basis of the present systematic list.

This list covers 343 species, 83 residents, 85 summer visitors and passage migrants, 59 winter visitors, 116 scarce visitors, vagrants and extreme rarities. Of these the status of 106 species has certainly or most probably changed in the past 20 years, and 24 species have been added to the Sussex list since 1961.

The Area Covered

The area covered by this book comprises the administrative counties of East and West Sussex, together with that part of Chichester Harbour which lies in the administrative county of Hampshire, which is now treated as Sussex territory for ornithological recording. Ornithologists in Sussex are fortunate in that the recent reorganisation of county boundaries has made only small territorial alterations to their county and none of ornithological significance, so that continuity is unaffected and records remain comparable. It should be noted that few references to East or West Sussex as separate units will be found in the literature; to the naturalist the whole area is simply Sussex, as it remains to the true native.

I have not included a locality map. Most of the places mentioned in the text are readily found on the 1:50,000 Ordnance Survey maps of which sheets 186, 187, 188, 189, 197, 198 and 199 cover Sussex. The S.O.S. records normally include map references from these for the more important records, particularly survey results. In these circumstances the limited map possible here seems superfluous.

Recent Ornithological Activities in Sussex

Besides gathering general records, the Sussex Ornithological Society has organised or contributed to a number of studies since 1962. These were:

Breeding surveys. Studies of the breeding populations of individual species covered Great Crested Grebe, Kestrel, Water Rail, Redshank, Snipe, Stone Curlew, Herring Gull, Collared Dove, Nightjar, Swift, Woodlark, House Martin, Tree Pipit, Rock Pipit, Yellow Wagtail, Grey Wagtail, Stonechat, Wheatear, Redstart, Nightingale, Cirl Bunting, and Rook.

An attempt was made from 1963 to 1974 to make a quantative survey of our woodland birds. This is described on page 17, and, although only partially successful, has provided much useful information which would otherwise not be available. Much information was also gathered about raptore and owl populations from 1966 to 1968. In addition the Society has contributed to national breeding bird censuses. Perhaps the most important of these have been the long-standing Heron census, Operation Seafarer in 1969, covering all our breeding sea-birds, and the B.T.O. Atlas scheme. Individual species surveys have included Great Crested Grebe, Ringed Plover, and Little Tern. Detailed reports of many of these studies have been published, for which see page 336.

Winter surveys. From December 1963 to May 1976 regular counts of waders in Chichester and Pagham Harbours have been organised. In 1966 these counts were expanded to include all estuarine birds. The results of the wader counts are summarised here for the first time, with histograms for the main species. Latterly these counts have been made as part of the National Estuaries Enquiry. National Wildfowl Counts have long been organised in the county and all the main wildfowl localities are covered.

Migration studies. Two migration watching stations have operated in Sussex since 1959, at Selsey Bill from spring 1959 to autumn 1970, and at Beachy Head from 1960 to the present. At Selsey Bill the main emphasis was on the detailed recording of the visible migration of passerines and sea birds; very little ringing was done. Beachy Head is run as an observatory, with a regular ringing station and daily totals of migrants recorded. In addition sea-watching has been an important activity since 1965 and, in the autumn, much time is devoted to observing the interesting raptore passage which occurs. The strong emphasis on sea-watching at both these stations has recorded much new information on sea-bird passage off Sussex and has led to important revisions of status for some species. In its 16 years of operation Beachy Head has also added 12 species to the Sussex list. Finally in this field the Chichester Ringing Group, operating at Chichester gravel pits, has particularly concentrated on the ringing and study of Sand Martins and *Acrocephalus* warblers.

The Order of Species

Although it is the policy of the Sussex Ornithological Society to continue to use the Wetmore order in the Sussex Bird Report for administrative convenience, I have adopted the new B.O.U. checklist order for this book.

Treatment of Species

As far as possible I have treated each species in a consistent way. After the species name there is a brief summary of status and any changes. This is to some extent subjective, but such terms as 'common' or 'scarce' are defined in the text and a quick checklist is useful. For each species I have then summarised previous accounts, usually des Forges and Harber's, followed by a description of the breeding and winter position and movements as relevant, usually in that order. For species recorded five times or fewer all records are given. Otherwise records of rare birds are summarised. In all cases I have tried to use actual numbers or estimates recorded to define status.

In describing breeding status I have used pairs per 2,500 acres, taken to equal 10 square kilometres, as a standard unit of population density wherever possible, translating the counts of defined areas we have into this measurement. The Ordnance Survey Grid is based on kilometre squares, so this unit should be simple to use; 10 square kilometres in fact equals 2,471 acres. All areas have been measured on the Ordnance Survey maps. For some species I have tried to indicate the present level of breeding success, but where this is based on casual observations of fledged broods it may be of limited value.

I have made extensive use of tables and histograms, as this is an economical way of presenting large numbers of records. For many short tables designed to show quickly and clearly the present pattern of occurrence, I have used the device of monthly totals. **With these it is important to note that the figures represent the total numbers of birds recorded in each month, and if a bird stays two or more months, it is recorded for each.** Thus the sum of the monthly totals is not the grand total of birds recorded; this is shown separately where required. Tables are arranged in the most appropriate chronological order. Spans of years, e.g., 1963-1969, are invariably inclusive.

In general I have confined notes on subspecies to those which are fairly readily recognised in the field, and I have followed the national practice of noting that these records are of birds showing the characters of the race.

Finally it is probably necessary to define the following terms:

Resident—A bird which is present throughout the year.

Winter visitor—A bird which lives in the county for an extended period during November to February.

Passage migrant—A bird which passes through the county on migration.

Through passage—Movement by passage migrants.

Summer visitor—A bird which lives in the county for an extended period during May to August.

Non-breeding—Resident in the breeding season without breeding.

Partial migrant—A largely resident species, of which part of the population migrates after the breeding season.

Visitor—A bird which visits the county but for which the records make no clear pattern of behaviour.

Vagrant—A rarity to the county, which has occured more than five times.

The Hastings Rarities

Although these records are no longer accepted by the British or Sussex Lists, I have decided that they must be mentioned in any book on Sussex birds. They still stand in such standard works as Walpole-Bond, *The Handbook of British Birds,* and D. A. Bannerman's *Birds of the British Isles,* where they will be found by many newcomers to ornithology who may wish to know why they are no longer accepted. In the references, therefore, I include a short list of sources where a full list of these records may be found, and the main arguments for and against them at present elucidated are set out.

PART ONE
BIRD HABITATS IN SUSSEX

GEOLOGY AND LAND USE

By R. D. M. Edgar

ALTHOUGH THE landscape of Sussex has been substantially modified by man, the basic geology and soil types still have an important bearing on the vegetation and crops, and hence the habitats available for birds now found in the county.

Most of Sussex, except the coastal plain to the south of Chichester, lies within the central southern portion of the geological unit known as the Weald. This extends westwards into Hampshire and Wiltshire, north and east into Surrey and Kent, and south-east under the Channel into northern France. The Weald is an approximate oval with its long axis running west-north-west to south-east, measuring 140km. by 65km. The whole was created beneath the sea and laid down as a series of overlying strata which emerged as an elevated dome, the cap being subsequently removed by erosion. The strata are now much folded and appear on the surface as a series of concentric circles. The oldest rocks are in the central part, the youngest on the periphery. In descending order of deposition (i.e., from the outside towards the centre) the succession is as follows:

a	Chalk	d	Lower Greensand
b	Upper Greensand	e	Weald Clay
c	Gault	f	Hastings Beds

The Hastings Beds are further sub-divided, again in descending order, into:

Tunbridge Wells Sands
Wadhurst Clay
Ashdown Sands

Fig. 1 (p. 2) shows how these strata occur in Sussex and they are discussed in more detail under the headings which follow.

1

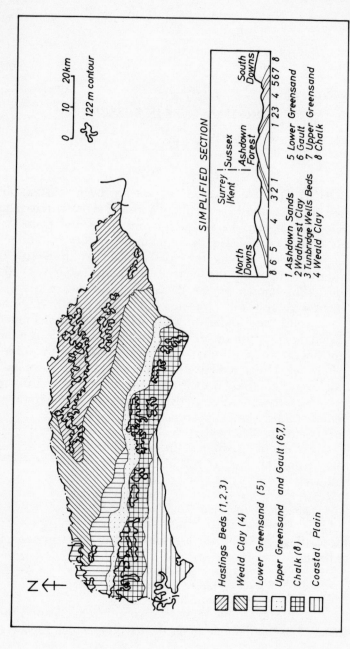

Fig. 1. Simplified geology of Sussex

Chalk

The South Downs emerge from the sea in the south of the county as a wave-washed platform from which rise the cliffs from Brighton to Beachy Head, at 236 metres the highest chalk cliff in Britain. From Beachy Head west to the Hampshire boundary their total length is 93km. and the greatest width 9km. They are divided by four south-flowing rivers, the Arun, Adur, Ouse and Cuckmere, and are characteristically rolling or whale-backed in outline. The entire north face is a very steep scarp which reaches in places to a height of over 240 metres, but to the south is a more gentle dip slope towards the sea.

A distinctive feature of the Downs are the coombes or dry valleys formed through erosion by water derived from the thawing of frozen land at the time of the last Ice Age. Many of these coombes have thick deposits of sand and clay at their bases and woodland has often been allowed to develop here. Generally, however, the soils are thin and very infertile. In places the Downs are capped by clays supporting beech woods and sand supporting vegetation known as chalk heath, a mixture of species characteristic of both basic and acidic soils.

The Downs were one of the first areas of Sussex to be colonised by man and were probably quickly cleared of their original vegetation of scrubby woodland. Most woodland is now found west of the River Arun, the downs further east being notably lacking in tree cover except for a few extensive forestry plantations, which now form a high proportion of all downland woodland. With the lack of grazing pressure much of the scarp slope has developed scrub and is slowly reverting to woodland. Grassland persists mainly on slopes that are too steep to be ploughed, but much of the downland is now under arable cultivation. These changes in agricultural practice are discussed in the section on Farmland.

Upper Greensand and Gault Clay

At the foot of the scarp slope of the Downs are the two formations of the Upper Greensand and Gault Clay; both are very narrow, and the first is largely buried beneath the Chalk.

The Gault Clay gives rise to very heavy soils which are often waterlogged, and is primarily an area of woodland and grass-land, cultivation being difficult.

Lower Greensand

The Lower Greensand forms a narrow ridge of some impor-tance, particularly in the west of the county where it is up to 10km. wide. The coarse sand produces soils which are very free-draining, and this zone includes one of the most important arable farming areas of the county. Ornithologically important heaths occur on this formation, although many are declining in interest through lack of management and development of forestry plantations.

Weald Clay

Within the band of Lower Greensand is the low-lying Weald Clay, producing a flatter landscape up to 30km. wide with heavy soils and little natural drainage. These soils are often cold and waterlogged and traditionally this is an area of deciduous woodland with small pasture fields. Greater agri-cultural mechanisation has led to considerable modification of this landscape and larger arable fields now occur in the area. This area is known as the Low Weald, and at the coast between Eastbourne and Bexhill the Weald Clay is covered by alluvium to form the extensive Pevensey levels.

Hastings Beds

The northern part of the county comprises the High Weald, consisting of a succession of clays and sandstones (Tunbridge Wells Sands, Wadhurst Clay, and Ashdown Sands) that have eroded differentially, giving a very dissected appearance. Small streams have deeply incised the sands to form steep-sided valleys and well-wooded slopes known as ghylls. Much of this land consists of small hilly grass fields divided by strips of woodland called shaws, intermixed with larger areas of wood-land. Within the main outcrop of Ashdown Sand lies Ashdown

Forest, a large tract of open heathland, reaching in places a height of nearly 220 metres, and surrounded by extensive woods.

The Hastings Beds emerge on the coast as a broken line of cliffs east of Hastings to Cliff End. Here the ghyll valleys with their woods reach the cliff edge.

Alluvium

The most recent of all the deposits of Sussex are the alluvial soils. Principally these occur on Pevensey Levels, part of the Low Weald, and on that part of Romney Marsh that lies within Sussex to the east of Rye. All the Sussex rivers are bordered by alluvium, in some places in quantity, as shown on Fig. 4 (p. 31). The Glynde and Adur Levels and Amberley/Pulborough Marshes along the River Arun are probably the most ornithologically important of the river levels today, but all these areas are increasingly threatened by drainage schemes.

Coastal Plain

In West Sussex an extensive low-lying, flat plain runs between the Downs and the sea. Despite considerable urban development, particularly on the coast, most of this plain is agricultural land of the highest quality and intensively cultivated. It is principally an area of London Clay with Brick Earths, a structureless loam to which the district owes much of its fertility. There is little remaining woodland, but the area is well known for the ornithologically important areas of Chichester and Pagham Harbours. Associated with both these harbours, and in fact reclaimed from them, are small but important areas of wet grassland, such as Sidlesham Ferry and around Thorney Deeps. Around Chichester there is an area of gravel and gravel pits of considerable economic importance.

Land Use

Fig. 2 (p. 6) shows the major land uses in Sussex at the moment. The most significant change in terms of land use,

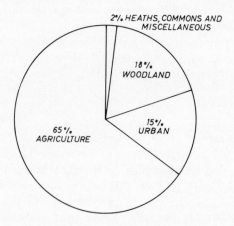

Fig. 2. Major land uses in Sussex

in recent times, has been the increase in the proportion of urban areas at the expense, principally, of agricultural land. The largest urban areas are concentrated along the coast and major expansion is taking place inland at Burgess Hill, Crawley, Crowborough, Horsham, and north of Hastings. There are no major heavy industries, but light manufacturing and service industries have become increasingly important, and the large leisure and tourist industry has considerable consequences for bird habitats. Agriculture is the major industry of the county in terms of land use, nearly two-thirds of the county's land being devoted to agricultural production. The heaths and commons are mainly small and fragmented except for the large area of Ashdown Forest. Of particular interest is the extent of woodland cover, mainly concentrated in the High and Low Weald, this being one of the most heavily wooded areas in England. It seems likely that changes in woodland management, the development of agriculture and the leisure and tourist industries will be the major factors affecting bird distribution in Sussex in the future.

The following sections deal in some detail with these land uses and their relevance to the distribution of birds in Sussex.

COASTLAND

By R. D. M. Edgar

SUSSEX HAS A coastline of 140km. (not including the indentations of the harbours) of which 60 per cent. is covered by built-up areas, earning the county the unenviable distinction of having one of the most developed coastlines in Britain. Indeed from Pagham eastward to Brighton the development is almost continuous, apart from the river mouths and a 5km. strip west of Littlehampton. In terms of habitats frequented by birds (apart from the urban areas) the coastlands can be divided into cliffs, estuaries, river mouths and tidal flats, shingle and dune areas, and coastal levels. The latter are considered in the section on Freshwater Habitats, since their ornithological interest does not arise primarily from their geographical proximity to the coast. The open sea is also an important habitat.

Cliffs

Two types of coastal cliff are found: the 15km. of chalk cliffs from Black Rock, Brighton, to Beachy Head, and the 8km. of sand and clay cliffs east of Hastings to Cliff End, Pett. Neither formation provides ledges of any size or permanence, although small auk populations once nested on the chalk cliffs. The chalk cliffs are mainly sheer with little vegetation, but the sandstone cliffs are more tumbled with an undercliff structure, and in places of sufficient stability to have allowed vegetation to form. All these cliffs erode rapidly, retreating at a rate of up to 1.86 metres per year. Large single falls are less common on the sandstone cliffs than on the chalk, the former tending to slump and yet recede the fastest.

7

The birds regularly recorded nesting on these cliffs are the Kestrel, Herring Gull, Jackdaw, Rock Pipit, Starling, House Sparrow and Stock Dove. Lesser Black-backed Gulls nest on the cliffs periodically, as do Black Redstarts. Fulmars have bred and have been present since at least the early 1950s. House Martins have been recorded nesting on the cliffs occasionally. Cormorants no longer breed, and the Raven has not nested since 1895, apart from a pair, one bird at least of which was an escaped pet, which nested between 1938 and 1945. The Peregrine Falcon has not bred since 1957, although the chalk cliffs once held one of the highest densities of breeding pairs in Britain. The cliff-nesting Kestrel population had probably declined by the late 1940s, and certainly did so after 1951. A reduction in suitable nest sites has been suggested as a possible cause, and a breeding survey of cliff-nesting Herring Gulls and Rock Pipits conducted in 1965 tends to confirm this idea. This survey showed three pairs of Rock Pipits nesting in the cliffs east of Hastings, and 42 pairs on the chalk cliffs. Although no Herring Gulls were reported nesting on the Hastings cliffs up to 1935, a total of 371 pairs did so in 1965 compared with 395 pairs on the chalk cliffs. However, Walpole-Bond in 1938 recorded 'perhaps as many as 2,000 couples' of Herring Gulls between Seaford and Beachy Head alone and, since it is doubtful whether there are suitable sites for this number at present, a change in cliff structure along the chalk is very likely. Probably some of these birds moved east to the sandstone cliffs.

Tidal Basins and Mudflats, Estuaries and Saltings

Tidal mudflats occur at the mouths of nearly all Sussex rivers, along the coast principally at Pevensey Bay and from Pett to Rye Bay, and most notably in the tidal basins of Pagham and Chichester Harbours. Chichester Harbour straddles the county boundary with Hampshire and the harbours of Langstone and Portsmouth (also Hampshire) are a part of the same ecological and physical unit. Chichester Harbour alone has some 1,298 hectares of mudflats, 164 hectares of sand, 611 hectares of *Spartina* marsh, and 42 hectares of saltmarsh. For

reasons of simplicity (and ornithological necessity) the whole
of Chichester Harbour is considered as being within Sussex
for the purpose of wildfowl and wader counts.

Breeding bird species of these largely intertidal habitats
are, not surprisingly, few, although some, particularly Redshank
and Meadow Pipit, nest on the drier parts of the saltings with a
few Lapwings. A sizeable gull and tern colony exists on islands
in Chichester Harbour. The most important species nesting in
close association with tidal areas is the Shelduck which nests
around Chichester and Pagham Harbours, near the Cuckmere
River, at Pett Level and in the Rye area. No full census of the
breeding numbers of this species has been carried out recently,
but there are probably some 100 to 150 pairs.

The habitats dealt with here are primarily of importance
for the numbers of wildfowl and waders present during the
winter months and at times of passage. Detailed counts have
been conducted during these periods in Chichester and Pagham
Harbours since 1964, once each winter for waders along the
whole coastline from 1964 to 1969/70, and twice each winter
from 1971/72 onwards. Detailed results are given under
individual species in the Systematic List and the numbers are
very large. Since 1971 Chichester Harbour has been shown
to hold an annual winter peak of between 27,000 and 38,000
waders and 8,000 to 13,000 wildfowl. Pagham Harbour holds
4,000 to 7,000 waders and approximately 1,500 wildfowl.
The entire Sussex coast including these Harbours holds between
35,000 and 57,000 waders, the numbers varying annually,
perhaps mainly affected by the severity or otherwise of the
winter. The populations of some species are particularly
important. In 1975/76 Chichester Harbour held internationally
important populations of Brent Goose, Shelduck, Ringed
Plover, Grey Plover, Black-tailed Godwit, Dunlin, and Sanderling, that is, the population of each was more than one per cent.
of the West European wintering total. Pagham Harbour also
held internationally important numbers of Grey Plover, and
the county as a whole attracted 7.25 per cent. of the West
European population of this species in addition to 3.8 per
cent. of its Ringed Plover, 3.9 per cent. of its Sanderling, and
2.2 per cent. of its Dunlin. These figures emphasise the impor-

tance of protecting these coastal habitats.

The saltings also provide winter feeding areas for flocks of finches and pipits, although the numbers are not large compared with the winter finch flocks of downland and shingle beaches. Twite, however, are largely confined to saltings and the maximum number in recent years has been 335.

Sand and Shingle

Sand dunes and beaches are few in Sussex. Dunes occur in the west of the county at East Head, to the west of the mouth of the River Arun at Climping, and in the east of the county at Camber. Dunes are much disturbed in summer and of comparatively little ornithological value, much of the large dune system at Camber being occupied by a golf course. Sandflats are found in the centre of Chichester Harbour, off Littlehampton, Worthing, Goring and Ferring, and at Camber in the east of the county. All support wintering Sanderling, the population usually totalling less than 500 birds, with a peak of 825 in 1973. The only species notably associated with the sand dunes, and adjacent saltings, is the Snow Bunting; the Camber area is the only regular wintering site in Sussex, flocks of 30 to 50 birds being quite usual.

Shingle is more widely distributed than sand, there being shingle islands in Chichester and Pagham Harbours and shingle beaches along much of the rest of the coast. Long stretches of these beaches front seaside towns and are now of little ornithological interest; the most important are around the Selsey peninsular, particularly on both sides of the entrance to Pagham Harbour, Shoreham Beach, between Newhaven and Seaford (the Tidemills), at the mouth of the Cuckmere River, to the east of Eastbourne (the Crumbles), bordering Pevensey Levels, at Rye Harbour, and further east at the county boundary. Even these are much disturbed by large numbers of tourists in the summer, those at Shoreham Beach, the mouth of the Cuckmere and Pevensey Bay particularly so. The Tidemills and Crumbles are both used by industry, the former in the process of being converted to a lorry park, and the latter to provide housing and recreational areas. The beaches at

Pagham and Rye Harbours lie within Local Nature Reserves and receive a measure of protection. Despite these problems the beaches still support a few breeding birds, notably Little Tern, Ringed Plover, Oystercatcher, and Wheatear. The open shingle beaches also support a small winter population of waders, mainly Turnstone, with a few Purple Sandpipers and numbers may increase in really cold weather. Some of the less trampled beaches have an interesting flora, the seeds of which now provide a food supply for some of the largest wintering finch flocks still be be found in the county.

Open Sea

The sea off Sussex is shallow; only off the chalk cliffs and at Fairlight does the five-fathom line come nearer than one kilometre from the shore, and along most of the county it is three or more kilometres out from the shore. Except in very calm and clear conditions flocks of birds are not easy to detect on the sea at any distance, and this, coupled with the shallowness of the water which may enable birds to feed well out to sea, probably results in many species being under recorded. Even so, the sea is known to be an important habitat supporting in winter flocks of diving ducks, mainly Common Scoter, Eider and Red-breasted Merganser; grebes, mainly Great Crested and Slavonian; a few divers and auks, and considerable numbers of gulls. In addition sizeable flocks of dabbling ducks, mainly Mallard and Wigeon, feed inland by night and rest on the open sea by day.

These birds are not evenly distributed along the coast. For example, scoter are mainly confined to East Sussex and mergansers to West Sussex, and most dabbling ducks are noted in Rye Bay, off Cuckmere Haven, and the Church Norton/Selsey area. Rye Bay is the most important locality for sea-ducks and divers, most Slavonian Grebes are found off Church Norton, mergansers off the Worthing area, and Great Crested Grebes off Brighton/Rottingdean and in Rye Bay. These variations presumably reflect the nature of the sea-bed and availability of food. All these species have been affected by oil pollution which, while not always severe, is nearly always present and may have caused marked declines of some species in recent years.

During migration considerable numbers of divers, ducks, geese, waders, skuas, gulls, and terns pass through the Channel off Sussex, and some will rest and feed; terns also summer in varying numbers. Gulls are present throughout the year although the populations have been poorly studied. There are known to be sizeable roosts at Chichester and Pagham Harbours, Shoreham, Rottingdean, Hastings, and at Camber, besides the many birds which feed along the whole shore. Being scavengers gulls have quickly exploited the possibilities of urban areas where they may now be more numerous than along the open shore.

WOODLAND

By R. D. M. Edgar

THE NATURAL CLIMAX vegetation of Southern Britain is deciduous woodland, and as late as 731 A.D. the Venerable Bede described the Wealden Forest as being 'thick and impenetrable'. Although the South Downs were cleared at a very early stage in man's history in Britain, the clearing of the Wealden forest was delayed until the medieval period, the height of the clearance being in the 13th and 14th centuries, although parts may have been cleared as early as the ninth century. The early clearances were made to form agricultural settlements, but by the 13th century the production of charcoal, used in the making of iron, became very significant. In later centuries the rate of clearance may have slowed, and in the 17th and 18th centuries a great deal of replanting was carried out in the formation of the large parklands. The process of both clearance and replanting continues today, although different tree species are often involved. It is unlikely that any of the Sussex woodlands remain in a natural state, although some areas may have a continuously wooded history. This is particularly likely for some of the Low Weald oak woodlands and the shaws, which may be remnants of the original forest left when the early fields were carved from the Wealden forest. With the considerable degree of replanting in the last few centuries it is possible that the Weald now exhibits a more wooded aspect than at any time since the early medieval period.

The latest Forestry Commission Survey, a sample census conducted in 1965-67, indicates some 68,000 hectares of woodland, about 18 per cent. of the county, making it one of the most heavily-wooded areas in England. Unfortunately, the census is not strictly comparable with the previous one of 1947, but, nevertheless, some revealing comparisons can be made. From Table I (p. 15) it can be seen that while the amount of broad-leaved high forest has increased by some five per cent., the increase in coniferous high forest has been 18 per cent. Much coppice is no longer managed as such, and the area has declined by 38 per cent., while the 'other' category has increased by 15 per cent. A recent 10 per cent. sample survey in the Rother District (the most eastern district of Sussex) has shown between 1960 and 1975 a net loss of 0.5 per cent. of privately-managed woodland per year, but no change in the area of Forestry Commission woodland. It is worth noting that Rother District has, approximately, 20 per cent. greater woodland cover than the average for East Sussex. But it is not clear whether this loss of privately-owned woodland applies to the whole county. Recent changes in the form of capital taxation may accelerate it.

Much of the increase in coniferous woodland has resulted from the clearance and replanting of coppice, as well as the planting of unforested areas of heathland and downland. Conifers are planted mainly on the lightest soils and large plantations are established on the western half of the Downs and at Friston. Here the conifers are used as a nurse crop and are progressively being removed to reveal an extensive beech forest. Other areas of conifers are found in the High Weald and on the Lower Greensand, but the heavy soils of the Low Weald are dominated by deciduous woodland. The plantations are often considered of little value as bird habitats, but there can be no doubt of their importance at some stages of their development. They have favoured the marked expansion of the Woodcock on the Downs in recent years, and also provide the Grasshopper Warbler and Yellowhammer with one of their principal nesting habitats. Plantations also provide valuable habitat in their early stages for many Tree Pipits, Nightjars, and warblers, which the Woodland Survey (q.v.) suggests are not numerous in many Sussex woodlands. It is true that individual plantations lose these species rapidly once the thicket stage is reached, but other species move in and large areas of plantation often exhibit a variety of growth stages

TABLE I

Sussex Woodlands (from Forestry Commission sample surveys)

Figures as percentage of total

	1947	1965-67
Broad-leaved high forest	26	31
Coniferous high forest	8	26
Coppice (with or without standards)	49	11
Other (scrub, yew woodland, degenerate coppice, etc.)	17	32
Totals	100	100

Note.—'High forest' refers to management aims rather than present condition, so that a young plantation is included in the 'high forest' category.

from clear fell to mature trees, which further increases the diversity of birds present.

Most of the downland woods are west of the Arun gap and, apart from plantations, beech (*Fagus sylvatica*) is the dominant tree, although it rarely regenerates, and where no replanting takes place ash (*Fraxinus excelsior*) quickly asserts itself. The beech woods, especially, have little undergrowth, in which case they do not hold large bird populations and are often too young to support hole-nesting species such as woodpeckers. The Woodland Survey indicates that there are no particular features of their bird populations, and certainly there are no characteristic species of beech woods in the way that Wood Warblers and Redstarts favour the open oak woods of the sand, or Nightingales the damp coppice of the clay. Yew (*Taxus baccata*) commonly occurs in the ash woods, and on the National Nature Reserve at Kingley Vale there are large stands of yew which support good populations of common species, particularly Great Tit, Coal Tit, Chaffinch and thrushes. The sycamore (*Acer pseudoplatanus*) is widespread, particularly so on the Downs near the coast where conditions are unsuitable for most other tree species, and it is much favoured by passage migrants.

In the extensive woodlands of the Low Weald the pedunculate oak (*Quercus robur*) is the dominant tree, often with a
secondary layer of holly (*Ilex aquifolium*), field maple (*Acer
campestre*), crab apple (*Malus sylvestris*), gean (*Prunus avium*),
Midland hawthorn (*Crataegus laevigata*), and the occasional
wild service tree (*Sorbus torminalis*). The oak supports more
species of insects (at least 284) than any other British tree
and these woodlands are noted for their communities of insec-
tivorous birds, particularly tits, Blackcaps, Garden Warblers,
Willow Warblers, Robins and thrushes. Much Wealden woodland
has been managed as coppice, often in combination with
standard trees, principally oak. In the Low Weald much of the
coppice is hazel, which was used primarily for the construction
of sheep hurdles and in the building industry, but is now of
little economic value. Many of these woods have been abandoned or grubbed up for agricultural use. The hazel coppices
are particularly favoured by the large Sussex Nightingale
population.

The dominant tree in the High Weald where there are clay
soils is also the pedunculate oak, but where sandy soils predominate the sessile oak (*Quercus petraea*) is well represented.
Other tree species commonly growing in association with
oak include beech, silver birch (*Betula pendula*), mountain ash
(*Sorbus aucuparia*), ash, holly, yew and Scots pine (*Pinus
sylvestris*). On the lighter soils the secondary layer is often
sparse, but the Woodland Survey suggests that these open
woodlands support a greater diversity of bird species than other
deciduous woods in Sussex, although certain species may be
less numerous. In particular they are favoured by Wood
Warblers and the dwindling Sussex population of Redstarts.
The densest high forest in the High Weald is associated with
the ghyll valleys, narrow ravines created by streams that have
cut through the lighter soils. Much woodland in the High
Weald again consists of coppice, in this instance sweet chestnut
(*Castanea sativa*) on the sandier soils, and hornbeam (*Carpinus
betula*) on the heavier soils, often grown in pure stands. These
trees were managed to provide poles for the hop industry, but
hop-growing is in decline in Sussex, the area of hops having
fallen over 40 per cent. from 935 hectares in 1936 to 559

hectares in 1974. The decline in the demand for wooden poles has been accelerated by the frequent use of metal poles. Chestnut is still in demand for fencing, although the trees are often grown to a greater girth, and hornbeam is now little used. These coppice woods have never been noted for their birds, even less when they are abandoned and become densely shaded, although hornbeam is a tree favoured by Hawfinches. Commercial forestry operations have taken over many coppice woodlands and planted conifers extensively.

The alder (*Alnus glutinosa*) is widespread on wet soils, although there are no large alder woods, and it usually grows in association with sallow (*Salix cinerea*) and downy birch (*Betula pubescens*). These areas are much frequented by wintering flocks of Redpolls and Siskins, and Woodcock often feed in these sites. Lesser Spotted Woodpeckers are of regular occurrence amongst these trees.

Many Sussex heathlands have become invaded by woodland, the silver birch and Scots pine predominating with rhododendron (*Rhododendron ponticum*) being common, and at a later stage sessile oak becomes dominant. The increase in this woodland may well have had a beneficial effect on the Woodcock and has provided the increasing breeding Redpoll population with an abundance of habitat.

The Woodland Survey *by M. Shrubb*

Between 1963 and 1974 an attempt was made to measure the abundance and distribution of the common and widespread birds breeding in Sussex woodlands by a series of sample censuses. The census method used was adapted by Dr. Michael Hollings from W. B. Yapp's *Birds and Woods* (Oxford University Press, 1962). The observer was asked to move through the wood of his choice at a fixed speed, dividing the time spent into units of 10 minutes each and recording for each 10-minute period all the birds seen or heard, normally within a band of 50 yards (46 metres) from the observer. Although the method has drawbacks, particularly that it is difficult to eliminate duplications from the results, it has the merits of being simple, and giving reasonably consistent results with a number of observers and being readily repeated. Counters were asked to make several visits in a season and, in a number of sites, counts were spread over several years.

In fact the survey was only a limited success because rather few observers took part. Nevertheless, these counts do provide us with the best available source of information about the common birds of Sussex woodland. Altogether a total of 23 sites was visited twice or more in at least one year, of which six were visited regularly in two years, and nine in three or more. In addition a single visit was made to five sites, but these counts have been excluded from this analysis. Perhaps, unfortunately, a fairly high proportion of the counts were made just after the 1962/63 winter when populations of many species were very low.

The figures obtained are used here to calculate three indices for the commoner species: the percentage frequency, relative abundance and contacts per hour. The percentage frequency is the number of 10-minute samples in which a species was recorded, expressed as a percentage of the total number of samples, and is thus a measure of distribution. The relative abundance records the percentage of the total population represented by each species. Taken together these two indices yield much information about the abundance or scarcity of each bird, how widely or evenly it is distributed, and how numbers of any species compare with others, perhaps particularly with its near relations. But changes in its relative abundance may not give an entirely accurate picture of population trends for any species, so the number of contacts per hour of counting for each species is added as an individual measure of abundance. This expresses total numbers in terms of time spent watching instead of area covered. The indices for rarer species, and the nocturnal ones such as owls, have been omitted from the tables because the figures give little useful information compared to those in the general records of the Society.

I have not tried to present the counts on a basis of woodland types as there seemed to be too few of most visited to give useful results. I have therefore grouped them on a broad geological basis: sand, chalk, clay, and the gravels and loams of the coastal plain which probably also enjoys a modest climatic advantage over the rest of the county. In fact these groupings are shown by the survey as having fairly characteristic woodlands. Thus six of the seven woods visited on sand soils were primarily mature mixed pine and beech/oak woods, often rather open. On the clay the woods visited were predominantly mature mixed deciduous or coppice, and often damp. On the coastal plain the sites were scattered fragments of oak wood, and on the chalk either young mixed plantations or mature deciduous, often beech.

Despite the limitations of the survey it did suggest some clear habitat preferences and population trends. Comments on individual species are given in the Systematic List, but some more general observations seem worth making here. There were quite marked differences in the overall structure of the bird populations. Thus a greater variety of species, but often lower individual numbers, was recorded on sandy soils, and the fragmentary woodlands of the coastal plain were distinctly poor in species, although several common birds were very numerous. The effects of the very cold winter of 1962/63 were abundantly clear in the steadily increasing numbers of some species such as Wrens in the following years. The survey figures also suggest very clearly that the lack of really severe cold in any winter since has enabled many resident birds to maintain increased populations in woodland, although this may not be so in other habitats. The counts also suggest that most Sussex woods have comparatively poor populations of many breeding summer visitors. The tables show that these birds at best occupied only 25 per cent. of the total populations recorded, and Willow Warblers occupied between a third and a half of this percentage. It seems worth drawing the attention of conservation bodies to this point when they consider the acquisition and management of woodland nature reserves.

It is also worth repeating the observation by Hollings (1963) that the counts confirm many well-established habitat preferences. Thus, for example, Coal Tits were associated with conifers, and Redstarts (not tabulated) and Wood Warblers with the more open woods of the sands, in contrast to Nightingales, Robins and thrushes, which were generally most numerous in the denser, damper woods of the clay. A habitat detail not very fully covered was the age of trees, which must have some bearing on the distribution and numbers of hole-nesting species such as woodpeckers, tits, Nuthatch and Starling. But all these are shown to be birds of mature woodlands, while some warblers and Yellowhammer emerge as birds of scrub or young plantation and edge. Obvious points, perhaps, but important, since an adaptation to a new habitat can have a profound effect on a species' fortunes.

But it should perhaps be stressed that the figures as recorded are most useful in outlining the overall status and distribution of birds in woodland, and I have therefore concentrated on this. It would be valuable to repeat the counts in order to record any changes.

TABLE II

Percentage Frequency of Species in 23 Sussex Woodlands

Species	Sand	Chalk	Clay	Coast
Turtle Dove	5.4	9.8	23.3	34.1
Cuckoo	6.9	5.1	13.3	3.6
Green Woodpecker	7.0	3.2	8.0	0.7
Great Spotted Woodpecker	7.0	2.1	12.3	1.4
Lesser Spotted Woodpecker	2.0	0	0.8	1.4
Tree Pipit	9.1	2.9	15.2	0
Wren	40.3	28.5	65.5	65.0
Dunnock	13.3	22.1	27.9	54.5
Robin	57.5	48.8	82.0	85.1
Nightingale	3.9	4.2	13.7	5.1
Blackbird	47.1	57.7	87.4	81.8
Song Thrush	23.3	28.3	37.5	55.2
Mistle Thrush	11.5	9.5	7.2	11.7
Garden Warbler	7.7	11.7	31.5	2.1
Blackcap	13.3	28.2	20.5	50.1
Whitethroat	12.4	24.7	32.5	13.2
Lesser Whitethroat	0.5	1.5	1.9	0
Willow Warbler	42.6	50.8	67.5	53.4
Chiffchaff	16.5	33.5	40.1	35.5
Wood Warbler	7.7	0.7	4.7	P
Goldcrest	6.0	4.3	7.6	0
Spotted Flycatcher	2.7	1.6	1.3	P

Table II *continued*

Species					Sand	Chalk	Clay	Coast
Long-tailed Tit	..	..	..	..	2.8	0.9	6.4	1.4
Marsh Tit	..	..	..	..	5.5	9.7	10.9	0
Willow Tit	..	..	..	..	0.9	P	3.4	0
Coal Tit ..	..	..	..	..	25.5	6.6	10.9	2.1
Great Tit	..	..	..	..	28.9	26.5	54.4	35.5
Blue Tit ..	..	..	..	..	37.5	30.9	69.9	53.9
Nuthatch	..	..	..	..	12.7	7.7	6.7	5.7
Treecreeper	..	..	..	..	4.2	0.7	6.8	1.4
Yellowhammer	..	..	..	..	11.9	18.5	27.1	7.1
Chaffinch	..	..	..	..	54.7	65.0	53.4	74.9
Greenfinch	..	..	..	..	1.8	4.7	2.1	7.0
Goldfinch	..	..	..	..	1.2	3.7	1.6	3.2
Bullfinch	..	..	..	..	1.7	11.1	14.2	10.6
Starling ..	..	..	..	..	12.7	15.1	57.9	38.9
Jay	..	..	..	..	12.8	6.6	19.2	12.6
Quadrats	..	..	..	..	1,363	989	477	75
Sites Visited	..	..	..	..	7	7	6	3

TABLE III

Relative Abundance of Species in 23 Sussex Woodlands

Species					Sand	Chalk	Clay	Coast
Turtle Dove	..	..	..	..	0.7	0.9	1.7	3.3
Cuckoo ..	..	..	..	..	1.0	0.5	0.8	0.3
Green Woodpecker	..	..	..	..	0.9	0.4	0.3	0.03
Great Spotted Woodpecker		..	..	..	1.1	0.2	0.7	0.1
Lesser Spotted Woodpecker		..	..	..	0.2	0	0.04	0.06
Tree Pipit	..	..	..	..	1.1	0.7	0.9	0
Wren	..	..	..	..	7.4	3.7	6.9	6.3
Dunnock	..	..	..	..	1.9	3.1	2.5	5.4
Robin ..	..	..	..	..	11.8	7.7	9.6	16.7
Nightingale	..	..	..	..	0.5	0.5	1.2	0.7
Blackbird	..	..	..	..	8.9	10.1	9.6	11.8
Song Thrush	..	..	..	..	3.1	3.6	2.4	6.1

Table III *continued*

Species	Sand	Chalk	Clay	Coast
Mistle Thrush	1.9	1.1	0.6	1.0
Garden Warbler	1.0	1.1	2.0	0.1
Blackcap	1.7	3.6	1.5	4.2
Whitethroat	1.6	3.9	2.8	1.1
Lesser Whitethroat	0.05	0.1	0.1	0
Willow Warbler	6.7	9.2	9.3	5.1
Chiffchaff	2.4	4.8	2.6	2.8
Wood Warbler	0.9	0.06	0.2	P
Goldcrest	1.2	0.6	0.3	0
Spotted Flycatcher	0.4	0.1	0.05	P
Long-tailed Tit	0.6	0.2	0.4	0.2
Marsh Tit	1.0	1.2	0.6	0
Willow Tit	0.1	P	0.2	0
Coal Tit	4.7	1.0	0.5	0.1
Great Tit	4.7	3.9	4.0	3.9
Blue Tit	7.4	4.8	7.5	5.9
Nuthatch	1.7	1.2	0.6	0.3
Treecreeper	0.6	0.09	0.5	0.06
Yellowhammer	1.6	2.7	1.7	0.5
Chaffinch	9.9	11.4	4.4	8.4
Greenfinch	0.3	0.7	0.3	0.4
Goldfinch	0.4	0.6	0.1	0.3
Bullfinch	0.2	1.7	1.1	0.7
Starling	2.9	3.7	7.8	6.6
Jay	1.9	1.0	1.6	1.0
Contacts..	10,862	8,860	9,273	1,079

TABLE IV

Contacts per hour of Species in 23 Sussex Woodlands

Species	Sand	Chalk	Clay	Coast
Turtle Dove	0.4	0.6	2.0	3.2
Cuckoo	0.5	0.4	0.9	0.3
Green Woodpecker	0.4	0.2	0.5	0.05
Great Spotted Woodpecker	0.6	0.1	0.8	0.1

Table IV *continued*

Species		Sand	Chalk	Clay	Coast
Lesser Spotted Woodpecker	.. ..	0.1	0	0.05	0.1
Tree Pipit	.. ..	0.6	0.3	1.4	0
Wren ..	.. ..	3.7	2.2	9.0	5.4
Dunnock	.. ..	0.9	1.6	2.2	4.6
Robin ..	.. ..	5.7	4.0	10.7	15.8
Nightingale	.. ..	0.2	0.2	1.2	0.5
Blackbird	.. ..	4.3	6.5	9.8	10.8
Song Thrush ..	.. ..	1.7	2.3	2.6	5.7
Mistle Thrush ..	.. ..	0.9	0.6	0.5	0.9
Garden Warbler	.. ..	0.5	0.7	2.2	0.1
Blackcap	.. ..	0.8	1.9	1.5	3.7
Whitethroat ..	.. ..	0.9	2.2	3.7	0.8
Lesser Whitethroat	.. ..	0.05	0.1	0.1	0
Willow Warbler	.. ..	3.3	5.5	11.9	4.9
Chiffchaff	.. ..	1.2	2.4	2.9	2.5
Wood Warbler ..	.. ..	0.5	0.04	0.3	P
Goldcrest	.. ..	0.6	0.4	0.5	0
Spotted Flycatcher ..	.. .. ..	0.2	0.1	0.1	P
Long-tailed Tit	.. ..	0.3	0.1	0.5	0.2
Marsh Tit	.. ..	0.4	0.7	0.8	0
Willow Tit	.. ..	0.1	P	0.3	0
Coal Tit ..	.. ..	2.1	0.4	0.7	0.1
Great Tit	.. ..	2.3	2.1	4.6	3.6
Blue Tit ..	.. ..	3.3	2.6	9.1	5.6
Nuthatch	.. ..	0.9	0.6	0.6	0.4
Treecreeper	.. ..	0.4	0.06	0.4	0.1
Yellowhammer	.. ..	0.8	1.9	2.5	0.5
Chaffinch	.. ..	4.6	6.2	5.1	7.5
Greenfinch	.. ..	0.2	0.4	0.1	0.4
Goldfinch	.. ..	0.2	0.4	0.1	0.2
Bullfinch	.. ..	0.1	0.8	1.0	0.6
Starling ..	.. ..	1.4	2.3	8.4	6.2
Jay ..	.. ..	1.0	0.5	1.5	0.8
Hours ..	.. ..	227	165	79.5	12.5

Note: P indicates the species was found present once.

HEATHS AND COMMONS

By R. D. M Edgar

HEATHLAND IN Southern England results from the clearance of the original temperate forest on areas of somewhat acidic sandy soils with a poor humus layer. The soils leach rapidly, and under a management regime of grazing and burning a characteristic vegetation develops of which ling (*Calluna vulgaris*) is a principal constituent. Commons may occur on any type of soil, the name referring to their type of use rather than ecological status. However, since they are usually areas of low vegetation dominated by rough grasses frequently with bracken (*Pteridium aquilinum*), gorse (*Ulex* sp.), and scattered trees, in ornithological terms it is convenient to consider the two together.

Sussex heathlands occur on the Lower Greensand in the west and north-west of the county, in the central area of the High Weald on the Hastings Beds, and in a few places on the Downs where there are superficial deposits of acidic soils. The southern heathlands are generally considered as one of the most rapidly diminishing habitats, principally through conversion to forestry. Even those heathlands which have not been reafforested are rapidly becoming covered with silver birch and self-sown Scots Pine, due to lack of grazing management. Uncontrolled burning may damage the typical vegetation, and diminishes the bird population. Fig. 3 (p. 25) shows the considerable decline in area of Lower Greensand heaths in north-west Sussex between 1822 and 1971. Commons are scattered throughout the county, and although rights of common are fiercely defended they are rarely exercised, and many commons are returning to woodland.

Pressure from recreation on these open areas is usually considerable, with consequently much disturbance to birds

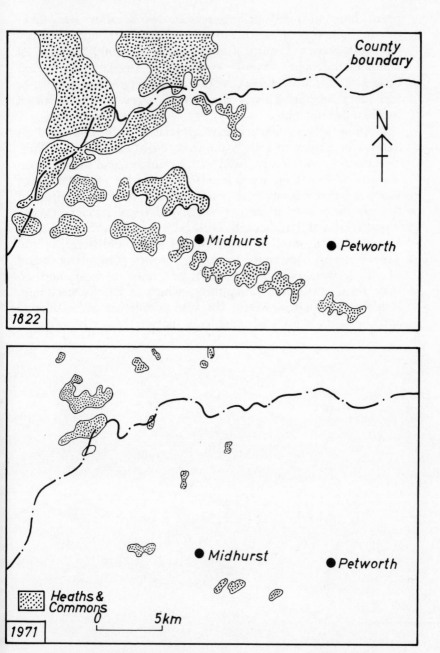

Fig. 3. Lower Greensand Heaths of West Sussex in 1822 and 1971

particularly in the breeding season. No accurate assessment of the amount of heathland is available, although a survey by West Sussex County Council showed 1,500 hectares of heath in that administrative county. The largest heath in East Sussex is Ashdown Forest, with 2,600 hectares being more or less open habitat. This is the second largest of the southern heathlands remaining.

Nesting species particularly associated with this type of habitat in Sussex include Stonechat, Nightjar, and Tree Pipit. The Hobby is often associated with heathland, and the Dartford Warbler is found on some heaths, but neither Woodlarks nor Red-backed Shrikes, both once typical heathland birds of Sussex, have bred in recent years. All these species (except Woodlarks and Red-backed Shrikes) breed in other habitats, for example Stonechats in downland scrub, and Nightjars and Tree Pipits as commonly in young forestry plantations (many of which were once heathlands); but only on heathland do they form a distinct community, which is rapidly declining. It is notable that in winter the bird population of heathlands and commons in Sussex is decidedly sparse.

FRESHWATER HABITATS

By R. D. M. Edgar

THESE IMPORTANT HABITATS may conveniently be considered under the headings of Rivers and Ponds, Levels, Reservoirs, and Gravel Pits.

Rivers and Ponds

The Sussex rivers mainly flow south, having risen in the sandstone areas of the county. Here they have often incised deeply into the sandstone rocks, producing steep-sided ravines whose depth often belies the size of the stream that created it.

These small streams are often fast flowing until they reach the lower elevations of the Low Weald. Here they become wider and slower and often carry considerable quantities of sand and silt. They all have alluvial flood plains or levels of wet permanent pasture in which extensive flooding used to be of frequent occurrence, but many improvement schemes have been instituted in recent years with stretches of river being straightened and flood banks raised. Extensive floods are now uncommon and short-lived, occurring only in times of heavy and prolonged rain. The frequent attention given to the management of river banks has made many unsuitable for the nesting of Kingfishers, and the frequent clearance of marginal vegetation has been to the detriment of species such as the Reed Bunting, Sedge and Reed Warbler. The latter two species have declined very considerably in the Arun valley and no doubt elsewhere in the county.

The upper streams are suitable for the creation of ponds, and many hammer and millponds were created in the past for industrial purposes. These now have good marginal vegetation and their dams produce small waterfalls, the preferred

27

nesting sites for Grey Wagtails which are widely distributed in this limited habitat, some 193 pairs having been recorded in a survey in 1967–69, mainly in the Lower Greensand and High Weald areas. The ponds hold the usual species associated with this type of habitat, with Great Crested Grebes and Tufted Ducks nesting on the larger ponds and lakes, and the small breeding population of Teal in the county largely restricted to this habitat or the smaller streams and marshes, rarely being found breeding on the river levels. These ponds support a significant population of wintering wildfowl, principally Mallard, Tufted Duck and Pochard, with smaller numbers of other species. Willows (of various species), sallows and alders are often associated with the ponds and attract wintering flocks of Redpolls and Siskins; some have breeding Lesser Spotted Woodpeckers, this being one of their main habitats in the county.

Levels

The Sussex Levels cover a considerable area, of the order of 160 square kilometres, and, except for Pevensey Levels, are associated with the flood plains of the main rivers. These levels or brooks are now areas of flat low-lying grassland drained by a complex system of ditches, but lying wet in winter. The network of ditches was in many cases originally designed to take advantage of the winter flooding of the rivers and enabled these areas to be managed as water meadows, a particular form of management which produced good quality hay crops, but is no longer practised or possible with the improvement of drainage and flood prevention. Although most of the levels are freshwater, some are brackish in their more southerly parts. The extensive Pevensey Levels of 36 square kilometres are largely a result of the enclosure or inning of a large bay studded with small clay islands called 'eyes'. By the eighth century the eastward drift of shingle along the coast had given natural protection to the spread of the salt marsh, and during the 12th and 13th centuries Pevensey Levels gradually changed from saltmarsh to reed and sedge meadows and ultimately pasture. Much of this reclamation work was undertaken by the great Abbeys, principally that at Battle. The pattern of ditched fields is virtually unchanged from that time.

In many of the Sussex levels pumped drainage schemes are being installed to give greater control over the water levels so that the water table can be gradually lowered, permitting the permanent pasture to be improved by ploughing and re-seeding and allowing a longer grazing season; some will no doubt be converted to arable.

The approximate area of the various levels in Sussex is shown in Table V (p. 30) and their location on Fig. 4 (p. 31). Extensive beds of the common reed (*Phragmites australis*) are no longer found in these levels except in the Combe Haven valley where the reed bed of some 10 hectares is the largest remaining example of this habitat in Sussex. Many drainage ditches are, however, fringed with reeds.

The importance of this wet grassland habitat, with its associated system of ditches, is considerable for Sussex birds. It forms the primary nesting area for a number of specialised species, particularly Lapwing, Redshank, Snipe, and Yellow Wagtail, and probably Reed and Sedge Warblers. The ditches may provide the principal feeding sites for the county's nesting Herons since all the major heronries are associated with levels. Some scarcer species, such as Garganey, Shoveler and Water Rail also breed.

As an example of the value of this habitat a survey of Pevensey Levels in 1976 recorded 52 nesting species and included counts of 27 pairs of Snipe, 29 pairs of Redshank, 74 pairs of Reed Warbler, 196 pairs of Sedge Warbler, 165 pairs of Yellow Wagtail, 118 pairs of Meadow Pipit, and 262 pairs of Reed Bunting. Besides revealing rather more Snipe, Redshank and Yellow Wagtail than previously recorded (*see* Systematic List) these counts clearly indicate the value of the marginal vegetation of the ditches for Reed Buntings, Reed and Sedge Warbler. Unfortunately, this vegetation is very vulnerable to major drainage works. Pevensey Levels probably comprises the most important area of this habitat for nesting birds in Sussex, but the Arun valley, Combe Haven, with its reed beds, and some of the marshes around Rye are also particularly significant and every area is of value.

TABLE V

Sussex Levels (Approximate areas)

Amberley/Pulborough marshes	.. 13 sq. km.
Amberley–Littlehampton (Lower Arun valley)	11.5 sq. km.
Adur Levels	13 sq. km.
Ouse valley (south of Lewes) ..	.. 14.25 sq. km.
Glynde Levels	.. 16 sq. km.
Cuckmere valley (north of Alfriston)	4.5 sq. km.
Pevensey Levels	.. 36 sq. km.
Rother Levels	.. 9.75 sq. km.
Pett Levels	.. 2.6 sq. km.

Other similar areas, totalling about 38 sq. km., occur in the valley of the Coombe Haven and in the Rye area.

The levels are also important for the wintering wildfowl they attract, particularly Teal and Wigeon. For example, the average winter peaks for these two species at Amberley/Pulborough and Glynde Levels between 1964 and 1975 were 560 and 1,280, and 560 and 1,300 respectively, some 45 per cent. of the total county population. Formerly all these levels held greater totals of these birds than they do today, and in addition attracted numbers of Mallard, Pintail, Shoveler and, at Amberley, Pochard. Although all still occur, the progressive lowering of water tables is making these areas less attractive and the reservoirs, gravel pits and estuaries of the county are becoming increasingly important wintering sites for them. The Arun valley, Adur levels, and Glynde Levels are now probably the most important levels for wintering duck, and the Arun valley also attracts an increasing herd of Bewick's Swans.

In addition the levels hold large winter flocks of Lapwing, Snipe, and Golden Plover. Pevensey Levels where 15,000-plus Lapwing, 1,200-plus Snipe, and 2,000-plus Golden Plover have been counted recently is perhaps the prime area, but five-figure flocks of Lapwing are not unusual elsewhere, and every suitable area will attract flocks of several hundred Snipe. Golden Plover, however, are coastal birds in Sussex and inland flocks are usually small.

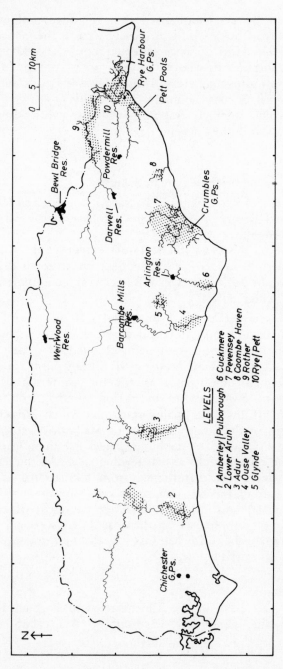

Fig. 4. Major Freshwater Habitats

It cannot be over-emphasised that the future of many of these species of Sussex birds is closely tied to the management of these levels. Most drainage schemes should have some regard for the importance to wildlife of these areas, and much can be achieved on quite small areas. Thus at Glynde Levels the Sussex Ornithological Society annually flood fields covering some six hectares which is largely responsible for the wildfowl numbers that now occur in these levels.

Reservoirs

The following reservoirs are in Sussex:

Weir Wood Reservoir (114 hectares), constructed 1954.
Darwell Reservoir (69 hectares), constructed 1938–40 and 1946–50.
Arlington Reservoir (63 hectares), constructed 1971.
Powdermill Reservoir (23 hectares), constructed 1924–32.
Barcombe Mills Reservoir (16 hectares), constructed 1964–66; enlarged 1971.

A new reservoir at Bewl Bridge of 310 hectares (a small part in Kent) is nearly full, and a reservoir at Ardingly (70 hectares) is in the process of being flooded. It is well known that any such sheet of water will attract birds, and these reservoirs' main importance is for the wintering wildfowl. Table VI (p. 33) gives an indication of the ornithological importance of the four major reservoirs which attract about 30 per cent. of the county's wintering Mallard, Wigeon, Tufted Duck, and Pochard. The dabbling species use them as daytime refuges, the diving ducks also as feeding areas. All the reservoirs receive a degree of disturbance from recreational activities, primarily fishing, but on some more active forms of recreation take place. The disturbance the latter causes is of constant concern to ornithologists as these artificial wetlands are an essential replacement for habitats lost through drainage, as are gravel pits discussed below.

Gravel Pits

Gravel pits exist in the Chichester and Pagham Harbour areas; at the Crumbles, Eastbourne; Rye Harbour, and

TABLE VI

**Sussex Reservoirs—Species Recorded and Most Important
Wintering Wildfowl Numbers**

	Total species recorded	Passage	Breeding	Wintering	Most important wintering wildfowl (with maxima since 1970).
Arlington Reservoir	172	152	14	60	Mallard (500) Wigeon (1,200) Pochard (200) Shoveler (60)
Weir Wood Reservoir	133	62	58	65	Teal (311) Tufted Duck (290) Pochard (200)
Barcombe Mills Reservoir	133	57	28	83	Mallard (700) Wigeon (1,800)
Darwell Reservoir*	114	52	62	83	Tufted Duck (188) Pochard (141)

*Species totals include an adjacent wood

Northpoint Beach, Rye. Soil has also been excavated at Pett Level (to provide material for the sea wall), leaving a series of lakes. The pits at the Midrips and Wicks near the boundary with Kent no longer hold water. The location of the major pits is shown in Fig. 4 (p. 31).

The gravel pits at Pagham Harbour, known as the Severals, are largely covered in *Phragmites* reeds and hold large popula- of Reed and Sedge Warblers and some Water Rails. The numerous gravel pits near Chichester support a good variety of breeding species, notably Great Crested Grebes for which this is the most important area in Sussex, as well as passage migrants and wintering wildfowl (for numbers, *see* Systematic List). Until recently new pits were continually being excavated while others are being filled with refuse. There is considerable pressure to use these waters for recreation, and they receive much disturbance. The gravel pits at the Crumbles have never been noted for their ornithological interest, except for passage migrants, and when excavation is complete will be used for sailing. Those at Rye Harbour and Northpoint Beach, Rye are extensive and largely undisturbed, although again there is strong pressure for recreational use; that at Northpoint Beach is to be connected to the River Rother and used as a yacht basin. Common Terns at present nest on an island in the pit, and it is to be hoped that when disturbance is too great for them they will move to the Local Nature Reserve at Rye Harbour, which includes a gravel pit with suitable islands. The lakes at Pett Level hold rather small numbers of wintering wildfowl, but are particularly important during times of passage. In recent years the Sussex Ornithological Society has lowered the water level of one of the smaller lakes in autumn and this has attracted good numbers of waders.

Wet gravel pits are generally recognised as important habitats for wildlife, particularly in view of the increasing drainage of wetlands. In Sussex they are much more important for their breeding birds than reservoirs as they generally have much more marginal vegetation. The pressure on these sites for leisure and recreation uses is becoming increasingly strong in the county.

FARMLAND

By R. D. M. Edgar and M. Shrubb

SINCE 1939 BRITISH agriculture has changed profoundly. The main features of this revolution have been a great decline in the area of grassland, the increase of mechanisation with the consequence of reduced farm labour, the widespread use of chemicals as tools and the simplification of crop rotations, and the introduction of important new crops such as maize. These changes have had a marked effect on farmland as an aggregation of bird habitats. Thus grassland (especially wet) is an important habitat for many specialised bird species, and its loss has reduced and restricted their populations. Other habitat losses have resulted from farm mechanisation which, requiring larger and more conveniently-shaped fields, has resulted in much hedge and scrub clearance. The more satisfactory economic position of farming allied with Government policies have also encouraged these losses. There have been dramatic declines of a few bird species as a result of using some chemicals, and perhaps more subtle and long-term changes as a result of the simplification of the plant community of farmland arising from cropping changes and the widespread use of increasingly sophisticated herbicides.

In Sussex about 250,000 out of a total of 380,000 hectares (some 65 per cent.) are devoted to agriculture (including small farm woodlands, agricultural buildings, etc.). All the above changes have been noted in the past 25 years, although some have been more limited than others. The clay soils of many farms north of the Downs, for example, do not lend themselves to intensive arable farming, and few farms here (or, for that matter, fields) are far from woodlands so that they are not wholly dependent on such features as patches of scrub or hedges for the presence of many common farmland species.

The changing pattern of agriculture in Sussex is shown by the Ministry of Agriculture Annual Returns and is outlined in Table VII (p. 37). These show since 1939 a more than twofold increase in arable land and a corresponding decline in permanent pasture. Further, there has been a decline of about 72 per cent. in the area of rough grazings. Some may have been ploughed, but much has probably been improved and is now recorded under permanent pasture, the more suitable permanent pasture having been turned to arable. Within the arable area the greatest changes have been the increase of cereals and the decline of the one-year clover ley. The latter change does not show in Table VII, being masked by changes in grassland management, but only 2,529 hectares of one-year clover leys were grown in Sussex in 1974, 1.8 per cent. of the arable area, compared to probably the full 9,478 hectares noted for temporary leys for 1939 in Table VII, about 17 per cent. of the arable area. Altogether these changes have involved a loss of 60,400 hectares of grassland in Sussex since 1939, some 16 per cent. of the county's total area. It is interesting to note that the total agricultural area between 1939 and 1974 has declined by nearly seven per cent., largely as a result of the increase in urban development, mainly on arable land.

Sussex geology has imposed an extensive regional pattern on the agricultural crops. About 25 per cent. of the total grassland area occurs in large blocks in the main river valleys and levels, and perhaps nearly as much as a continuous band along the north scarp of the Downs which is too steep to plough. There is also an important grassland element over much of the heavy land of the Weald, where farming is characteristically more mixed than on the Downs, the coastal plain, river valleys or levels. Nearly half the arable area is concentrated along the Downs and the coastal plain to their south, with another important area aligned along the Greensand belt to their north. In general terms grass predominates on the heaviest soils or in low-lying wet areas, and arable where the soil is free draining and easily worked. The most important crops are clover and temporary grass (leys) 34 per cent. of arable land, barley (rather more in East Sussex) 29 per cent., and wheat (mainly West Sussex)

TABLE VII

Agricultural Areas of Sussex, 1939–1974 (adapted from M.A.F.F. Annual Agricultural Returns)

| Year | Arable | | | | | Grassland | | |
	Cereals	Temporary Leys	Other Crops	Total Arable		Permanent Pasture	Rough Grazings	Total Grasslands
1974	72,724	46,234	15,625	134,583		87,733	9,520	97,253
1969	73,463	47,613	16,329	137,405		88,715	11,200	99,915
1967	75,335	47,465	15,253	138,053		93,817	10,556	104,373
1963	58,577	59,990	17,721	136,288		96,736	11,493	108,229
1957	59,512	50,458	24,985	134,955		96,249	17,720	113,969
1939	24,644	9,478	20,398	54,520		160,304	34,113	194,417

All areas in hectares

20 per cent. Altogether cereals account for 54 per cent. of the total arable area.

The present agricultural pattern has clearly involved great changes and the loss of permanent pasture is of particular significance ornithologically. This has largely occurred on the Downs, where perhaps the greatest changes likely to affect birds in Sussex have taken place. Here a predominantly grass-land habitat was converted to a predominantly arable one in a very limited period after 1945, primarily due to a Government policy of encouraging cereal growing. Grants for ploughing grassland and cereal deficiency payments made barley more profitable than sheep, numbers of which fell by more than half between 1926 and 1954. Although sheep numbers in Sussex have now risen to nearly pre-war numbers, comparatively few are to be found on permanent downland pasture. At the same time as the conversion of downland pasture to arable many areas of scrub, particularly gorse, were destroyed. The latter change is not entirely due to agriculture, as much building development has taken place on the Downs. Although large areas of grassland still remain on unploughable slopes, particu-larly on the north-facing scarp, they have largely changed in character. Lacking the grazing pressure of sheep and rabbits, the latter decimated by myxomatosis, they have become overgrown with long coarse grasses followed by scrub, and in some places are already becoming woodland.

These changes have caused marked declines in breeding Wheatears and Stone Curlews, the former being nearly extinct as a downland breeding bird, and the latter much rarer than in 1939. The loss of much of the characteristic gorse scrub has reduced Stonechats and Dartford Warblers and possibly Grass-hopper Warblers, although the latter have quickly exploited the new habitat afforded by young forestry plantations. Some species have benefited from the change in the downland agri-cultural scene, and Corn Buntings and Skylarks are now more more numerous in these areas than elsewhere in the county and are the most characteristic birds of the downland. Many common passerine species must also have increased their downland ranges as a result of the slow advance of scrub and woodland over the remaining grass, and probably the downland avifauna is more varied today than in 1939 despite losing its characteristic and most interesting specialities. Of the latter, the Cirl Bunting does not appear to have taken advantage of the increasing scrub, possibly because much of it is on north-facing slopes, and it has now declined in numbers.

Perhaps the other highly significant change in Sussex agriculture to have affected birds is the more recent and extensive drainage of the important areas of wet permanent pasture in the river valleys and levels, which amount to some 16,000 hectares. The combination of drainage and improvement to pasture has greatly reduced the numbers of many characteristic and local species, either breeding, such as Garganey, Snipe, Redshank, and Yellow Wagtail, or wintering, such as Teal, Shoveler, and again Snipe. Ornithologically nothing has been gained from these changes in habitat on which the Sussex populations of some species largely depend. Drainage is now enabling some areas to be ploughed, which will advance the process further.

Elsewhere in Sussex the nature of the soils and the distribution of woodland have tended to limit the extent and effects of habitat changes caused by farming, but everywhere important changes in farming techniques have occurred. While the arable area has increased at the expense of ornithologically more interesting permanent grassland, there has been a simultaneous reduction of the one-year ley, usually clover, within the arable system, combined with an increasing use of herbicides. The effect of this process is not yet clear, although G. R. Potts has produced some valuable information during studies of the Grey Partridge on the Downs near Worthing. The importance of the ley crop, particularly clover, in an arable system in this context is that it not only provides diversity, but also a better opportunity for wildlife, particularly plants and insects, to complete its annual cycle than do crops which are cleared every year. The use of herbicides is also reducing plant variety in fields, and therefore also insects present. Both changes must eventually reduce the food supply, both animal and plant, available to birds in farmland habitats. On the other hand the introduction of new crops such as maize, oilseed rape, tic beans, and the increased area of peas and mustard have provided new food sources which some species, particularly pigeons, corvids and some seed eaters, have been quick to exploit. But the basic changes towards a farming system dominated by a limited range of plants, most of which are cereals, can only have reduced variety in farmland wildlife, including birds. The effects of these changes in agricultural techniques so far are by no means catastrophic for birds, perhaps because the limited availability of bushy nesting cover in predominantly arable areas has controlled the number of many common passerines below the levels the potential food supply could support.

The widespread use of pesticides, notably insecticides, in modern farming has probably also affected the food supply available to birds as well as sometimes causing widespread deaths among them. These synthetic chemicals were first generally introduced in the late 1940s and early 1950s, and are mainly used in two stages in arable operations—as protection for seed at sowing, and as protection for the growing crop. Early insecticides were crude, wide-spectrum contact killers, whereas modern ones are more often systemic in operation, that is, they make the crop temporarily poisonous to the pest and are increasingly specific. In fact, the use of pesticides in cereal farming is largely limited to seed dressings and sometimes aphicides, but it was to the use of persistent organo-chlorine seed dressings that the decline in birds of prey in the late 1950s and early 1960s was convincingly attributed. During this period the Peregrine Falcon disappeared from Sussex and a marked decline in the Sparrowhawk population occurred. Other species such as the Kestrel and Barn Owl were probably also affected, and large 'kills' of seed-eating birds were reported; breeding numbers of some such as Greenfinches and Stock Doves certainly declined. With the voluntary banning of organo-chlorines most of these species have recovered, but great care in the use of pesticides is necessary to prevent a repetition of these events.

Other changes arise from mechanisation which, amongst other things, has resulted in the complete disappearance of the corn rick and its attendant chaff heap. These provided an important winter food source for many species, mainly seed eaters. There is every likelihood that this, together with the decline of undersown cereals, accounts for the marked decline of winter finch flocks from much of Sussex. Mechanisation itself has, apart from the habitat changes it has induced, had little direct effect on birds in Sussex. It is often stated that the greater speed of modern farming operations and the larger machines used cause increased losses in ground-nesting species such as the Lapwing. This is probably so, but may be offset by the fact that the fields are left to the birds more quickly, enabling subsequent broods to be reared undisturbed.

Although a decline in hedgerow timber and the consequent loss of farmland bird habitat is a result of modern farming, the recent losses caused by Dutch Elm Disease are independent of farming practice. The effect on the Sussex landscape of the disappearance of the elm has been very severe in some areas, notably the coastal plain, but the significance for birds is unclear. In West Sussex the English elm (*Ulmus procera*) is nearing extinction and it might be expected that the large numbers of standing dead trees will, at least temporarily, provide large amounts of insect food and sites for hole-nesting species. In the comparatively small area of East Sussex in which the elm is common, mainly centred on the Cuckmere valley and Firle region, the disease control campaign of East Sussex County Council involves the felling of all infected trees. Whilst this means no standing dead timber, the possible survival of the elm as a hedgerow tree must be more beneficial, particularly since in these areas the elm is the principal farmland tree. It is interesting to note that the Rooks which use elms as a high proportion of their nest sites in this region quickly move to other tree species when elms are removed.

Another consequence of modern farming has been a change in the types of farm buildings, which may have affected Barn Owl and Swallow numbers by the loss of sites as traditional Sussex barns disappear.

Clearly the ornithologist must expect the evolution of agriculture to continue, and its most likely result will be to produce a much more uniform habitat with consequently a much less varied bird population than at present, composed of a comparatively few widespread and adaptable species. It is impossible to say how far this process will go, as agriculture is strongly influenced by a wide variety of external factors. It is worth noting that many of the recent habitat changes caused by agriculture in Sussex, and elsewhere, partly result from the reversal of a long decline in farming prosperity between 1875 and 1940. It seems likely that a similar decline will not be allowed to occur in a period of world food shortages, and continued changes along the present lines can be expected.

URBAN AREAS

By R. D. M. Edgar

URBAN AREAS comprise towns, villages and industrial sites. The county has a population of approximately 1,270,000 (in 1974), and a population density of over 330 people per square kilometre. The rise in population can be seen from Fig. 5 (p. 44), the greatest increase having been in West Sussex. Recently the largest increases have occurred in the Burgess Hill, Crawley, Crowborough, Horsham, and Hastings areas. Although these areas of expansion are mainly inland the largest towns are located along the coastline with an almost continuous ribbon of development from Pagham east to Seaford, with further major development at Eastbourne and the Bexhill/ Hastings area. This has produced one of the most developed coastlines in Britain. This extensive development has considerably affected the distribution of birds. Downland breeding species such as the Dartford Warbler, Grasshopper Warbler, Stonechat, Wheatear, and Stone Curlew used to be found in areas now covered by residential and industrial development, and some species dependent on beaches have been severely reduced, such as the Little Tern and the Ringed Plover. On the other hand many urban areas have sizable gardens and so may attract a greater number and/or diversity of common passerines than were once found here.

A small number of Black Redstarts inhabit some of the coastal towns and industrial sites, and Kestrels nest in many towns; three pairs were recorded nesting on Brighton churches in 1968, the same number recorded by Walpole-Bond. Rather more unusual is the single pair of Herons that have nested in the centre of Westham village for many years. With so many urban areas on the coast it is not surprising that Herring Gulls

43

nest on buildings in Sussex, and during the Operation Seafarer counts of 1969 between 106 and 131 pairs were found in the Hastings and St. Leonards district, and nests have more recently been recorded at Eastbourne, Brighton, and Worthing. Refuse tips are frequented by large numbers of gulls and the few wintering Lesser Black-backed Gulls are usually found at these sites, often inland.

Another species much associated with urban areas is the Swift, and a 1969 survey recorded some 4,500 individuals

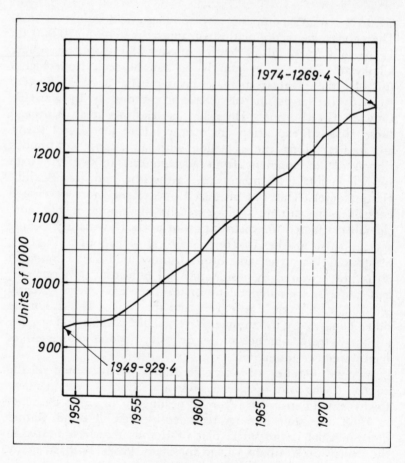

Fig. 5. Population of Sussex 1949–1974

present in the breeding season in the county. House Martins nest in many villages and some larger towns and in 1971 three pairs were found nesting 1.2km. from the site of a gas works that had closed a few months previously. Ringed Plovers can also exploit industrial sites and, for example, breed in the vicinity of the power station at Southwick.

Although these urban areas support a surprisingly large variety of nesting birds they cannot be considered as a major nesting habitat for any except Swifts, Starlings, House Sparrows and hirundines. Perhaps their most important contribution for Sussex birds in recent years has been the vast increase in the provision of food at bird-tables and feeding stations. In severe winters this has certainly improved the chance of survival of many common birds and has perhaps raised their winter survival rate generally. Not only town birds exploit this food source. Recent records have shown Siskins and Reed Buntings moving into towns to use the same food source in winter, and Blackcaps are regular in winter in some towns. Ringing evidence suggests that other birds from outside towns are doing the same.

CONSERVATION

By R. D. M. Edgar

THE CONSERVATION of birds is but part of the whole subject of wildlife conservation. Although a habitat may be manipulated particularly to encourage a bird species or group of species, this would involve the conservation of other forms of wildlife essential to that bird's existence. In Sussex most conservation work has been carried out to conserve particularly vulnerable habitats, in which birds are often an important element, and in a few cases the birds have been the main reason for the conservation work. Some of the species involved are rare both in a national and local context which, of necessity, limits the possibilities for discussion here. However, from the preceding sections it should be clear that habitats that are rapidly diminishing or becoming unsuitable for birds are particularly those associated with wetland, heathland, and on coastal and downland sites.

Co-ordinated efforts towards conservation have occurred almost entirely since 1950 and even individual efforts before that time are few. The instances of large numbers of birds having been shot or trapped for food, or rare specimens collected, is well documented, and in Sussex was often carried out on a very considerable scale. One example will suffice; Walpole-Bond records, with reference to Wheatears, that during the period from the final years of the 18th to the early ones of the 19th centuries an inhabitant of East Dean 'once during that short time was thought to have taken nearly a hundred dozen', and another 'near Eastbourne procured eighty-four dozen in the same short space of time'. Even up to 1902 Wheatears were sent to hotels in Brighton, up to two dozen birds being caught in a morning. Obviously no species could withstand such depredations for long, although the present losses of habitat may be considered even more serious.

An interesting example of early concern for bird conservation in Sussex is described by E. C. Arnold in his book *Bird Reserves*. Arnold, at one time headmaster of Eastbourne College, purchased a number of sites with the expressed intention of improving them as bird habitats. His earliest purchase, in about 1911, was of 1.5 hectares, including a brick-yard pond, in the Eastbourne area, which he planted up in order to attract, amongst other birds, breeding Marsh Warblers. His other purchases in the 1920s and 1930s included a 12 hectare woodland, also near Eastbourne, and 1.6 hectares on Pevensey Levels. One of his most interesting acquisitions was of 36 hectares of levels in the Cuckmere valley, on part of which he constructed ponds, some of which have become a reed bed. This reed bed is still maintained by working parties of the Sussex Ornithological Society.

For many people conservation is synonymous with nature reserves. In Sussex the statutory nature reserves, that is National and Local Nature Reserves, total 1,429 hectares, the first being declared in 1952. The reserves of the voluntary conservation organisations, the Sussex Trust for Nature Conservation and the Royal Society for the Protection of Birds, total 456 hectares. This total of 1,885 hectares is almost exactly one half of one per cent. of the county, so that although some of these sites are of great importance to birds, most birds are found in the other 99.5 per cent. of the land. Thus, although these reserves include many of the most vulnerable areas and species they must not be given undue importance in the consideration of a wildlife conservation policy. However, it is fair to say that much would have been lost to the county if they did not exist. There are many, often very large areas, that are publicly owned and of great value to wildlife but these sites are not primarily managed for wildlife, although this is often an important consideration and some suffer considerable disturbance.

Other major projects, primarily aimed at bird conservation, by the Sussex Ornithological Society include the regular winter flooding of six hectares of Glynde Levels which has attracted

sizable regular flocks of wildfowl, notably Teal and Wigeon;
the lowering of water-levels in one of the Pett pools to attract
migrating waders in autumn; and the placing of nesting islands
in gravel pits and reservoirs. East Sussex County Council has
created a five hectare lake near the mouth of the Cuckmere
River to attract wading birds, with nesting islands for Ringed
Plovers. Although these, and similar objects, are small in
scale, this belies their importance to bird conservation in
the county as a whole in view of the rapid decline of certain
bird feeding can perhaps be mentioned as a considerable benefit
to certain bird populations.

Although major disasters such as large oil pollution incidents
and deaths from pesticides are few, both cause continuing
problems. The greatest conservation problems, however, are
those associated with changes in land use, particularly agriculture, including the drainage of wetlands and loss of heathlands and the increase of urban areas with their attendant rise
in population and expanding leisure and tourist industries.
There can be no doubt that future changes along these lines
will continue and pose particular problems, most of which will
be to the detriment of the birds of Sussex.

1 & 2. COASTAL MARSHES. (*above*) Thorney Deeps and Brent in flight;
(*below*) Pagham Harbour at half tide.

3 & 4.   HIGH WEALDEN WOODLAND. (*above*) Darwell Wood; (*below*) open oak woodland in the same area.

5. Damp coppice near Arundel.

6. Downland plantations at West Dean woods.

7 & 8. MODERN HEATH-
LAND 'MANAGEMENT'.
(*left*) A casual burn in Ashdov
Forest; (*below*) after two year
bracken is rapidly invading th
heath.

9 & 10. WET GRASSLAND. (*above*) Amberley Wildbrooks in winter, now threatened with drainage; (*below*) The Sussex Ornithological Society's flood scheme in Glynde Levels.

11 & 12. GRAVEL PITS AT CHICHESTER. (*above*) Gravel handling plant; (*below*) wildfowl habitat.

13, 14 & 15.   CHANGES ON THE DOWNS. (*above*) Barley is the dominant crop; (*below*) The Slype, a mysterious trench carved down the side of Ditchling Beacon, photographed just after the Second World War. The picture shows how sheep have kept down the scrub; (*overleaf*) The Slype 1977. In the absence of sheep, the scrub has taken over.

16 & 17. LULLINGTON HEATH AND ITS ENVIRONS. (*above*) Lullington Heath from the south-west, April 1954; (*below*) from the south-west, 1978.

18 & 19.   LULLINGTON HEATH AND ITS ENVIRONS. (*above*) View south-west
along the track down to Litlington – Old Kiln Bottom, April 1954; (*below*) the sam
view, 1978.

20 & 21.   LULLINGTON HEATH AND ITS ENVIRONS. (*above*) The track along the southern boundary, April 1954; (*below*) the same view, 1977.

22 & 23. HERBICIDES.
(*left*) The clean bottom of a
wheat field sprayed with a pre-
emergent herbicide at drilling;
(*below*) Where the sprayer
missed.

PART TWO

SYSTEMATIC LIST OF SPECIES

Please refer to the Introduction for definitions of terms used and explanations of the treatment of species in this Systematic List

RED-THROATED DIVER— *Gavia stellata*

Status.—Common winter visitor and passage migrant. No recent change in status is certain, but some decline in the wintering numbers is likely.

Red-throated Divers have been recorded in every month except July and are the most frequently recorded divers in the winter months. However, the numbers seen varied from under 20 to over 200 in any one winter between 1962 and 1976. Small parties are quite often noted and gatherings of 50 or more have been seen; the largest in recent years was of 200 off Pett Level on 7 February 1965.

Such parties are becoming rare, and the winter population has probably declined during the last decade. Oiling incidents may be a contributory cause as sometimes as many as 10 per cent. of the winter records are of oiled birds.

Extensive passage movements occur which are discussed under **DIVER SPECIES.**

BLACK-THROATED DIVER— *Gavia arctica*

Status.—Scarce winter visitor; more numerous passage migrant, at least in Spring. No recent change in status is apparent.

The exact status of all the diver species in Sussex is difficult to determine owing to problems of identifying birds in flight and in separating Black-throated and Great Northern Divers.

49

However, Black-throated Divers have occurred between 3 August and 22 May, and approximate monthly totals for the period 1962 to 1976 are as follows:

Aug.	Sept.	Oct.	Nov.	Dec.	Jan.	Feb.	Mar.	Apr.	May
1	1	1	13	24	22	32	56	211	258

Nearly all records were for tidal waters, but there were occasional reports for large areas of fresh water inland such as Chichester gravel pits or the larger reservoirs.

Except on spring passage the species is usually seen singly, but two or three are sometimes seen together, and a party of 13 was recorded seven miles offshore in Rye Bay on 11 February 1967. A distressingly high proportion of the records from November to March relate to oiled birds, and the species may be more numerous offshore in the winter than our records indicate. These show not more than 15 occurring in the county in any winter in the period 1962 to 1976; in many winters only one or two are seen.

More are seen on spring passage, as the table shows, but passage movements are discussed under **DIVER SPECIES**.

GREAT NORTHERN DIVER — *Gavia immer*

Status.—Scarce winter visitor and passage migrant. No recent change in status is apparent.

The information available shows this to be the scarcest of the three diver species recorded in Sussex. It has occurred in each month from October to June, but is most usually found between December and May, either wintering or on spring passage. Approximate monthly totals for the period 1962 to 1976 are as follows:

Oct.	Nov.	Dec.	Jan.	Feb.	Mar.	Apr.	May	June
5	7	13	13	8	9	18	16	1

Nearly all records are for tidal waters, but birds very occasionally appear on large areas of freshwater inland, such as the main reservoirs. Birds are usually seen singly, but, as with Black-throated Divers, two or three are sometimes seen together. No more than nine have been recorded in one winter, however, and in some years none is seen.

Birds are noted on passage, but passage movements of divers are discussed under **DIVER SPECIES**.

DIVER SPECIES—*Gavia species*

With a high proportion of the divers observed in Sussex not specifically identified, the figures quoted under the specific headings only represent about a third of the divers seen. To give a more accurate picture of the numerical status of the group in Sussex the table sets out the approximate total numbers of all divers seen in each month between 1962 and 1976.

Jan.	Feb.	Mar.	Apr.	May	June	July	Aug.	Sept.	Oct.	Nov.	Dec.
750	820	760	1,191	1,423	9	0	7	19	142	503	522

A comparison of these figures with earlier data quoted by des Forges and Harber suggests a marked decline in the Channel during this century. Such a comparison must be made with caution, however, as some early counts of large numbers were made from boats some way off shore, for example by E. T. Booth; similar data for recent years are not available.

Systematic sea-watching in spring and autumn has recorded considerable passage movements off the coast. Autumn passage is difficult to disentangle from winter movements, which have been recorded immediately before severe weather, and the normal wanderings of birds wintering in the Channel. However, in autumn until late December about 70 per cent. of the birds noted are moving west.

There is a very marked passage from March to May, when 90 per cent. of all divers seen have been moving east up the coast. Most pass through in April and the peak movements are fairly consistently noted in the second half of this month, although they sometimes occur in late March or early May. However, this pattern may be distorted by the pattern of observation. Comparatively little time is spent sea-watching in the early months of the year in Sussex, but substantial easterly movements have been noted off Beachy Head as early as 31 January.

In studying these movements attempts have been made to assess the comparative abundance of each species. The identification of divers in flight is always difficult, but experienced observers feel confident in naming a proportion of the birds seen. Thus at Selsey Bill between 1960 and 1963 270 out of 800 passage divers were identified in spring, of which 55 per cent. were considered to be *arctica* and 45 per cent. *stellata*. More recently at Beachy Head, out of a total of 1,670 passage divers noted in spring between 1971 and 1975, 18 per cent. were identified as *arctica*, nine per cent. as *stellata*, and 0.5 per cent. as *immer*. Thus it seems clear that *arctica* is the most numerous species on spring passage. However, there is no doubt that *stellata* is the most numerous diver in winter, and Cooper (1975) has noted that virtually all the divers identified off Beachy Head during January to March have been *stellata*. Thus it seems likely that the winter population and a substantial passage in February and March are largely composed of *stellata*; passage of this species continues through April and May, and is then joined by a large movement of *arctica*; *immer* is always a scarce species.

LITTLE GREBE—*Tachybaptus ruficollis*

Status.—Scarce and local breeding species; common winter visitor; probably regular passage migrant. No recent change in status is definitely known, but a decline in the breeding population is suspected.

As breeding birds Little Grebes appear surprisingly scarce, the records for the years 1970 to 1976 indicate a population of less than 100 pairs. But the species is inconspicuous, usually nests on waters with dense marginal vegetation, and does so on quite small stretches of water besides lakes and large ponds, so pairs are probably overlooked. The table lists the more important breeding sites noted from 1970 to 1976, and the numbers found.

Locality	Number of Pairs	Locality	Number of Pairs
Aldsworth Ponds ..	2	Fen Place Mill ..	2–4
Forest Mere ..	1–3	Burton Ponds ..	3
Chichester G.P. ..	3–6	Wiston Park ..	1–2
Milland	1–4	Weir Wood	1–2
Sidlesham	1–2	Rye Harbour G.P.	4–10
Knepp	1–2		

In addition there were breeding records or casual breeding season reports from 25 other localities in the same period. Nesting is not established at each site every year, but evidence of any decline is, at present, rather inconclusive.

In the winter most Little Grebes occur on sheltered waters at the coast, although they are rare on the open sea. The most important winter sites are Chichester and Pagham Harbours, Newhaven Tidemills, and the Cuckmere estuary, each place holding gatherings of 20 to 50-60 fairly regularly. Since 1965 the number recorded along the coast in any winter has not exceeded about 170 birds, and the largest count in one locality was of 101 birds. Increasing numbers now winter inland, a change in habits similar to the Great Crested Grebe. From 1951 des Forges and Harber recorded Little Grebes regularly wintering inland and, since 1965, up to 60 have done so annually.

Wintering birds first appear at the coast in August and September, and most have left by early April. Some through passage also occurs and is probably regular, particularly in October and November, but the extent of such movements has not been determined accurately.

BLACK-NECKED GREBE—_Podiceps nigricollis_

Status.—Regular winter visitors and passage migrant.
The numbers occurring have declined in recent years.

As a winter visitor this species' distribution is very similar
to that of the Slavonian Grebe, but there is now no regular
wintering locality, although most recent records have been
from the western end of the county and Rye Harbour. No
party of more than three Black-necked Grebes has been
noted since 1960, and most reports are now of single birds; these
occur inland about as often as do Slavonian Grebes. Monthly
totals of Black-necked Grebes during the period 1960 to
1976 were:

July	Aug.	Sept.	Oct.	Nov.	Dec.	Jan.	Feb.	Mar.	Apr.	May	June
0	10	18	16	11	19	27	29	10	15	3	1

These records involve a total of about 120 individuals and the
species is now much scarcer than the Slavonian Grebe, although
des Forges and Harber recorded approximately equal numbers
of each species. In fact analysis of the records shows a steady
decline since about 1956. Thus the average number recorded
annually in each five-year period since 1947 was:

1947–1951	1952–1956	1957–1961	1962–1966	1967–1971	1972–1976
15.6	16.8	10.6	9	7.4	6.5

With the great increase in observer activity during the period
there is no reason to doubt that the decline evident since 1956
is anything but real. Almost certainly it has mainly affected
wintering birds rather than passage migrants, particularly in
Chichester Harbour, where parties of up to 10–15 once wintered
fairly frequently.

The movements of wintering birds and passage migrants
clearly overlap, but the records suggest that comparatively
few of the birds recorded from August to October and in April
stay for any length of time.

SLAVONIAN GREBE—*Podiceps auritus*

Status.—**Regular winter visitor; passage migrant, at least in spring. An increase has probably occurred in recent years.**

As a winter visitor the species occurs along the whole coast and occasionally on inland waters, but the most regular localities are Chichester Harbour and Church Norton, where gatherings of up to about 15 often winter. Larger numbers have occurred off Church Norton in some recent winters, including a count of 50 on 11 December 1971, the largest party yet recorded in Sussex. Birds are recorded inland, mainly at Chichester gravel pits, almost annually in winter.

Winter visitors probably arrive in November, sometimes October, and are most numerous in November and December. Some through passage perhaps occurs in late autumn and is clearly discernable in late March and April. There have been six recent records for May, and a bird in summer plumage was present at Chichester gravel pits and Chichester Harbour until 19 July 1970, and another was seen at Thorney Island on 25 July 1971. These are the first summer records for the county. Although there are no August records, the species has been recorded in September, the earliest report being for the seventh in 1951 and 1974. These are the only September records since 1947 and are the earliest autumn dates for Sussex. Monthly totals for the period 1960-1976 were:

Sept.	Oct.	Nov.	Dec.	Jan.	Feb.	Mar.	Apr.	May	June	July
1	20	186	245	210	175	164	156	6	1	2

A total of about 560 individuals is involved in these records and comparison with data given by des Forges and Harber suggests some increase, the average number recorded each year having risen from about 15 annually until 1961 to over 55 annually since 1967. The increase in observer activity seems unlikely to account entirely for this change.

RED-NECKED GREBE—*Podiceps griseigena*

Status.—**Annual winter visitor; probably also scarce passage migrant. No recent change in status is apparent.**

Red-necked Grebes have been recorded in every month from August to May, but most are seen from October to February. In the period 1961 to 1976 a total of about 83 were reported, numbers varying between one and 12 per year, and monthly totals were:

Aug.	Sept.	Oct.	Nov.	Dec.	Jan.	Feb.	Mar.	Apr.	May
3	4	14	11	15	20	10	8	5	2

Few were noted as making prolonged stays and it is difficult to assign any particular record as a wintering or passage bird.

Although these figures suggest some recent increase, as des Forges and Harber record only about 40 for the period 1950 to 1960, this would easily be accounted for by the great increase in regular observations at the coast. Nearly all records were for the sea or the immediate vicinity of the coast.

There have been eight recent inland records, however, from Weir Wood Reservoir (two), Darwell Reservoir (one), Chichester gravel pits (one), and Arlington Reservoir (four), making a total of 16 inland reports for the county altogether.

GREAT CRESTED GREBE—*Podiceps cristatus*

Status.—**Local resident; common winter visitor; probably passage migrant. Little recent change in status is apparent, but the increase in the resident population noted by des Forges and Harber has probably continued.**

The breeding population was surveyed annually from 1962 to 1965 and in 1975. The results of these surveys are given in the table, and show that 18 sites held Great Crested Grebes regularly in the breeding season and five sites, which were not occupied in 1975, are probably occupied more often than not.

**Breeding Season Population of Great Crested Grebes in
Sussex, 1962–75**

Locality				Number of Birds 1962–65	Number of Birds 1975
Chichester gravel pits	..	..	..	16–42	38
Petworth Park ..	..	..	..	3–4	7
Lurgashall	..	..	..	0–2	4
Shillinglee	..	..	..	2	5
Burton Ponds*	..	..	..	2–6	4
Knepp ..	..	..	..	4–8	6
Leigh Pond	..	..	..	2	2
Warnham Mill Pond ..	..	..	..	4	2
Hammer Pond ..	..	..	..	0–2	0
Barnhouse Pond	..	..	..	0–2	0
Tilgate ..	..	..	..	1–2	0
Slaugham Place	..	..	..	2–4	0
Crawley Mill Pond	..	..	..	2–4	2
Balcombe Lake	..	..	..	2–4	2
Horsted Keynes	..	..	..	0–4	4
Weir Wood Reservoir	..	..	..	2–4	30
Maresfield	..	..	..	0–2	1
Wadhurst Park ..	..	..	..	2–8	0
Eridge Park	..	..	..	2	2
Darwell Reservoir	..	..	..	0–6	2
Powdermill Reservoir	..	..	..	0–2	2
Pett Level	..	..	..	2	2
Rye Harbour gravel pits	..	..	..	2–4	7

*Note.—Burton Ponds includes Chingford Pond; all map references are given in SxBR 1964 and 1975. The winter of 1962/63 caused marked fluctuations in the first period.

In addition to the above sites three others held a total of six birds in one year between 1962 and 1965, and five held a total of 15 birds only in 1975; two of these new areas in 1975 were recently filled reservoirs. This probably represents a fair picture of the more casual breeding season or breeding records, of which a few occur in most years. Thus between 1966 and 1974 there were breeding season records from another 11 sites, of which three held birds in three years and four in two, making a grand total of 42 sites for which there were breeding season records between 1962 and 1975. Quite possibly some of our breeding birds use one or two alternative sites, perhaps particularly where they are breeding on rather small stretches of water.

However, the 1975 figures clearly give a very fair picture of the present breeding status, and Hughes (1975b), in discussing the results, notes that although the total summer population increased by 45 per cent. between 1965 and 1975, the number actually nesting has remained static at rather under 50 pairs (96 birds). Hughes listed industrial and agricultural pollutants and increased recreational activities, such as fishing, sailing and power boating, as factors affecting Great Crested Grebes' breeding distribution and success. It is worth noting that the increase in the acreage of wet gravel pit and reservoirs available to the species for nesting since 1962, particularly at Chichester, has not resulted in any significant increase in nesting pairs. A feature of modern management of both wet gravel pits and reservoirs is to encourage leisure activities of various sorts, and landscaping (which too often involves removing most of the marginal vegetation for tidiness). Unfortunately conservation is not usually considered very much under this policy.

Nesting has started earlier in recent years, which appears to be associated with a trend for Great Crested Grebes to become resident at their nesting sites. Walpole-Bond noted that eggs were only very exceptionally laid before the end of April, but in recent years nests with eggs have been found in February (the 26th, 1967), and have been noted fairly regularly in late March and early April.

In winter Great Crested Grebes are most common on the sea, particularly in Rye Bay, where up to 500 have been seen together (20 February 1949). More recently the largest concentrations noted there were about 200 on 4 December 1967, and 30 December 1968, and concentrations of up to 150 have been seen off the coast between Brighton and Rottingdean. Elsewhere the numbers seen together have rarely exceeded 10 to 30 birds. Peak numbers are normally present between December and early February.

The species once wintered inland very rarely (Walpole-Bond), but des Forges and Harber recorded small numbers doing so regularly by 1961 and this trend has continued. It seems most likely that the breeding stock is becoming resident on its breeding waters. Since 1962 counts of up to 60 have been made in winter at Chichester gravel pits, and of up to 30 at Weir Wood Reservoir, with small numbers regular elsewhere. Prolonged frost will drive these birds on to the sea, but many return inland immediately there is a thaw.

There may be some through passage. Although sea-watching has shown no significant coasting movements in either spring or autumn, small influxes have been noted on inland waters during March and April. A few non-breeding birds are also recorded on the sea during June and July.

FULMAR—*Fulmaris glacialis*

Status.—Summer visitor; probably passage migrant; winter vagrant. Prior to 1945 a winter vagrant only, thus a considerable increase has occurred recently.

Birds were seen on the cliffs in East Sussex as early as 1950, but despite a considerable increase in numbers, breeding was not proved until 1976. The largest summering group is found at Beachy Head, where up to five were noted prospecting in 1961, and numbers built up steadily to a maximum of 38 apparent pairs in 1972. Since 1965 prospecting birds have also been noted regularly at other localities on the chalk and east of Hastings. There were well over 100 birds summering in 1976. The birds arrive on the cliffs in January and February and stay until June or July, and what are presumably the same birds are recorded right along the coast. Curiously 90 per cent. of all Fulmars recorded at Selsey Bill have been flying west.

The species is uncommon in August and September, although the numbers of records is increasing, and is distinctly rare from October through December, when only seven were recorded between 1961 and 1974. However, in 1975 the Beachy Head population returned on 28 December, and this species' pattern of occurrence is still changing rapidly.

BULWER'S PETREL—*Bulweria bulwerii*

Status.—One record.

One was found dead near Beachy Head on 3 February 1903.

CORY'S SHEARWATER—*Calonectris diomedea*

Status.—Three records.

One was seen a few miles off Newhaven on 21 September 1936; one flew east off Langney Point on 15 October 1948; One flew east off Langney Point on 19 November 1950.

GREAT SHEARWATER—*Puffinus gravis*

Status.—Two records.

The remains of one were found at Rye on 27 November 1938; one was seen off Langney Point on 4 June 1956.

SOOTY SHEARWATER—*Puffinus griseus*

Status.—Rare passage migrant in autumn.

Until 1961 des Forges and Harber record four, and from then until 1976 27 were seen. Birds have been recorded singly except for two together flying west off Selsey Bill on 28 August 1965, and three likewise off Langney Point on 12 September 1970.

Birds have been recorded in June (one), July (two), August (eight), September (14), and October (six).

MANX SHEARWATER—*Puffinus puffinus*

Status.—Spring to autumn visitor. The number occurring
has apparently increased in recent years.

Two races of the Manx Shearwater occur in Sussex: *Puffinus
p. puffinus* and *Puffinus p. mauretanicus,* and between 1948
and 1976 both were seen almost annually. The table summarises
the records by months and races and shows *puffinus* to be the
most frequent. However, there are seasonal variations, and
mauretanicus is slightly more numerous in autumn, while
puffinus is much more numerous from April to June.

Manx Shearwaters in Sussex, 1948 to 1976

Race	Feb.	Mar.	Apr.	May	June	July
Manx Shearwater (*P. p. puffinus*) ..	1	0	9	318	21	5
Balearic Shearwater (*P. p. maureta-* *nicus*)	0	0	0	2	9	7
Race undetermined	0	0	7	3	4	1
Total	1	0	16	323	34	13

—continued under—

Race	Aug.	Sept.	Oct.	Nov.	Dec.	Total
Manx Shearwater (*P. p. puffinus*) ..	3	11	5	2	1	376
Balearic Shearwater (*P. p. mauretani-* *cus*)	15	6	3	1	0	43
Race undetermined	1	3	0	0	0	19
Total	19	20	8	3	1	438

There have been no January records. All recent records are
for the Channel and most relate to single birds. But several
parties have been seen, the largest of which was of 80 *puffinus*
off Beachy head on 9 May 1975. The May total includes
some exceptional movements of *puffinus* off Beachy Head,
on 28 May 1972, involving 84 birds, and 8 May 1975, involving
64 birds, and on the 9th with 126 birds. These movements

account for 75 per cent. of all the records of this race since 1948 and that in 1972 occurred in a severe south-westerly gale. Thus although a marked increase is apparent in recent years it may prove to be due entirely to three freak movements. The race *mauretanicus,* on the other hand, may now be appearing less frequently, and only one has been recorded since 1971.

STORM PETREL—*Hydrobates pelagicus*
Status.—**Rare visitor. The numbers recorded appear to have declined in recent years.**

Walpole-Bond refers to innumerable reports for both spring and autumn, but des Forges and Harber recorded only 19 between 1946 and 1960, and there were only three more up to 1976. There are old records for every month except August and September, but the records since 1946 have been for April (one), May (one), June (two), October (four), November (13), and December (one). All were of single birds except for three together off Langney Point on 1 November 1952. There are no recent inland records, although storm-driven birds have been found inland in the past.

LEACH'S PETREL—*Oceanodroma leucorrhoa*
Status.—**Rare visitor.**

Until 1961 des Forges and Harber recorded a total of about 75 birds. From then until 1976 there were two reports: 31 December 1964, Langney Point; and 19 October 1966, Saltdean. All the 15 records since 1948 have been of single birds and the most in any year was four in 1952. There were records for four months: September (three), October (six), November (five), and December (one). There are old records for January and one for May.

A third of the recent records relate to birds found dead or dying inland after severe gales. Otherwise the species is strictly maritime.

GANNET—*Sula bassana*

Status.—Common spring to autumn visitor offshore; scarce in winter. No recent change in status is apparent.

Gannets are recorded offshore in every month, but are scarce or rare from December to March. The table, summarising detailed observations at Selsey Bill between 1960 and 1970, still gives a fair indication of the pattern of occurrence and numbers involved.

Gannet Movements off Selsey Bill, 1960–1970

	January/ February	March/ June	July/ October	November/ December
1960–65				
East	44	412	786	31
West	39	963	1,685	102
1966–70				
East	9	317	228	71
West	61	1,516	1,237	121

In addition feeding parties of up to 80 birds were seen offshore, mainly in early autumn, and 800 flew west off Beachy Head on 18 September 1976, the largest movement yet seen off Sussex.

As with some other seabirds westerly movements predominate, which makes defining status accurately very difficult. Since there are now breeding colonies on the Channel Islands in comfortable feeding range of the Sussex coast, it is likely that both feeding and passage movements are involved.

Sick or dead birds are sometimes found inland.

CORMORANT—*Phalacrocorax carbo*

Status.—**Has bred; non-breeding birds present throughout the year; winter visitors; probably passage migrant.
No recent change in status is definitely known.**

Although sometimes seen on the chalk cliffs in the summer,
Cormorants have not bred in Sussex since 1938 or earlier.

Few accurate counts are available for this species, but the
records since 1967 show it to be most numerous in the county
from October to March, with peak numbers in October or
November and February or March. Totals for the whole county
in this period have not been shown to exceed 200–300 birds,
although 200 were recorded in Chichester Harbour alone in
1953. This was probably an exceptional count, as not more
than 50–60 have been noted there during estuary counts since
1967, but gatherings of 60 to 100 are regular now in several
places along the coast, for example Bognor pier, and 150 were
recorded in the Rye area in the winter of 1972/3. Thus the
total noted at present perhaps underestimates numbers.

Most are recorded at the coast, particularly in the western
harbours and at Rye Harbour, but inland records are frequent
from autumn to spring, and up to 65 have been seen at
Chichester gravel pits. Smaller numbers frequent the main
reservoirs. There is a regular roost in Arundel Park, and 120
were seen flying to roost there on 17 December 1973, the
highest count so far.

There are two records of the race *sinensis*: 11 February 1936,
which had been ringed in Germany; and 12 February 1938.

SHAG—*Phalacrocorax aristotelis*

Status.—**Occasional non-breeding summer visitor; winter
visitor; probably passage migrant. Has been recorded
regularly in Sussex only since 1950, although this
species may have been overlooked previously.**

Between 1950 and 1976 from one to about 30 birds were
seen anually, except in 1960 when there were about 160,

mainly in the spring. Birds were recorded in every month, and approximate monthly totals during the period were:

Jan.	Feb.	Mar.	Apr.	May	June	July	Aug.	Sept.	Oct.	Nov.	Dec.
41	46	150	118	107	48	35	34	29	25	43	34

All records were for the coast, except for one shot from a party of six at Weir Wood Reservoir on 18 March 1962 and a total of five at Arlington Reservoir between 1973 and 1975. There is also a record for 26 November 1928 from Goodwood.

Birds ringed in Northumberland were recovered at Southwick in February 1954, and at Horsted Keynes on 25 March 1962, and one from the Isle of May, Forth, was recovered at Roedean on 18 January 1970. All were dead and had been ringed as pulli the summer before recovery.

HERON—*Ardea cinerea*

Status.—Resident and partial migrant; perhaps also passage migrant and winter visitor. A decreasing breeding species.

Herons are reasonably common in Sussex at all seasons in suitable localities but, although up to 35 have been noted together in autumn and winter, gatherings of any size are rare away from breeding colonies.

Walpole-Bond gives a detailed account of all the Sussex heronries, active or extinct, known until 1938, when the total population was 321 pairs. This represented a considerable decline during the previous 100 years, since one heronry alone contained about 400 pairs about 1840. This long-term decrease has continued, although there have been fluctuations. The table, based on counts of certainly occupied nests, summarises the breeding position since 1938.

Number of Breeding Herons in Sussex, 1938 to 1970

	1938	1950	1960	1970
Total pairs ..	321	225	145	159
Colonies ..	11	10	12	11

In 1973 there were 178 nests in 10 colonies; and there were 179 in 10 colonies in 1976, when two sites usually holding five to 10 pairs were not visited.

The colonies known from 1970 to 1976 and the numbers of certainly occupied nests they contained were:

Fishbourne, Old Park Wood

First recorded in 1872, although possibly a very ancient site. The highest recorded count was 37 nests in 1960 and 1962; the 1970 figure was 25, and there were 33 in 1976.

Pagham

First recorded in 1960 and possibly an offshoot of the Fishbourne colony. The highest recorded count was six nests from 1966 to 1969; the 1970 figure was four, but there were only two in 1976, and the colony may be dying out.

Parham, North Park Wood

Originally founded at Michelgrove in 1810, this colony moved to its present site between 1826 and 1832. The highest recorded count was 90 to 120 nests in the 1870s, and since 1948 was 48 nests in 1959; the 1970 figure was 41, and there were 42 in 1976.

Henfield, Wyckham Wood

Probably founded in 1951, when it was first recorded. The highest recorded count was 13 nests in 1959; the 1970 figure was nine, and there were four in 1976.

Glynde Place

First recorded about 1946, it was not known in 1939. The highest recorded count was 24 nests in 1950; the 1970 figure was one. There was none thereafter, and the colony is extinct.

Firle Decoy

Founded in 1917. The highest recorded count was 41 nests in 1973; the 1970 figure was 30, and there were 35 in 1976. Figures published for this colony between 1948 and 1966 were usually less than 10, and it seems likely that this site and Glynde are used by the same group of birds.

Glynleigh

Founded in 1937. The highest recorded count was 34 nests in 1955. There was none after 1969, and the colony is now extinct.

Priesthawes

First recorded in 1963 with two nests. There were six nests in 1970 and eight in 1975. This colony probably started as an offshoot of Glynleigh, being only about a mile away, and has not had more than eight nests. A single pair at nearby Westham since 1963 derived from the same source.

Wartling

The present colony was first recorded in 1959 and has moved twice, occupying the present site in 1968. The highest recorded count was nine nests in 1969; the 1970 figure was four, and there were four in 1976. The Herstmonceux/Wartling area is a very old site, a large colony (150 pairs) being recorded at Windmill Hill in the mid-16th century, although detailed records for the colony only exist from 1835. It apparently died out in 1948, and the present colony was first located at Boreham Street.

Eridge Park

Founded between 1885 and 1890. The highest recorded count was 38 nests in 1950 and 1957. There were only six nests in 1970, but 11 in 1976.

Leasam

There has been a substantial heronry in the triangle formed by Rye, Brede and Beckley since at least 1297. Originally at Udimore, it moved to Great Sowdens Wood, Brede, between 1840 and 1845, then to Aldershaw, Beckley, between 1892 and 1896. The present site was apparently first recorded about 1939 and Aldershaw was deserted in 1947. The highest known count was about 400 nests in Great Sowdens Wood in about 1840, and in this century 119 nests at Aldershaw in 1930. Since 1948 numbers at Leasam reached a peak of 63 nests in 1950, declined to an all-time low of five in 1963, but have since recovered steadily; the 1970 figure was 30, and there were 23 or more in 1975.

Since 1947 breeding has also occurred at the following sites: Itchenor, up to 18 nests from 1946 to 1951; Chichester gravel pits, one nest in 1960; Fynings Moor, Rogate, two nests in 1963 and 1964; Beauport Park, Hastings, four or five nests in 1950; Great Park Wood, Udimore (one of the original sites of the present Leasam colony), irregularly occupied until 1960 by up to nine pairs; Nuthurst, a pair in 1973; Knepp, eight pairs in 1976 Buxted Park, one pair in 1976.

There are a few records from the coast every year suggesting migration. Records relate to coasting movements, which are difficult to evaluate and some of which may refer only to local movements, and both immigration and emigration in in spring and autumn. Most movement is noted from June to September, and nestlings ringed in Sussex have been recovered on the Continent as early as June in the same year. Thus of 40 ringed at Aldershaw in April 1928, six were recovered in Belgium, France and Spain between early June 1928 and 11 January 1929.

PURPLE HERON—*Ardea purpurea*
Status.—**Vagrant.**

There are 18 records, 11 of them since 1957. All are of single birds—10 seen at the coast and eight in inland localities.

Records are for April (four), May (five), June (two), July (one), September (one), October (one), and November (two). The old records are undated, but one was for autumn.

SQUACCO HERON—*Ardeola ralloides*

Status.—Three records.

One was shot at Horsham in 1849, probably in July; one was shot between Steyning and Henfield about 30 September 1934; one was seen at Brighton on 29 April 1951.

CATTLE EGRET—*Bubulcus ibis*

Status.—Four records.

On 27 April 1962 four together were found in fields just north of Pagham Harbour and one was seen there on the 29th. On 28 April that year one was seen with cattle at Lancing. One seen at Wittersham from 8–15 August 1974 was thought to be an escape from captivity.

LITTLE EGRET—*Egretta garzetta*

Status.—Vagrant.

There are 13 records, all since 1952 and of single birds seen at the coast. Nine were recorded from either Chichester or Pagham Harbours. There are records for May (six), June (four), and July (three). One bird remained in Chichester Harbour from 10 June to 1 September 1952, and another did so from 30 July to 23 August 1959.

NIGHT HERON—*Nycticorax nycticorax*

Status.—**Vagrant.**

There are about nine records but only four for this century: an immature was seen near Lancing College on 12 December 1954, which may have been an escape; an immature was found dead at Rye on 29 September 1969; a sub-adult was seen at Sidlesham Ferry on 27 May 1970. One was seen at Rye Harbour from 2–4 September 1975.

LITTLE BITTERN—*Ixobrychus minutus*

Status.—**Vagrant.**

Until 1947 des Forges and Harber give about 17 records, and there have been six since 1964. All records are of single birds and most are for the coast, or recently Chichester gravel pits. There are four old records for built-up areas. Records are for March (one), April (three), May (eight), June (one), July (one), August (two), September (one), and October (two). Four old records are undated.

BITTERN—*Botaurus stellaris*

Status.—**Scarce winter visitor; occasional from spring to autumn. No recent change in status is apparent.**

Although up to eight have been seen in one year, Bitterns are not annual in Sussex. In the period 1947 to 1976 about 73 were recorded, approximate monthly totals being:

Aug.	Oct.	Nov.	Dec.	Jan.	Feb.	Mar.	Apr.	June
1	1	2	18	20	18	15	3	1

There were two reports of two together, otherwise all were of single birds. The species may be encountered in any suitable marsh or dense area of aquatic vegetation at the coast or inland.

AMERICAN BITTERN—*Botaurus lentiginosus*
Status.—Three records.

One was shot on Pevensey Levels on 26 November 1867; one was shot on Amberley Wildbrooks on 30 November 1883; one was caught near Hollingbury Camp, Brighton, on 24 October 1909.

WHITE STORK—*Ciconia ciconia*
Status.—Vagrant which is perhaps increasing.

Until 1929 des Forges and Harber give about 20 records involving about 27 birds. Since 1965 there have been 11 reports involving 16 birds. One overwintered near Adversane in 1974/75, but otherwise records were for April (three), May (one), June (three), July (two), and September (one). The April records include one of a party of five at Polegate on the 25th in 1972.

BLACK STORK—*Ciconia nigra*
Status.—One record.

One was seen at Iden from 9 August to 14 September 1958; it had been first seen at Stone Cliff, Kent, on 7 August.

GLOSSY IBIS—*Plegadis falcinellus*
Status.—Vagrant.

The only recent record is of one at Pagham Harbour, on 22 and 23 April 1965. There are a number of old records, mainly of single birds, although parties of about 10 birds have been seen twice; des Forges and Harber give one or two for May, one for August, three for September, several for October, and two or three for November.

SPOONBILL—*Platalea leucorodia*

Status.—**Rare passage migrant or spring to autumn visitor; rare winter visitor.**

Since 1947 Spoonbills have been recorded each year, except in 1959, 1960, 1962, 1963, 1969, 1973, and 1976, and there were records involving 82 birds. Single birds are usually seen, but two or three together have been recorded several times, and a party of five flew west off Langney Point on 17 October 1947, and one of 20 did likewise on 1 September 1964.

Most records are for Chichester, Pagham or Rye Harbours, and all are for the coast, except for one at Amberley Wildbrooks from 31 December 1950 to 15 April 1951. This is the longest stay recorded for any individual, but birds often remain for several weeks. There are records for every month, monthly totals for the period 1947 to 1976 being:

Jan.	Feb.	Mar.	Apr.	May	June	July	Aug.	Sept.	Oct.	Nov.	Dec.
2	2	5	5	17	13	3	7	32	9	4	3

GREATER FLAMINGO—*Phoenicopterus ruber*

Status.—**One record.**

One shot near Jury's Gap on 1 August 1916 was possibly an escape.

MUTE SWAN—*Cygnus olor*

Status.—Resident; possibly also winter visitor. No recent
change in status is apparent.

Mute Swans are fairly widely distributed breeding birds in
Sussex, but little up-to-date information about numbers is
available. The most recent survey was that organised by the
British Trust for Ornithology in 1955, which recorded *c.* 100
pairs; des Forges and Harber considered this to be an under-
estimate.

In winter sizable flocks occur in suitable localities along the
coast, in the permanent grasslands of the river valleys and levels
and on the reservoirs. The largest such flock in recent winters
was of 145 in the Amberley/Pulborough marshes on 17 December 1960, and gatherings of 40 to 70 are not infrequent. About
100 are now found wintering fairly regularly in Bosham Creek.

WHOOPER SWAN—*Cygnus cygnus*

Status.—Irregular winter visitor. Now scarcer than
Bewick's Swan and not recorded every year, although
no change in the number occurring is apparent.

The numbers recorded have always been small, although
quite marked influxes occurred in the three most recent severe
winters, with about 42 in 1946/47, 40–50 in early 1956, and
60 in 1962/63. Otherwise fewer than 20 have been seen in any
year since 1947, except 1968, when 34 passed east up the
coast off Pevensey on 7 March, the largest party noted in the
county since 1938.

Whooper Swans are most usually seen in the permanent
grasslands of the river valleys and levels or on reservoirs and
estuaries. Nearly all the records are for the period December
to March with a distinct peak in February, but there have
been two April records since 1947, one for May (2nd, 1956,
Rye), one for October (16th, 1969, Pevensey), and one for

13 November 1971 in the Adur Levels; there are also two old records for November. Approximate monthly totals for the period 1947 to 1976 were:

Oct.	Nov.	Dec.	Jan.	Feb.	Mar.	Apr.	May
1 ·	1	48	80	131	93	2	1

BEWICK'S SWAN—*Cygnus bewickii*

Status.—Winter visitor; possibly also passage migrant. A marked change in status has occurred in recent years, and is now a regular winter visitor, although as recently as 1953 it was rarer than Whooper Swan.

Most Bewick's Swans are now recorded in wet grasslands or large areas of open water in the interior, although des Forges and Harber record none in the interior before 1940 and as recently as 1961 most were still seen at the coast. However, in addition to increasing reports of transient parties inland, a wintering herd is now established in the Amberley/Pulborough marshes and groups regularly make prolonged stays elsewhere.

The first sign of the present pattern of occurrence is detectable as early as the winter of 1953/54, but an increase has been most marked since the winter of 1961/62. The cold winter of early 1956 produced an exceptional influx, but neither of the winters of 1946/47 nor 1962/63 did so, in direct contrast to Whooper Swans. The table summarises the records for Bewick's Swans for the period 1948-1975 by five-year periods:

Bewick's Swans in Sussex 1948-1975

				Oct.	Nov.	Dec.	Jan.	Feb.	Mar.	Apr.	Total birds
1948-52	..	..	..	0	0	1	2	1	1	1	6
1953-57	..	..	..	0	8	4	25	137	51	31	226
1958-62	..	..	..	0	5	11	50	38	10	0	74
1963-67	..	..	..	0	20	93	283	102	75	0	391
1968-72	..	..	..	9	64	239	235	145	102	30	436
1973-75 (3 yrs.)	..	..		2	36	194	176	166	113	0	313

The increase has been considerable. Disregarding the influx of early 1956, which involved about 150 birds and appears quite exceptional, the average number seen per year rose from just over one to 14 between 1952 and 1962, jumped to 70 or more per year between 1963 and 1972, and rose to over 100 per year between 1973 and 1976. January is the peak month, but winter visitors now start to arrive in October and November and depart in February and March, sometimes April. There has been a fairly constant tendency since 1962 for Bewick's Swans to appear earlier in winter, and in 1972 the Amberley flock started to arrive in late October. There have been two other recent October records, for the 27th, 1973, in the Cuckmere, and 30th, 1971, at Rye.

The number staying throughout the winter is still quite small, 92 in February 1976 being the highest count so far of the Amberley/Pulborough flock. Thus many more birds have been recorded as making shorter visits or passing straight through. But it is not clear if the latter records indicate passage or are merely wide-scale wanderings by birds with no permanent winter site. Most records of movement have been to the west, which may not be significant.

PINK-FOOTED GOOSE—*Anser fabalis brachyrhnchus*

Status.—Scarce winter visitor and passage migrant. No recent change in status is apparent.

Pink-footed Geese are not quite of annual occurrence in Sussex, but were noted in 20 of the 30 years between 1947 and 1976. All records are for the river valleys, levels, or the coast.

The severe winters of 1955/56 (166 recorded) and 1962/63 (165 recorded) are the only winters in which substantial numbers have been seen. Otherwise more than *c.* 20 in one winter is most exceptional, and single birds are quite usual. These geese rarely stay for very long, except in severe weather.

Most of the records are for January (31 per cent.), March (26 per cent.), February (17 per cent.), and November (14 per cent.), but there are records for the whole period September to May. The May record is of a bird which remained at Piddinghoe until 13 May 1956.

Parties have been seen flying up the Channel, presumably on migration, twice in April (4th, 1961, and 7th, 1969), and once in March (30th, 1971).

BEAN GOOSE—*Anser fabalis fabalis*

Status.—Irregular winter visitor. No recent change in status is apparent.

Between 1919 and 1959 des Forges and Harber give five records comprising 27 birds. Since then there have been 14 records comprising a total of *c.* 85 birds in six winters. Most were seen in early 1963, with records from nine localities totalling at least 40 birds. Between 25 December 1963 and 21 March 1964 a party of eight wintered in West Sussex, being seen in several places as far apart as Sidlesham and Wiston Park; there is no reason to suppose that more than one party was involved. In addition 10 seen at Litlington on 14 October 1974 seem most likely to have been on migration, apparently the only such record for Sussex.

WHITE-FRONTED GOOSE—*Anser albifrons*

Status.—Regular winter visitor or migrant. Some recent increase in the numbers occurring is possible.

About 90 per cent. of all grey geese identified in Sussex are of this species. Although recorded annually there is no regular winter population, and birds rarely remain for more than a few days except in severe winters, when considerable influxes occur. Apart from birds flying over, which may be seen anywhere, these geese are nearly always found in the permanent grassland of the river valleys and levels or near the coast, where there are large areas of suitable grazing.

The numbers recorded each winter are very variable, ranging since 1947, for example, from three in the winter of 1960/61 to about 1,670 in the winter of 1962/63. Parties are usually of up to about 50 birds, but flocks of up to 150 are not rare; the largest flock in recent years was of *c.* 400 birds in the Sidlesham area in early 1963.

Nearly all records are for the period November to March, but there is one October record (1885, Shoreham), and a few for April, May and June which probably refer to pricked birds or escapes from collections. A marked peak occurs between mid-December and the end of January, and many records during this period, particularly since 1965, are of parties flying west or south-west. In total these records strongly suggest a westerly winter movement through the county. Possibly these birds are part of the flocks which winter in the valleys of the Hampshire Avon and/or Severn. Some spring passage may occur in March, but involves few birds.

As far as is known all Sussex records refer to the race *albifrons*, except for a bird showing the characters of the race *flavirostris* at Wiggonholt on 27 January 1956.

GREY LAG GOOSE—*Anser anser*

Status.—Irregular winter visitor; perhaps regular passage migrant.

Although this species has occured more regularly in the past decade than formerly, no very significant change in status seems likely. Introduced populations now feral in southern England probably account for some Sussex records, making the status of truly wild birds very difficult to assess.

However, the numbers recorded are always small, parties of more than 10 birds being exceptional; single birds are frequently noted. Except in 1953, when a party of 67 was seen, not more than about 25 birds have been seen in any year since 1947, and it is of interest that influxes have not occurred in recent severe winters.

Half of all the records since 1947 have been for the period mid-February to mid-April, particularly March, with 30 per cent., which suggests that there is a fairly regular, although small, spring movement through the county. A return movement may occur in the autumn, although there are fewer records. There are also a few records for January, but only two for the first half of February.

CANADA GOOSE—*Branta canadensis*
Status.—**An introduced resident which is increasing.**

S. W. M. Hughes published a full account of the history and current status of the Canada Goose in Sussex in SxBR.1972; these notes summarise his findings.

The species was probably first introduced into Sussex somewhen in the second half of the 19th century, and the largest flock in the county, at Petworth Park, was started somewhen between 1918 and 1930. Since 1947 breeding has been proved at a total of 22 sites, and some other sites have probably not been found; not every site is used, or at least recorded, each year. Three attempts to census the total population have been made after the breeding season, in July 1953, January 1967 and 1968, and July 1971. These counts recorded totals of 23-50 birds in 1953, about 290 in the period 1967-1968, and 326, including 98 young of the year, in 1971. In 1976 the records indicated a population of at least 700 birds, and 45 pairs were reported in the breeding season.

The number found breeding successfully in any year is small compared to the total population, for example only 20-25 pairs in 1971. Although some breeding sites are certainly not known, many pairs simply do not attempt to breed, and breeding success is low. This suggests a dearth of suitable habitat. In north-west Sussex some culling is also carried out by agricultural interests. Despite these significant checks on the population this species seems likely to increase further in the future.

BARNACLE GOOSE—*Branta leucopsis*
Status.—**Rare winter visitor, usually in severe weather. No recent change in status is apparent.**

Until 1961 des Forges and Harber gave about 14 records in addition to the small influx involving *c.* 55 birds in the frost of February 1956. Since 1961 there have been nine records comprising 49 birds, 39 of them in the winter of 1962/63. All records are for coastal grasslands except for a party of 27 on Glynde Levels on 26 February 1956.

Most birds have been seen in December, January or February, but there is one record for October (30th, 1949, Sidlesham), one for November, three for March, and one for April, of a bird which stayed at Pagham Harbour from 18 March to 3 April 1962.

Except for birds seen during severe winter weather, which have often associated with influxes of other geese, records of this species are open to the suspicion that the birds have escaped from captivity. This was certainly so with a party of five present in East Sussex during much of 1972.

PALE-BREASTED BRENT GOOSE—*Branta bernicla hrota*
Status.—**Scarce winter visitor. No recent change in status is apparent.**

Pale-breasted Brent Geese were noted in 14 out of the 29 winters between 1947/48, and 1975/6, with a total of *c.* 130 birds in all. Not more than 30 (in 1966/67) have been recorded in any winter. Parties of more than five are unusual, but flocks of 10-20 have been noted on five occasions, and one of 30 was seen in Chichester Harbour on 25 February 1967, the largest yet recorded in the county.

This race has been seen most often in Chichester and Pagham Harbours (14 records comprising 67 birds), at Cuckmere Haven (four records comprising 17 birds) and at Pett Level (four records comprising 24 birds).

DARK-BREASTED BRENT GOOSE—*Branta bernicla bernicla*

Status.—**Locally common winter visitor; passage migrant. A marked increase in numbers has occurred recently.**

Prior to 1938 this goose wintered regularly in Chichester Harbour and possibly in Pagham Harbour, but little information about the numbers involved is available. However, by 1950 regular wintering had ceased. Today a substantial winter population has re-established itself in both harbours and is still increasing; there is little doubt that the numbers involved are now far greater than ever before. The table sets out the peak counts in Chichester Harbour, where by far the largest flocks occur, in each winter since 1947, to show the extent and timing of the increase.

Peak Winter Counts of Brent Geese in Chichester Harbour from 1946/47 to 1975/76

46/47	47/48	48/49	49/50	50/51	51/52	52/53	53/54	54/55	55/56	56/57	57/58
80	16	10	0	0	0	25	38	40	220	83	280

58/59	59/60	60/61	61/62	62/63	63/64	64/65	65/66	66/67	67/68	68/69	69/70
220	180	650	400	600	1,500	2,000	1,500	2,600	2,000	2,455	2,300

70/71	71/72	72/73	73/74	74/75	75/76
3,295	3,080	4,350	7,500	5,150	6,345

In Pagham Harbour the winter peak did not exceed 200 birds until the winter of 1973/74, but there were 1,030 by 1975/76. The establishment of the present winter population appears to date from the mid-1950s, and the increase has been very marked since 1960. It has been parallelled by a similar increase in Langstone Harbour in Hampshire, which is only separated from Chichester Harbour by Hayling Island; in fact, the two harbours join at the north end of Hayling. All the information available shows that the Brent flocks in these two harbours remain largely separate, except to the north of Hayling Island, and counts of the entire Chichester/Langstone complex since 1972/73 have shown the peak populations to reach 10,000 to 12,000 birds.

Winter visitors start to arrive in October, occasionally September, and peak numbers usually occur in January or February. But large flocks are now present from mid-November to mid-March every winter, and the winter mean in Chichester Harbour, calculated from monthly counts during this period, rose almost every winter from 720 in 1965/66 to 5,345 in 1975/76. The flocks disperse very rapidly in the second half of March and sizable flocks are rare after the end of this month.

Although present in Langstone Harbour there are now no beds of *Zostera* species in either Sussex estuary, although these certainly existed in the early years of this century, and *Z. angustifolia* was recorded near the Hayling shore of Chichester Harbour as recently as 1963. But substantial beds of green algae are present and appear to have spread in recent years; they are probably continuing to do so. The Brent now appear to feed mainly on these plants. However, the geese also fed extensively on grass marsh round Chichester Harbour after 1973/74, and Campbell (1946), during a study of the food of Wigeon and Brent Geese in Britain, recorded animal matter in the stomachs of three Brent from Essex and five from Ulster, out of a total of 28 stomachs examined. Thus the feeding requirements of this bird may prove less inflexible than usually supposed.

Away from Chichester and Pagham Harbours these geese are scarce in Sussex, but small parties occur briefly in most winters in many coastal localities, particularly the Pett/Rye area. They are rarely found on inland waters, although, since it is established that some of our winter visitors migrate over the interior of the county, such records are likely from time to time.

There is a regular easterly passage along the coast in spring, between late February and late April, with peak numbers usually occurring in March. The numbers recorded annually vary widely, ranging from under 100 to nearly 3,000 in recent springs. A westerly return movement occurs between mid-October and December, but fewer birds are noticed. The extent to which the Sussex population is involved in these movements is unknown, but at least some of our wintering birds move overland, and parties have been reported over Kingley Vale, Eartham, and West Chiltington recently, usually in spring. The reports suggest that large numbers are sometimes involved.

RED-BREASTED GOOSE—*Branta ruficollis*

Status.— One record.

One was seen in the Amberley/Pulborough marshes between 8 and 17 February 1958.

RUDDY SHELDUCK—*Tadorna ferruginea*

Status.— Vagrant.

There have been no acceptable records since 1940 which have not been considered as most likely to have escaped from collections.

Among old records there is evidence of irruptions in September 1890, when single birds were obtained at Harting and Selsey; October 1892, when at least seven were seen or obtained between Eastbourne and Selsey, and August and September 1940, when six were shot at Rye Harbour. Walpole-Bond also records several on 8 September 1884 and during April 1885, two of which were shot.

SHELDUCK—*Tadorna tadorna*

Status.—**Locally common resident and winter visitor; a few on passage. The wintering population has increased considerably in recent years, but little change at other seasons is apparent.**

Shelduck first bred in Sussex in 1904 but, although numbers established themselves round Chichester and Pagham Harbours fairly quickly, colonisation of the rest of the county has been slow and the breeding population is still mainly concentrated around these two harbours. However, single pairs breed regularly at the Cuckmere estuary and about 12 pairs do so between Rye and the Midrips. Breeding has also occurred at a cliff-top site at Beachy Head, and the species is now colonising inland sites, with regular nesting at Chichester gravel pits, and birds present in other localities, particularly in the Arun valley, almost every season. Nesting has been proved as far inland as Harting.

There are no recent counts of breeding pairs round either of the western harbours, but counts of young there indicate little change since 1947 and suggest a total population of rather under 100 pairs. The county breeding population is therefore unlikely to exceed 100–150 pairs. Breeding success, judging from a long series of reports from Rye, has also changed little since 1947; the Rye figures show an average brood size ranging from 5.7 to 9.7, and averaging 7.8.

A substantial non-breeding population also summers in the western harbours. Again this has shown little significant change since 1947, and May and June counts show that 450 to 700 birds are regularly involved in Chichester Harbour and 50 to 180 in Pagham Harbour.

These breeding season data suggest a marked decrease since 1938, when Walpole-Bond quoted a figure of 500 pairs for south-west Sussex. This figure was repeated by des Forges and Harber, and quoted by Parslow (1973), but I am reasonably certain that it was a considerable over-estimate. Certainly there is no reason apparent for such a marked local decrease (of about 80 per cent.), which seems unlikely in view of the slow increase and spread in other areas.

Large winter concentrations only occur in Chichester and Pagham Harbours, where a series of counts, summarised in the table, have been made since 1966.

Total Number of Wintering Shelduck, Chichester and Pagham Harbours, 1966 to 1976

Winter	Nov.	Dec.	Jan.	Feb.	Mar.
1965/66	No count		3,500	3,850	680
1966/67	665	780	3,160	3,490	545
1967/68	750	1,650	3,550	2,780	5,400
1968/69	1,065	2,200	3,950	1,750	1,370
1969/70	655	2,540	4,000	3,620	3,820
1970/71	550	1,450	3,000	4,260	3,200
1971/72	1,175	2,255	3,510	4,550	2,400
1972/73	1,100	1,385	3,260	3,325	2,850
1973/74	735	2,370	3,645	3,625	2,530
1974/75	1,465	1,875	3,105	2,975	2,405
1975/76	1,662	2,263	2,815	3,140	2,520

The largest winter flocks are in Chichester Harbour, where the winter peak was of 3,000 birds or more in each winter until 1974/75, and the highest count was of 4,900 birds on 10 March 1968. Peak counts in Pagham Harbour ranged between 500 and 1,000 birds in the period.

Outside these harbours it is doubtful if the total winter population exceeds 200 birds, but up to 70 winter at Newhaven and between Rye and the Midrips. A few also winter in the Cuckmere estuary, the Amberley/Pulborough marshes and Glynde Levels, but parties of more than 20 are rare.

The counts from the western harbours represent a considerable increase in the wintering population. This is most clear in

Pagham Harbour, where the National Wildfowl Counts until 1963 recorded a normal winter peak of 100 birds, with up to 300 in severe weather (Atkinson-Willes 1963). In Chichester Harbour the highest count recorded until 1961 was of 1,550 birds in February 1959, but it is doubtful if any counts covering the entire estuary were made before 1966.

The movements and moult migration of Shelduck in Sussex have been little studied. But it is evident that the species is now a regular winter visitor on a large scale, although the data available to des Forges and Harber suggested that the winter flocks were made up of the breeding population, non-breeding birds and the young of the year, except in very cold weather; this cannot be so today, although cold weather influxes still occur.

Very few Shelduck are present in August and September, most of the resident adult population leaving to moult in July and a variable proportion of the young of the year following later; some September counts in Chichester Harbour have found as few as three present. The return movement begins in October, but substantial numbers are not often present before November. The highest winter numbers are present in January and February, occasionally early March, and there is a fairly rapid departure of winter visitors in late March and early April.

DUCKS

Table VIII sets out the range and means of the peak winter counts recorded in the period 1964/65 to 1974/75 for the commoner ducks, in the most important wintering sites in Sussex for which regular figures are available. The table aims to provide a simple comparative index, both of numbers and the relative importance of areas, rather than definitive estimates of population. Since it takes no account of possible movements between sites it probably contains some duplications. For the same reason the population estimates given in the species accounts are meant only to indicate the order of size.

TABLE VIII

Range and Average of the Winter (Oct.-Mar.) Peaks of Duck in 12 Important Sussex Wintering Localities, 1964/65-1974/75

Locality	Mallard	Teal	Wigeon	Pintail	Shoveler	Tufted Duck	Pochard
Chichester Harbour .. ::	20-365 220	40-820 345	255-1,775 820	55-175 95	0-13 6	0-195 55	0-115 30
Pagham Harbour ::	85-430 290	100-500 310	50-3,000 730	10-75 40	0-50 18	13-200 50	1-40 15
Chichester gravel pits ::	215-800 440	25-340 135	0-80 20	0-100 18	55-185 95	180-425 300	200-465 330
Burton Ponds ::	12-150 90	10-65 25	0-25 12	0-14 4	0-23 6	35-100 60	10-70 45
Amberley/Pulborough ::	30-410 200	200-1,200 560	500-2,225 1,280	2-200 60	6-400 85	0-120 25	0-120 21
Knepp Lake .. ::	50-250 175	0-70 15	30-300 205	0-15 3	0-20 9	0-30 10	0-410 95
Weir Wood Reservoir ::	105-800 355	15-310 100	50-150 115	1	0-15 3	50-290 135	75-200 110
Barcombe Reservoir.. ::	150-700 280	10-95 28	60-1,800 645	1-14 5	2-40 14	20-80 60	35-145 50
Glynde Levels ::	85-1,000 370	200-2,000 560	450-3,000 1,300	0-10 5	1-100 30	7	2
Cuckmere valley ::	70-255 135	10-300 80	15-350 125	3	2	8	1
Darwell Reservoir ::	35-410 160	0-300 75	10-255 85	0-7 2	0-5 1	45-190 85	45-200 85
Rye Harbour .. ::	50-1,000 480	10-400 130	15-1,400 300	1-18 5	0-40 12	25-150 75	25-535 325

Note.—Since Arlington Reservoir was filled in 1970 flocks of up to 500 Mallard, 70 Teal, 1,200 Wigeon, 10 Pintail, 60 Shoveler, 70 Tufted Duck, and 200 Pochard have been counted there. Almost certainly there is considerable duplication in the figures given here for Glynde Levels and Barcombe and Arlington Reservoirs. Cuckmere Valley for this table means south of Exceat Bridge.

The table also indicates the increasing importance of the large areas of open water created by gravel extraction and for reservoirs to wintering surface-feeding species. Much drainage work has been done, and is being done, in the grass marshes of the river valleys and Levels, greatly reducing the importance of one principal wildfowl habitat in the county. The creation of artificial waters does much to replace this loss, and five of the 12 sites in the table are gravel pits or reservoirs and support about 30 per cent. of the population listed. Sussex is also well supplied with smaller lakes and ponds, of which Burton Ponds and Knepp Lake are two typical examples. In total such ponds are clearly another potentially useful wintering ground for wildfowl, and more information is needed about such sites.

Severe winters greatly inflate the numbers of nearly all wintering wildfowl. In the species accounts which follow the aim has been to describe the 'normal' pattern as far as possible. Thus, while most winters produce short cold snaps which have been accepted as part of the normal pattern, the effects of the quite exceptionally severe winters of early 1947, 1956, and 1963 have been allowed for when making comparisons.

WIGEON—*Anas penelope*

Status.—Common winter visitor and passage migrant. No recent change in status is apparent.

The main winter concentrations now occur in Chichester and Pagham Harbours, the Amberley/Pulborough marshes, and Glynde Levels. The winter populations in 12 major wildfowl localities in the county for the period 1964/65 to 1974/75 are summarised in the table on page 86. A comparison of these figures with similar figures from the same areas between 1947 and 1964 indicates little overall change in status; a small increase is possible. But the records suggest that large flocks of Wigeon have stayed for much shorter periods in many inland localities since 1964 as a result of the generally drier conditions. The species is inclined to graze dry grassland more readily than other dabbling ducks, however, so is somewhat less vulnerable to drainage operations. Local changes of abundance have also occurred, with marked increases at Pagham Harbour and Glynde Levels and declines at Amberley/Pulborough, Darwell Reservoir and Rye Harbour.

In addition to the figures in the table sizable concentrations sometimes occur in the Adur valley (up to 400 birds), Pevensey Levels (up to 250 birds), Wet Level (up to 350 birds), and at Pett Level (up to 800 birds). Very few are known to occur elsewhere. Numbers everywhere greatly increase in very severe weather.

Although occasional birds, usually pricked, may summer, winter visitors have been recorded as early as late August, but first arrivals are more usual in September and October. Peak numbers are usually found in January, but may occur locally in any month between December and early March, often depending on the water levels. By the end of March the bulk of our winter visitors have departed. Regular sea-watches have recorded small passage movements in autumn, mainly in November and again in spring, usually in March.

GADWALL—*Anas strepera*

Status.—Scarce winter visitor and passage migrant. The number occurring has increased steadily since 1938, although the population is still very small. A feral population now breeds.

Until 1938 only about 25 had been recorded, and between 1938 and 1961 about 120 were seen, numbers varying from one to seven annually; none was seen in three years (des Forges and Harber).

Between 1962 and 1976 Gadwall were recorded annually, numbers ranging from seven to 55 in a winter. During this period a regular wintering flock established itself at Chichester gravel pits, which reached a peak of 43 birds in December 1969 and accounted for about half the records for each winter. However, numbers declined very sharply there after 1969, possibly as a result of the management of the fishery. The population has now become much more dispersed, with birds occurring on many of the larger lakes, reservoirs and areas of gravel pits in the county. Parties of up to 25 are not uncommon. Gadwall are rare on the sea and infrequent in the river valleys.

Winter visitors probably start to arrive in September and October, earlier records referring to autumn passage, or to the one or two birds which now summer fairly regularly. A small spring passage occurs between late March and the end of May.

In 1976, when three pairs reared 24 young, a feral population was established at Arundel as part of the Wildfowl Trust's collection. The young were free flying, and the future status of this species in Sussex will be strongly influenced by this population.

TEAL—*Anas crecca*

Status.—Scarce and local breeding species; common winter visitor and passage migrant. The wintering population has declined considerably in recent years, but it is unlikely that breeding numbers have altered greatly since 1938.

Recent records indicate a breeding population of about 50 to 60 pairs, but almost certainly under-estimate the true position. Teal are very inconspicuous when nesting, and no census has been attempted. Most breeding records have been from lakes or ponds with good marginal vegetation, such as Shillinglee, Lurgashall, and Burton ponds, or from small, sometimes quite insignificant, streams and marshes in the interior. The species rarely nests in extensive grass marshes, where, during much systematic study of other species, there have been only four recent summer records. Breeding is also unusual near the coast, but has been recorded at five sites.

This distribution appears substantially similar to that described by Walpole-Bond and no marked change in the breeding position since 1938, when 75 to 150 pairs were thought to breed, seems likely.

As winter visitors most Teal now occur in Chichester and Pagham Harbours, the Arun valley, and Glynde Levels. The winter populations in 12 major wildfowl localities in the county for the period 1964/65 to 1974/75 are summarised in the table on page 86. The species has certainly declined in recent winters, with the improved drainage of many extensive areas of wet grassland, its primary winter habitat. A comparison of the figures in the table with similar figures for the same areas between 1955 and 1964 shows an overall decline of about 35–45 per cent. Locally, numbers have increased at Chichester Harbour, Glynde, and possibly Chichester gravel pits. In addition to the figures tabulated concentrations of 100 or more are frequent in the Adur valley (max. 600), and Pevensey Levels (max. 260), and the species also occurs in smaller parties in many minor wetland areas.

From the information available it seems likely that the total winter population of the county now rarely exceeds 4,000 birds. In 1960 and 1962 the Amberley/Pulborough marshes alone held a winter peak of about 3,000 birds.

Passage movements and the arrival and departure of winter visitors are difficult to separate. The local breeding stock appears to disperse in July and August and winter visitors may start to arrive in September. Peak numbers occur between December and February, and most winter visitors have departed by late March. Some through passage takes place in spring, between March and early May, and in autumn up to the end of November, but recent records give little idea of the scale of these movements.

Birds showing the characters of the race *carolinensis* were seen at the Midrips between 19 and 22 March 1961, and in the Cuckmere Valley on 21 and 22 March 1975.

MALLARD—*Anas platyrhynchos*

Status.—Common resident and winter visitor; probably passage migrant. No recent change in status is apparent.

The Mallard population in Sussex is supported regularly by the release of hand-reared birds by wildfowlers. The numbers of such birds shot annually is not known, but evidence that these introductions have increased the breeding or wintering stock is lacking.

As a breeding bird the Mallard is widely distributed throughout the county and not always confined to wet habitats; breeding has been established in several downland localities, for example Rewell Wood. The most important breeding habitat is lakes or ponds with good marginal vegetation. Quite small ponds may hold a number of pairs, for example, 11 pairs have been found at Patching Pond. Elsewhere up to 40 pairs have been counted at Chichester and Rye Harbour gravel pits recently. In grass marsh breeding densities are not apparently very high; even in very favourable areas counts have rarely exceeded 20–30 pairs per 2,500 acres (10 sq.km.), and are often less.

The winter populations of 12 important wildfowl localities in the county for the period 1964/65 to 1974/75 are summarised in the table on page 86. However, this only represents a proportion of the total wintering population, as other localities are known to attract substantial flocks; for example, up to 250 have been recorded recently at Warnham Mill Pond and the Adur Levels, up to 300 at Pevensey Levels, up to 450 at Swanbourne Lake, and 500 in Lewes Brooks. In addition many minor wetlands hold smaller groups. No overall change in the winter status is apparent, although local changes have occurred, for example in the Amberley/Pulborough marshes, where numbers have declined with improved drainage. Peak winter numbers normally occur between December and February, and birds disperse very rapidly in late February and March.

There is little recent evidence of a marked through passage.

PINTAIL—*Anas acuta*

Status.—Has bred. Regular winter visitor and passage migrant. No very marked change in status has been noted recently.

Pintail bred in Sussex in 1925 and 1936, and a pair probably attempted to do so in 1970.

The number wintering in the county has always been quite small, and the main concentrations are now found in Chichester Harbour, mainly in Chichester Channel at Fishbourne, and the head of Bosham Channel, Pagham Harbour (since 1971), and sometimes still in the Amberley/Pulborough marshes. The winter populations in 12 major wildfowl localities in the county for the period 1964/65 to 1974/75 are summarised in the table on page 86. A comparison of these figures with similar figures for the same areas between 1947 and 1964 indicates no overall change in status. A decline has occurred in the Amberley/Pulborough marshes, where flocks of more than 100 were regular before 1964, but are now infrequent, although 200 were present in 1974/75. Such numbers are now much more usual in the western harbours. The table includes all the regular winter localities, although birds may be reported from many other suitable sites. Only exceptionally, however, does the present winter population exceed about 400 birds.

Although birds are noted regularly in August and September, winter visitors probably do not arrive until October, and some certainly stay into April. Their arrival and departure overlap a small passage in spring and autumn. This movement has been most clearly indicated by regular sea-watches, which have recorded small easterly movements between the late March and early May, and a westerly movement between October and December.

GARGANEY—*Anas querquedula*

Status.—A few pairs breed; passage migrant. The numbers breeding appear to have declined recently. Otherwise no change in status is known.

Until 1961 up to 12 pairs bred annually (des Forges and Harber). However, between 1962 and 1976 breeding was only proved five times, although other breeding season records suggested a population of up to seven pairs; in some years none was found. Most of the known or likely breeding localities were searched fairly thoroughly during the period, so a decline in the breeding population seems apparent.

Spring passage is most marked between mid-March and the end of April, with a fairly well-defined peak at the end of March. Arrival had been noted as early as 27 February (1971), however, and some passage continues until mid-May. Numbers vary but a total of 40 is the highest recorded in recent springs; parties of up to 10 together are sometimes seen. Autumn passage begins in early July and continues until early October, although the latest recorded dates are 29 October 1966 and 11 November 1892. Similar numbers to the spring are involved, and passage peaks in mid-August, particularly the second week of the month; up to 23 have been recorded together.

There are two winter records, of a pair seen near Horsham on 19 January 1947, and one shot at Langney Point on 21 February 1913. The Langney bird may possibly have been a very early spring arrival.

BLUE-WINGED TEAL—*Anas discors*
Status.—Two records.

One was obtained at Worth on 17 January 1922; one was seen at Church Norton and Chichester gravel pits from 12 to 14 May 1970. Both these birds may have escaped from captivity.

SHOVELER—*Anas clypeata*
Status.—A few pairs breed; winter visitor and passage migrant. The winter population has declined in recent years, but little change at other seasons is apparent.

Breeding may not be annual, but between 1965 and 1976 it was proved in eight years, involving a total of 10 pairs. Other

breeding season records, however, indicate that between five and
10 pairs probably breed in most years.

In winter the main localities for the species are Chichester
gravel pits, the Amberley/Pulborough marshes and Glynde
Levels, but sizable flocks are now most regular at Chichester
gravel pits. The winter populations in 12 major wildfowl
localities in the county for the period 1964/65 to 1974/5 are
summarised in the table on page 86, and a comparison of these
figures with similar figures for the same areas between 1947
and 1964 indicates an overall decline of about 30 per cent.
until 1973. Like the Teal, the Shoveler has undoubtedly
suffered from the improved drainage of many inland marshes,
and the present winter population does not often exceed
200–400 birds in a normal year. But 400 were recorded in
the Amberley/Pulborough marshes alone in 1974/75, an
exceptionally wet winter when the species was unusually
numerous.

There is a marked spring passage, often starting in late
February and continuing into May; most movement occurs
in March and April. In some years a high proportion of the
birds involved are adult males. There is much annual variation
in numbers, but regular sea-watches, which record the bulk
of this movement in many years, have not reported more
than about 200 birds in any spring. Autumn passage appears
to be slight and may be under-recorded, since many August
and September records appear to relate to passage rather than
resident birds. Winter visitors probably begin to arrive in
October.

RED-CRESTED POCHARD—*Netta rufina*
Status.—**Vagrant.**

Between 1948 and 1961 des Forges and Harber gave eight
records involving about nine birds, and there were 15 more
records involving 17 birds up to 1976, besides a number of
reports which have been considered to relate to escapes from

collections; in fact, some of the records included here must be open to this suspicion.

Birds have been seen in every month except June and August, and commonly make prolonged stays. Taking the first reported date for each bird records have been distributed as follows: July (two), September (two), October (three), November (one), December (eight), January (one), February (two), March (three), April (one), and May (three). Most have been seen at Chichester gravel pits, but the species may occur on any stretch of fresh water.

POCHARD—*Aythya ferina*

Status.—**A few summer and sometimes breed; common winter visitor; probably passage migrant. There has been no marked change in status in recent years, but birds now summer more often.**

A few have summered annually since 1966, but breeding is still very rare. Until 1960 des Forges and Harber recorded eight cases and a pair may have bred in 1973.

The winter population in 12 major wildfowl localities in the county for the period 1964/65 to 1974/75 is summarised in the table on page 86. The main concentrations occur at Chichester and Rye Harbour gravel pits, where flocks of up to 400 birds are regular and which, combined, hold about half the county population. Flocks of 100 or more are also fairly frequent at Weir Wood Reservoir, but seem uncommon elsewhere, although the records for 1972/73, when numbers were unusually high, included a count of over 400 at Knepp. Including the small flocks, totalling 100 birds or fewer, occurring on ponds other than those listed on page 86, the total wintering population of the county appears to be of the order of 1,000 to 1,400 birds.

A comparison of the present figures with similar ones for the same areas between 1947 and 1964 suggests little overall change; a slight increase is possible. However, there has been much change in the importance of individual waters, and the present concentration at Chichester and Rye seems of recent origin. Prior to 1964 at least five areas, including the Amberley/Pulborough marshes, normally held winter peaks of 100-200 birds, but as new reservoirs are flooded the pattern will doubtless change. Pochard only occur in numbers on salt water in very cold weather.

There is little up-to-date information on movements; des Forges and Harber record autumn arrival occasionally from July, with the main arrivals in October and November; most depart by late March. There is no recent evidence of any change. Winter peaks fairly consistently occur in December or January.

FERRUGINOUS DUCK—*Aythya nyroca*
Status.—Four records comprising nine birds.

Three were shot on the Crumbles on 15 August 1903; three were seen at Warnham Mill Pond on 20 March 1908; one was seen on Amberley Wildbrooks on 24 March 1926; two, one of which was eventually shot, were present in the Rye/Midrips area from 17 November 1946 to 22 February 1947. It is not known if any of these birds had escaped from collections, but a number of more recent reports certainly relate to such birds and are, therefore, disregarded.

TUFTED DUCK—*Aythya fuligula*
Status.—Common resident and winter visitor; passage migrant. The breeding stock has increased steadily since 1958, and some increase has occurred in the number wintering.

Tufted Ducks were first proved to breed in Sussex in 1853, but have bred regularly only since about 1958. The table summarises the summer population based on records for late May and June and proven breeding records between 1958 and 1975. Breeding was proved on a total of 36 waters in the period, most of which may be regularly occupied, although the records show annual fluctuations and breeding is not always proved at all known breeding sites each year. About half the proven breeding population is concentrated at Chichester gravel pits (up to 31 pairs), and Rye Harbour gravel pits (up to 16 pairs), with six or seven pairs breeding in some years on each of Burton Ponds and Darwell Reservoir. Elsewhere one or two pairs is the usual number. Nearly all breeding sites are freshwater lakes or ponds and most suitable ones in the county are now, or will soon be, occupied. One or two pairs also breed regularly on the tidal stream of Glynde Reach, and breeding has been proved on the Ouse below there, which is also tidal water.

The Summer Population of Tufted Duck in Sussex, 1958-1976

	1958-64	1965-67	1968-70	1971-73	1974-76
Total summering population					
Sites holding summering birds	14	25	33	28	39
Total birds involved	151	170	285	356	635
Proven breeding population					
Sites where breeding proved	7	17	20	12	17
Total breeding pairs	20	41	51	65	68

Note.—Total summering population includes the proven breeding population.

Breeding success in the period under review was often poor and observers have frequently remarked on a high predation rate after hatching. The average brood size noted ranged from 3.6 to 7.7, with a mean of 5.2, but the number finally reared was often much less; the few figures available indicate a predation rate of up to 40 per cent., sometimes more. Pike are often suspected as responsible.

The winter population in 12 major wildfowl localities in the county in the period 1964/65 to 1974/75 is summarised in the table on page 86. By far the largest concentration is found at

Chichester gravel pits, and the only other area at which more than 100 birds have occurred annually is Weir Wood Reservoir; similar flocks seem now to be establishing themselves at Darwell Reservoir and Rye Harbour gravel pits. In addition to the figures tabulated, a total of some 100-200 birds is usually recorded each winter on other ponds, and the present wintering population of Sussex seems to be of the order of 1,000-2,000 birds. A comparison between the figures given in the table and similar figures for the period 1947-1964 suggests an increase of about 25 per cent., virtually confined to Chichester and Rye Harbour gravel pits and clearly correlated with the increase of water available as digging progressed. Tufted Duck are unusual on salt water, except in severe winter weather.

The arrival and departure of winter visitors is difficult to determine accurately in the presence of a sizable resident population, but peak winter numbers are present between December and February. Some passage appears to take place in March and April, when numbers on inland waters may increase temporarily, and a few have been noted passing during sea-watches. Information on autumn movements is very scant, but they are believed to start about September.

SCAUP—*Aythya marila*

Status.—Scarce winter visitor and passage migrant; occasional in summer. No recent change in status is apparent.

Most Scaup winter at sea or on waters near the coast, mainly from Seaford Bay to the Midrips, but one or two are now quite regular inland, particularly at Chichester gravel pits and Weir Wood and Barcombe Reservoirs.

Except in very cold weather, however, the numbers wintering in Sussex are never very large. Thus between 1964 and 1976 numbers varied between one bird in the winter of 1964/65 and c. 90 in the winter of 1969/70 and 1971/72. The largest flock noted was of 60 birds, but parties of up to 20 are much more usual and many records are of single birds. In very cold weather much larger flocks appear. Thus, up to 5,000 together were seen in Rye Bay in early 1947, and the winters of 1955/56 and 1962/63 produced flocks totalling several hundreds along the coast.

In recent years there have been records for every month as single birds have summered five or six times. Most have been present in January and February. The arrival and departure of winter visitors appears to overlap a small passage which has been most obvious in spring, when regular sea-watches have recorded small easterly movements, involving up to 25 birds annually, between early March and early May.

EIDER—*Somateria mollissima*

Status.—A few summer in most years; regular winter visitor and passage migrant. The increase noted by des Forges and Harber has continued.

A few now appear to summer fairly regularly. There have been June or July records annually since 1960, except in 1971, 1972 and 1975, and up to 27 birds have been seen together, although smaller numbers are much more usual.

The main wintering concentrations in Sussex recently have been in the Pagham/Selsey area, with up to 60 regularly; Seaford Bay, with up to 30 regularly; and Rye Bay, with up to seventy. However, Eiders may also be seen right along the coast, and the total numbers recorded wintering between 1960 and 1976 varied between 20 in the winter of 1960/61 and 250 in that of 1962/63; on average about 70-80 are usually present. The total in the 1962/63 winter is the highest yet noted and included 114 together off Selsey Bill on 27 January 1963, the largest flock yet seen in the county. Eiders are confined to salt water.

The arrival and departure of winter visitors overlaps passage, but peak winter numbers seem to be noted most consistently in January or February. A fairly marked spring passage occurs between March and May, when sea-watching has recorded up to 200 birds in one spring. Autumn movements or arrival may start as early as August, but is most usual in late October; most autumn passage is observed in November.

LONG-TAILED DUCK—*Clangula hyemalis*

Status.—**Scarce winter visitor and passage migrant. Some increase in the number occurring is likely.**

Most Long-tailed Ducks are seen at sea or on tidal waters, but one or two are recorded on inland waters almost every year. Single birds are most usual, but parties of up to five occur and one of nine was seen in Chichester Harbour on 26 January 1958.

The table summarises the records since 1948 and suggests some increase; duplications arise in the monthly totals when birds winter.

Long-tailed Ducks in Sussex, 1948–1976

Period	Total number of birds recorded	Average number of records per year	Monthly totals							
			Oct.	Nov.	Dec.	Jan.	Feb.	Mar.	Apr.	May
1948–1952	6	1	0	2	2	2	1	3	0	0
1953–1957	24	5	5	16	11	4	0	0	0	0
1958–1962	76	15	7	21	11	26	9	12	11	1
1963–1967	96	20	11	36	30	10	7	16	4	0
1968–1972	127	25	11	37	34	41	32	32	25	4
1973–1976	66	16	4	14	19	19	20	18	11	1

There was a sharp increase in the number of records between 1956 and 1965, and an even greater increase between 1966 and 1973, but numbers since have been lower. Without doubt these changes reflect changes in observer activity, but the figures suggest a genuine increase in numbers is also involved.

There are two records for July (10th, 1975, and 17th, 1960) and one for August (12th to 21st, 1976). Otherwise the earliest autumn record was 15 October, and arrival was most usual at the end of this month or in November. A large proportion of our birds are transient and sea-watches have shown westerly movements until late January and small easterly movements in March and April. The latest spring record is for 6 May (1961 and 1971), but April records are now quite regular, although there was only one between 1948 and 1959.

COMMON SCOTER—*Melanitta nigra*

Status.—Present throughout the year. Common winter visitor and passage migrant. The winter population has decreased in recent years.

The main Sussex wintering locality for this species is Rye Bay, where winter peaks between 1964 and 1976 ranged between 150 and 1,100 birds, averaging 530. Elsewhere large flocks are rather irregular, but up to 400 were noted off Langney Point, 250 in Seaford Bay, and 150 in Pevensey Bay in the same period. Off West Sussex the species is much scarcer, the only large winter flocks seen in the period being of 100 off Selsey Bill in early 1964 and 1965. The species has declined considerably in winter since peak counts of 2,000–5,000 birds were noted regularly in Rye Bay between 1947 and 1956.

Although the peak winter counts are made fairly consistently in Rye Bay in January or February, the arrival and departure of winter visitors is impossible to determine as birds are present throughout the year. Summering flocks of up to about 50 birds are probably regular, and about 3,000 summered in Rye Bay in 1956.

Common Scoter are virtually confined to the open sea, although oiled birds will visit fresh water near the coast. But there are a few inland records; des Forges and Harber give about 14 until 1961, and there were 12, comprising 45 birds, between 1962 and 1972, including a party of 25 at Weir Wood Reservoir on 25 June 1972; there has been none since.

There is an extensive spring passage. Typically this occurs between mid-March and late May, and involves several thousand birds. Numbers and peak dates vary annually, the sighting of large movements being closely correlated with the occurrence of south-easterly winds; Cooper (1975), however, noted that the peak off Beachy Head usually occurred between 11 and 20 April. Movements of over 1,000 birds in a day are noted almost every spring, however, and the largest single movement yet seen was of 12,000 flying east off Beachy Head on 7 April 1969. Between 1965 and 1976 the total numbers recorded on spring passage varied between about 2,000 in 1967 and 25,000 in 1968. In some years passage continues into June; for example, in June 1970, 640 were seen passing off Selsey Bill.

Large autumn movements are unusual. The largest daily movement recorded in autumn at Selsey Bill between 1960 and 1970 was of 83 birds. But the records after June showed a predominantly westerly movement and fairly clear peaks in July/August and October/November.

SURF SCOTER—*Melanitta perspicillata*
Status.—One record.

A female was seen at Rye Harbour gravel pits on 3 December 1966.

VELVET SCOTER—*Melanitta fusca*
Status.—Scarce winter visitor and passage migrant. No recent change in status is apparent.

The numbers wintering off Sussex are always small, the largest winter totals noted since 1947 being 90 birds in 1958, and 102 in early 1974, when a flock of 100 was seen in Rye Bay on 23 February. In many winters fewer than 20 are seen.

Most wintering reports come from the coast from Langney Point to the Midrips, particularly Rye Bay and, excepting passage birds, numbers further west have only exceeded about 10 birds in very cold weather. Velvet Scoter are virtually confined to the sea or sometimes tidal waters, but oiled birds may visit fresh water near the coast; there are two very old inland records, and single birds were seen at Weir Wood Reservoir on 1 February 1970 and Darwell Reservoir on 12 November 1972.

Larger numbers occur on spring passage, when up to 300 have been recorded together (8 May 1951, Rye Bay). Since 1965 spring sea-watches have recorded up to 290 (average 70) birds passing along the coast between early March and late May; the latest spring date was 30 May. There are a few old June records, but none since 1947. Autumn arrival has been noted as early as 10 July, but usually starts in late October, and passage has been noted in November.

GOLDENEYE—*Bucephala clangula*
Status.—**Common winter visitor; passage migrant. No recent change in status is known.**

The bulk of the Goldeneye wintering in Sussex do so in Chichester Harbour, where recent counts have shown a fairly consistent winter peak of about 100 birds; on 16 January 1971 225 were counted, and on 1 January 1974, 234, the largest concentrations so far recorded. Both these very high counts were made from a boat rather than the shore, and experience suggests that counting from the shore in this harbour may often under-estimate numbers of Goldeneye. Peak numbers are fairly consistently present in January and early February; numbers in December are often quite low, and the birds disperse rapidly in late February and March. The recent figures suggest some increase when compared with des Forges and Harber's account, but more probably reflect the great increase in observer coverage of the Harbour since 1965. However, there has possibly been some increase in the number of adult males wintering.

Walpole-Bond notes them as extremely rare, but between 20 and 30 per cent. of the flocks in Chichester Harbour recently have been adult males.

Elsewhere numbers are quite small, but Goldeneye are noted annually at several places along the coast, and on most important inland waters. The largest gathering away from Chichester Harbour appears to be of 19 at Rye Harbour in February 1968 and up to 13 together have been seen on inland waters, although single birds and parties of up to five are most usual. They are not often seen on the open sea except on passage.

Since 1965 the species has been noted in each month between October (21st) and May (30th), but there are earlier records for July (31st, 1959), and September (27th–30th, 1958). An injured bird also summered at Darwell Reservoir in 1958. Birds have been noted regularly into April, and sea-watching has shown a passage in March and April, which is sometimes also reflected on inland waters. Very little autumn passage has been observed, but there is obviously a steady arrival of winter visitors in November and December.

SMEW—*Mergus albellus*
Status.—Scarce but regular winter visitor. No recent change in status is apparent.

This species has been recorded in each month from November to March, but as with Goosander most are seen in January and February. Extreme dates are 3 November (1974, Cuckmere), and 31 March (1963, Rye). Since 1947 a total of about 485 Smew has been recorded, with exceptional numbers in 1954 (*c*. 50 birds), 1956 (*c*. 100 birds), and 1963 (*c*. 80 birds). These influxes were all associated with severe weather and numbers otherwise ranged between one and 24 annually, averaging about nine. Approximate monthly totals between 1947 and 1976 were:

Nov.	Dec.	Jan.	Feb.	Mar.
9	66	180	279	81

The distribution of this species and Goosanders in Sussex is very similar, but Smew are even more infrequent on the open sea. Although often seen singly, small parties are rather more often seen than with Goosanders; the largest recorded was of 22 at Manhood End in early February 1956.

RED-BREASTED MERGANSER—*Mergus serrator*
Status.—Occasional in summer; common winter visitor and passage migrant. No recent change in status is apparent.

There are a few records for June and July, when up to four have been seen together. Sometimes these are disabled birds and summering is doubtfully of annual occurrence.

Substantial wintering flocks are virtually confined to West Sussex, from Shoreham west to Chichester Harbour. The largest concentration occurs fairly consistently in Chichester Harbour, where flocks of 40 to 60 birds have been annual since 1947; 130 were seen there on 18 December 1954, the largest flock yet noted in the county, and there were 97 on 4 December 1971. Elsewhere gatherings of 20 to 40 are noted frequently in the Pagham/Selsey area, off Climping and between Worthing and Shoreham; 100 were seen off Lancing on 26 January 1964, and about 65 wintered off Worthing in 1971/72. East of Brighton the species seems remarkably scarce in winter. Since 1947 the only records in the county files of sizable winter flocks were of 45 in Seaford Bay on 25 February 1956, and 30 off Langney Point on 17 January 1965; the other records are nearly all of single birds or small parties of five or so. Although largely confined to salt water in Sussex, there are sufficient inland records to suggest that one or two mergansers can be found on inland waters every winter.

The arrival and departure of winter visitors overlaps passage, but peak winter counts are usually made in December or January. Spring passage commonly extends from early March to late May, but sea-watching results from Selsey Bill since 1960 consistently show that the passage peaks in the first three

weeks of April, and off Beachy Head Cooper (1975) found a
marked peak between 11 and 20 April. Numbers vary, but up
to 650 birds have been noted passing up the Channel in a
spring, and movements of 50 to 100 birds in a day are an
annual event; 234 flying east off Beachy Head on 15 April
1968 is the largest single movement noted. The return movement rarely starts before October, although there are four
records for August and four for September. Peak passage
normally occurs between mid-November and mid-December.
Fewer birds are involved than in spring, but up to 75 have been
seen passing down the Channel in a day, and once 200
(19 November 1972, Selsey Bill). Winter sea-watching at Selsey
Bill has shown westerly movement to predominate during
January and February in some years, suggesting some passage
continues from October to February.

GOOSANDER—Mergus merganser
Status.—Scarce but regular winter visitor; a very few may
pass through on passage. No recent change in status is
apparent.

Apart from a wounded bird still present on Lurgashall Mill
Pond on 22 July 1972, this species has been recorded in each
month from October to May. Most are seen between December
and February, with a decided peak in January. Extreme dates
are 3 October (1948, Thorney Island), and 20 May (1961,
Selsey Bill). Since 1947 a total of about 570 has been recorded,
about a third of them in the two severe winters of early 1956
(c. 44 birds), and 1962/63 (c. 154 birds). Apart from such
influxes up to c. 30 have been seen annually, with an average
of about twelve. Approximate monthly totals from 1947 to
1976 were:

Oct.	Nov.	Dec.	Jan.	Feb.	Mar.	Apr.	May
9	50	124	210	160	80	17	5

Goosanders are found on both fresh and salt water, near the
coast and well inland, but they are rather rare on the open sea

and are perhaps more likely to be seen on salt water in very cold weather. Most are seen singly or in twos and threes, but up to 10 have been recorded together and, in 1963 a party of 50 was seen at Burpham on 30 January, and another, which finally totalled 29, was present at Weir Wood Reservoir in March.

OSPREY—*Pandion haliaetus*

Status.—Regular passage migrant. A recent increase in reports is assumed to be connected with the re-establishment of a British breeding population.

Ospreys have been recorded annually since 1947, except in 1948, but since 1961 numbers have almost doubled. Most are seen on autumn passage, with a marked peak in September, but spring reports have become more numerous recently and have included several April records. These were once considered very rare and most spring passage is noted in May. Extreme dates are 16 April (1970, Pagham), and 16 November (1952, Darwell Reservoir). Monthly totals for the period 1947 to 1976 were: April (eight), May (29), June (four), July (four), August 24, September (64), October (27), and November (two).

Almost any sizable stretch of water, inland or coastal, may attract an Osprey, but spring birds rarely make prolonged stays. In autumn, however, it is not unusual for a bird to remain in one area for several weeks, and stays of more than six weeks have been recorded. Most birds are seen singly, but two together are not very unusual, and three were seen together at Weir Wood Reservoir on 30 August 1976.

HONEY BUZZARD—*Pernis apivorus*

Status.—Rare passage migrant. Although the number recorded has greatly increased in recent years, no real change in status may have occurred.

There is no evidence that this species has ever nested in Sussex. Until 1960 des Forges and Harber gave about 60 records

records for the period late May to early November; most reports were for June, September and October.

Between 1961 and 1976 there were 35 records for: May (four), June (three), August (five), September (21), and October (two). Spring dates fell between 9 May (1971, Beachy Head, the earliest county record), and 10 June, and autumn dates between 16 August and 24 October. All but seven of these birds were seen at or near Beachy Head, where watching for passage raptores has been carried out regularly since 1965. Probably Honey Buzzards are regular passage migrants there, at least in autumn.

BLACK KITE—*Milvus migrans*

Status.—Two records.

One arrived from the south-east at Beachy Head on 12 April 1970, and departed west; one was seen near Herstmonceux on 13 November 1976.

KITE—*Milvus milvus*

Status.—Vagrant.

Kites probably ceased to breed in Sussex about 1825, and des Forges and Harber give 21 records between 1863 and 1960, all for the period September to May as far as is known. Between 1961 and 1976 there have been 14 records: in January (two), March (four), April (two), May (one), August (three), September (one), and November (one). Two March records, which were for 1972, may have involved only one bird, as may two August records in 1973.

WHITE-TAILED EAGLE—*Haliaeetus albicilla*
Status.—Vagrant.

Although not infrequently recorded in the 19th century, when it was possibly a fairly regular winter visitor, only six were recorded between 1900 and 1929, and there has been only one since, at Selsey Bill on 30 July 1961. Walpole-Bond connected the sudden decline in reports, which dated from about 1895, with the extermination of the Scottish breeding stock.

MARSH HARRIER—*Circus aeruginosus*
Status.—Occasional in winter; rare but regular passage migrant. No recent change in status is apparent.

Although once most usually seen in winter, nearly all records since 1938 have been of passage birds at the coast. For example, between 1962 and 1976 there were 72 records: in January (one), March (one), April (nine), May (two), June (five), July (one), August (12), September (17), and October (six). Only six were noted away from the coast, and birds sometimes made prolonged stays in favoured coastal marshes, for example 35 days in 1965. Spring records fell between 24 March and 11 June, with a marked peak of *c.* 70 per cent. between 19 April and 19 May, and autumn records fell between 23 August and 15 October. There were two summer records: one was picked up dead in Houghton Forest on 14 June 1971, and one was seen at Bracklesham on 27 July 1972.

A comparison of this account with that given by des Forges and Harber indicates very little change in status since 1938.

HEN HARRIER—*Circus cyaneus*
Status.—Regular winter visitor and passage migrant. The number occurring has increased quite markedly since 1966.

Between 1947 and 1961 des Forges and Harber recorded an annual average of about 10, but noted that some decline was evident towards the end of this period. However, between 1966 and 1976 the average doubled to about 20 per year, an increase which is unlikely to be merely a reflection of increased observer activity.

Altogether between 1962 and 1976 about 255 Hen Harriers were recorded, 220 of them between 1966 and 1976. Monthly totals were:

Aug.	Sept.	Oct.	Nov.	Dec.	Jan.	Feb.	Mar.	Apr.	May
1	3	50	82	79	76	52	68	39	5

These birds were largely 'ring-tails', but *c.* 60 adult males were recorded, 17 of them in 1971 and 1972, an unusually high proportion. Most birds were seen on open downland, levels and coastal marshes, but Hen Harriers winter fairly regularly in Ashdown Forest, and some have recently wintered in large tracts of forestry plantations.

Extreme dates for this species are 4 August and 16 May, but not many are seen before the second half of October. Some wintering birds remain until late March or early April and, in recent years, there has been a clear tendency for them to linger later in the year; all the May records have been since 1968. Some through passage is also noted, particularly in November, March and April, and one was seen to fly in from the sea at Selsey Bill on 1 May 1968.

Most records are of single birds, but up to five have been recorded in one area at the same time and there is possibly a tendency for groups of up to four to appear more often.

MONTAGU'S HARRIER—*Circus pygargus*

Status.—**Formerly bred in small numbers and sporadic breeding may still occur; scarce passage migrant. A recent decline in the numbers occurring is apparent.**

Breeding has only been recorded once since 1938, although it was certainly more regular prior to that date. The exact numbers involved are obscure, but Walpole-Bond's account suggests a population of no more than five to 10 pairs at best, and breeding was not established as an annual occurrence.

As a passage migrant des Forges and Harber give an average of about five Montagu's Harriers a year between 1947 and 1961 but, with only about 55 recorded between 1962 and 1976, this annual average shows a decline of about 25 per cent. Monthly totals between 1962 and 1976 were April one, May (25), June (seven), July (four), August (13), September (seven), and October (three). All records were of single birds which rarely stayed for more than a day. Like the other harriers this is a species of open country; the Downs, levels and coastal farmland thus provide most records.

Extreme dates are 17 April and 22 October, and, since 1962, there have been marked passage peaks in both periods, with 40 per cent. of the spring records in the second half of May and a similar proportion of autumn reports in the second half of August.

GOSHAWK—*Accipiter gentilis*

Status.—**Winter vagrant; rare passage migrant. Has bred.**

Breeding took place in one area from certainly 1938, but perhaps 1926 or earlier, until 1951.

Otherwise between 1948 and 1976 there were 20 records relating to 21 birds: in January (two), February (one), March (two), April (one), May (one), September (six, relating to seven birds), October (three), and November (three). All but two of these records were for the coast or its vicinity. Three birds were recorded in early 1956, seven between 1961 and 1970, of which six were noted at Beachy Head between 3 and 17 September, and four in 1975.

SPARROWHAWK—*Accipiter nisus*

Status.—Uncommon resident and passage migrant.
Formerly common, this species had declined drastically
by 1960; some increase has occurred since.

Sparrowhawks are still widely distributed breeding birds
in Sussex, the only major habitat type of the county in which
they do not breed being the coastal plain. Even the substantially open areas of the Downs hold pairs where small copses
provide nest sites.

Rather few comparative data are available from which to
assess recent status changes, but these appear to have been
marked. However, K. G. Ridgewell has supplied some records
for the years 1929 to 1939 for roughly 64,000 acres (256
sq. km.) of downland west of the Cuckmere, which then held
at least 17 regularly-occupied sites. Much of this area was
thoroughly watched between 1965 and 1970, and the records
obtained then indicated a marked decrease, with only eight
or nine regularly-occupied sites. Ridgewell considered that this
decrease began about 1952 and it apparently reached its
maximum about 1961, when no breeding Sparrowhawks were
reported from anywhere in the county. This certainly overstated the decline, but records for the whole county between
1965 and 1970 showed a general recovery, and during this
period there were breeding season records from 97 sites relating
to 44 pairs and 53 single birds. A high proportion of the sites
were found regularly occupied. Although breeding was proved
frequently, surprisingly few accurate records of brood size
were made. However, 59 young were recorded as reared, and
there were only three complete failures out of 26 nests at which
observations were made; one brood of three was shot after
fledging. Some further recovery was noted between 1970 and
1976.

It is difficult to give estimates of total population for this
species, which is probably often overlooked. Most records
are also for west and central Sussex, which very possibly
reflects the distribution of observers. However, systematic
records from areas totalling about 750 square kilometres of
very varied habitat, which have been well searched for the

species, recently showed a breeding density of consistently less than one pair per 2,500 acres (10 sq. km.), suggesting a county population of not more than 300 pairs.

Although des Forges and Harber recorded Sparrowhawks as probably regular winter visitors until 1961 there is little satisfactory evidence of this more recently. Some are certainly seen each winter in areas where breeding has not been established, which may only indicate some local dispersal or that the species is easy to miss when breeding.

There is a regular passage, particularly in the autumn. Thus between 1965 and 1971 there were 56 records from the coast of birds presumed to be on passage, between 9 August and 17 December, and 32 similar spring records between 23 February and 30 April. There were very marked peaks in September and April, and both emigration and immigration was noted at each season. More recently the scale of this passage has been masked by the presence of birds wintering along the coast. The source of these birds is not known, but they may be present from late August until April.

BUZZARD—*Buteo buteo*

Status.—**Rare resident; possibly winter visitor; scarce passage migrant. No change in status is apparent since about 1950.**

The original breeding population of this raptore in Sussex was exterminated in the interests of game preserving during the 19th century, breeding being last recorded in Ashdown Forest in 1882. About 1950 a small breeding population re-established itself in central Sussex and breeding has been regular since, although little increase has occurred. Thus, between 1965 and 1976 between one and seven pairs were found present annually, nearly all in West Sussex, compared with up to four pairs between 1950 and 1956. Breeding is in fact more often suspected or assumed than proved at present, but six broods were recorded between 1964 and 1970. However,

Buzzards are still persecuted by game preservers in some parts of the county, birds being found twice on gamekeepers' gibbets in 1971, for example. It seems very likely that such persecution is the main reason for this species' continued lack of success in colonising the county.

The breeding population appears to be resident, but birds are recorded in other areas of the county in winter sufficiently frequently to suggest either some post-breeding dispersal within the county, or that a few visit the county from elsewhere in winter.

There is a small autumn passage. This has been very clearly shown at Beachy Head where, between 1965 and 1976 a total of *c.* 70 Buzzards was recorded between 5 August and 27 October; some were observed to depart out to sea. Forty per cent. of the records were for the third week of September. Although most obvious at Beachy Head, this movement is noted at other points along the coast. A smaller passage also occurs in spring, when there are frequent reports of birds at the coast between early March and late May; often these birds have been reported as flying north.

ROUGH-LEGGED BUZZARD—*Buteo lagopus*

Status.—**Irregular winter visitor. Numbers have fluctuated very markedly in recent years.**

Rough-legged Buzzards were once probably annual winter visitors to the county, but des Forges and Harber recorded only two between 1938 and 1961, singles on 3 and 4 November 1956 and 10 to 16 November 1957. Between 1962 and 1976, however, there were records in 11 winters involving about 90 birds. All but 22 of these occurred during the exceptional influxes into England of the autumn and winter periods of 1966/67, 1973/74 and 1974/75. In 1966/67 and 1973/74 six or more birds wintered in the county, but the autumn and winter of 1974/75 were quite remarkable, with a total of 45-50 birds altogether, of which at least 20 wintered; 15 or more arrived from the south at Beachy Head on 22 October 1974. The majority of wintering birds favoured open downland with small woods for roosting, but there were records for open country from Chichester Harbour and Graffham to the Midrips.

This species is rarely seen before late October, and wintering birds have usually gone by late March or early April. However, one, which subsequently wintered there, appeared near Rye on 11 September 1970.

LESSER KESTREL—*Falco naumanni*

Status.—One record.

One was seen near Steyning on 4 November 1973.

KESTREL—*Falco tinnunculus*

Status.—**Common resident; possibly winter visitor; regular passage migrant. Although some decrease has certainly occurred in recent years, its extent is difficult to assess accurately.**

A survey of the breeding population was made from 1964 to 1967, which found the species to be generally distributed and reasonably numerous. A total of 238 occupied breeding territories was found in just over half the county, and birds were found in another 71 localities in the breeding season, where evidence of a definitely occupied breeding territory was not obtained. Breeding densities averaged two pairs per 2,500 acres (10 sq. km.) on the coastal plain, 1.7 on the Downs, 1.3 in the Weald, and 3.9 in the permanent grasslands of the river valleys and levels. The total county population was estimated to be 600 pairs, and an increase was evident in some areas during the survey.

Comparisons with previous records showed an extensive decline along the chalk cliffs, where Walpole-Bond recorded never less than about 30 pairs, and nearly 100 in 1919, but the survey found only 10 pairs. Other long-term changes could not be shown by this survey, but both des Forges and Harber and Prestt (1965) note a more general decline. Since 1967 some local fluctuations have occurred, but such changes are perhaps to be expected. Both Walpole-Bond and Parslow (1973) show that cyclic fluctuations in breeding populations are very likely.

Some details of breeding success were recorded by the survey, with an average of 2.4 young reared from 15 nests, in which 61 eggs were laid; three eggs were infertile and 17 stolen or destroyed by man, an important predator of this species. In addition 120 other fledged broods were recorded, with an average of 2.1 young per brood. These levels of breeding success were very similar to those found at the same time in the London area and Leicestershire. A full account of the survey is given in SxBR 1968 and *Bird Study,* 17, 1-15.

The Kestrels breeding in Sussex are thought to be resident, but winter status needs further and more exact investigation; some changes may have occurred since 1938.

Small passage movements occur in both spring and autumn. Immigration and emigration is noted at both seasons, but the former predominates in spring, with 76 per cent. of the records, and the latter in autumn, with 60 per cent. of the records. Spring movements have been noted between 13 February and 3 June, but over 60 per cent. of the passage is in April. Autumn movements have been noted between 15 July and late November, with a very clear peak, accounting for 45 per cent. of the records, in the first half of October. Coasting movements also take place, but their exact scale is very difficult to determine in the presence of resident pairs at most coastal watching sites. A comparison of these records with Walpole-Bond's account suggests a very marked decline of passage Kestrels in Sussex, which may be connected with declines in the breeding stock reported in other areas of Britain.

RED-FOOTED FALCON—*Falco vespertinus*

Status.—**Vagrant.**

Until 1961 des Forges and Harber recorded 11 and there have been four since, at Sidlesham on 8 September 1968, and three in 1973; at Beachy Head on 10 May and 1 June and at Rye on 13 June. As far as is known all the records have been for the period spring to autumn.

MERLIN—*Falco columbarius*

Status.—**Regular winter visitor and passage migrant. No recent change in status is apparent.**

Although recently extreme dates have been 14 August (1970, Rye), and 1 May (1968, Cuckmere), this species is most abundant from October to January. Between 1961 and 1976 an average of about 12 birds was recorded each year, and monthly totals were:

Aug.	Sept.	Oct.	Nov.	Dec.	Jan.	Feb.	Mar.	Apr.	May
2	22	68	38	32	37	18	15	9	1

Little change has occurred since the period covered by des Forges and Harber's account.

Arrival and departure at the coast is frequently noted in both spring and autumn, and especially in October. Wintering birds favour coastal farmland and marshes and a high proportion of recent records have been for the Selsey peninsular, the Beachy Head area, and from Rye to the Midrips. But Merlins are not infrequently recorded along the Downs and are seen very occasionally further inland. They are most usually seen singly, but two together are sometimes met with.

HOBBY—*Falco subbuteo*

Status.—**Rare breeding summer visitor; passage migrant.
The breeding population may have increased since 1960.**

Between 1962 and 1976 breeding was established, or probably took place, regularly in 17 areas holding between 20 and
25 pairs. Breeding success varied very little during the period,
when a total of 22 broods was noted, averaging rather more
than two young per brood. A recent increase in the breeding
population is likely as the records for 1947 to 1960 suggest
a maximum population of about 12 pairs and regular breeding
in only six areas.

Hobbies occur each spring and autumn on passage at the
coast. Recently spring records have fallen between 16 April
(1968, earliest county record) and mid-June, and autumn
records between 12 July and 31 October (1965, Selsey Bill),
but the species is very uncommon in October. Records from
Beachy Head, where systematic watching for passage raptores
has been carried out, show marked passage peaks, May accounting for 87 per cent. of the spring records, and September,
particularly the second half, accounting for 80 per cent. of
the autumn records.

GYR FALCON—*Falco rusticolus*

Status.—**Three records.**

One was shot at Mayfield in January 1845, the first British
record; one of the white 'candicans' type was shot near Bals-
dean on 26 September 1882, and a similar bird was seen on
the Downs behind Worthing from 11 to 24 March 1972.

PEREGRINE—*Falco peregrinus*

Status.—**Formerly bred, but now only a rare winter visitor and passage migrant.**

Until 1939 up to 12, but more usually about seven, pairs bred along the 15 miles of chalk cliffs. This was one of the highest breeding densities known in the British Isles (Ratcliffe, 1963). Pairs also bred occasionally on the sandstone cliffs and in disused chalk pits. A decline occurred after 1939, and the post-war population never exceeded six pairs and was often less. Peregrines last bred successfully in 1957, and are now only winter visitors and passage migrants.

Between 1962 and 1976 about 75 were recorded, monthly totals being: June (one), July (one), August (six), September (15), October (11), November (nine), December (11), January (13), February (six), March (12), April (10), and May (three). Single birds wintered in the Cuckmere valley in 1963/64, at Glynde Levels in each winter between 1966 and 1971, and at Pevensey Levels in 1969/70. Some other records between November and February may refer to wintering rather than wandering birds, but otherwise all reports were of birds apparently passing through.

RED-LEGGED PARTRIDGE—*Alectoris rufa*

Status.—**An introduced resident which apparently became firmly established about 1841. Numbers appear to have declined in recent years.**

Few reports about this species are received annually, but these suggest that it is some three to four times scarcer than the Common Partridge. It is possibly most numerous on the coastal plain, where breeding densities of 10 pairs per 2,500 acres (10 sq. km.) have been recorded, or on the Downs. However, its status on the Downs is now obscured by large introductions of other species of the genus, namely *A. graeca* and a hybrid, *A. graeca* x *A. rufa*, known as an 'Ogridge'.

North of the Downs Red-legged Partridges seem very scarce, but they are probably present in very small numbers in most open habitat types. Despite the lack of comparative data marked decline in numbers since 1938 is assumed and likely, as Walpole-Bond described the species as 'quite common'.

GREY PARTRIDGE—*Perdix perdix*
Status.—**Resident. A considerable decline has occurred in recent years.**

As with the previous species rather few reports are received annually. However, Common Partridges are still widely distributed in open habitats throughout the county and are probably most numerous on the Downs and coastal plain, where breeding densities of up to 80 pairs per 2,500 acres (10 sq. km.) have been recorded recently. It should be noted that counts of breeding pairs of this species must be made early in the year to be accurate.

Despite the lack of comparative data demonstrating it, there is not much doubt that this species has declined markedly in Sussex, as in other parts of Britain. The main causes of the decline are perhaps connected with contemporary and major changes in agricultural practice, but climatic factors have also contributed, with a series of cool damp summers, particularly in the 1950s, contributing to a high chick mortality on the coastal plain, for example.

QUAIL—*Coturnix coturnix*
Status.—**Scarce breeding summer visitor; occasional in winter; scarce passage migrant. No recent change in status is apparent.**

The numbers recorded annually vary widely; since 1960, for example, they have ranged from two in 1962 to about 40 in

1970. Most records are for June and July, and Quail are recorded every year in suitable breeding habitat, particularly cornfields along the length of the Downs east of the river Arun. Probably some always breed, although this is very infrequently proved, and the numbers of pairs involved is very difficult to estimate. However, the records since 1960 have indicated no more than 20 pairs in any year, and usually less.

Quail occasionally occur in winter, and des Forges and Harber gave about 14 such records until 1960, although only four of these were after 1900. There have been five more since 1960, at Winchelsea on 13 January 1966, Sidlesham on 6 and 7 February 1966, Shoreham on 8 March 1967, Earnley on 31 January 1968, and Southease on 8 February 1976.

Spring passage or arrival in recent years has been noted between 21 March (1973) and 22 May, but, in 'Quail years', arrival possibly continues well into June. Autumn passage or departure has been noted between 3 August and 25 September.

PHEASANT—*Phasianus colchicus*

Status.—**A widely distributed and common resident, whose numbers are annually augmented by hand-reared birds on a very large scale.**

CRANE—*Grus grus*

Status.—**Vagrant.**

Apart from two old records, for May 1849 at Pevensey Levels and 18 October 1854 at Pagham, all records except one are for 1963. In that year there was an extraordinary influx into southern England between 30 October and 4 November. The highest numbers were recorded in Sussex, where about 300, possibly more, were seen in parties of up to 100 birds. The birds were seen in five general areas: Eastbourne to Lewes; the Adur and Arun valleys; round Midhurst and Harting; and the Selsey Peninsular. One was seen near Crowborough on 16 April 1976.

WATER RAIL—*Rallus aquaticus*

Status.—Scarce resident, winter visitor and passage migrant. The breeding population may have declined in recent years.

An attempted census of the breeding population between 1962 and 1966 recorded only about 15 pairs. This was certainly an underestimate, and altogether between 1962 and 1976 there were records for the breeding season from 35 sites involving a possible 38 pairs; breeding was proved in 12 sites. These figures are based on records for May, June and July only, since winter visitors or passage birds are certainly present in the county from August to April. Despite the difficulty in locating breeding Water Rails they are clearly scarce and irregularly distributed, and a decline since 1938, when Walpole-Bond estimated about 50 breeding pairs, is possible. Not every known site appears to be occupied annually and, as a breeding bird, the species is now rare or absent from the permanent grasslands of the river valleys and levels, although Walpole-Bond recorded several regular breeding sites in such areas. At present the regular sites are either fairly large lakes with dense marginal vegetation, such as Burton, Lurgashall, and Shillinglee ponds, or small patches of marsh in the interior of the county. One or two pairs breed in coastal marshes.

Water Rails are more generally distributed in winter, when birds have recently been recorded in up to 20 inland localities in one winter, more than in any one breeding season. They are also regular at most suitable localities along the coast. Wintering birds are usually found singly, but gatherings of up to six are not very rare and about 15 wintered at Church Norton in 1968/69. Most of these birds seem to be visitors from outside the county.

Some passage also occurs. Autumn movements, whether passage or the arrival of winter visitors, have been noted between late August and mid-November and spring movements or departures between mid-March and 13 May. Some winter visitors stay on until mid-April. On passage, and sometimes in winter, Water Rails may occur in built-up areas.

CORNCRAKE—*Crex crex*

Status.—**Formerly bred; occasional in winter; scarce passage migrant. No change in status is apparent since 1947.**

There have been no breeding reports since 1945 although there have been five summer records of single birds in 1955, 1964, 1966, 1971 and 1972.

Between 1947 and 1976 a total of about 90 was noted, approximate monthly totals being:

Apr.	May	June	July	Aug.	Sept.	Oct.	Nov.	Dec.
8	11	2	3	16	44	19	0	1

Most were recorded in coastal districts, where Corncrakes may be found anywhere, including in built-up areas, but most usually in arable fields or rough grassland. This distribution perhaps again largely reflects the distribution of observers at the migrations, and the species certainly occurs inland, usually in arable farmland.

Recently spring records have fallen between 9 April (1961, earliest county record) and 26 May, but 78 per cent. of the records were for the last week of April and the first two of May. Autumn records fell between 6 August and 17 October, with a marked peak in September involving about 60 per cent. of the records. There are a few old records for November, the

latest being for 27 November 1844 at Rottingdean, and there
are about four winter records, but only two since 1900, one in
1908 and one at Cissbury on 9 December 1973.

LITTLE CRAKE—*Porzana parva*

Status.—**Vagrant.**

There are 13 records. Three are undated, otherwise there
are four for March, four for April, one for June, and one for
October. The most recent record is of one caught and ringed
at Beachy Head on 15 April 1968.

BAILLON'S CRAKE—*Porzana pusilla*

Status.—**Five records.**

One was caught near Eastbourne on 6 August 1874; one was
obtained near Brighton on 2 September 1894; one was obtained
near Lancing on 13 November 1900; one was obtained near
Pevensey on 16 May 1939; one was seen near Sedlescombe
between 27 December 1941 and 9 January 1942.

SPOTTED CRAKE—*Porzana porzana*

Status.—**Rare winter visitor; very scarce passage migrant.**
No recent change in status is apparent.

Spotted Crakes were recorded in 17 out of the 30 years
between 1947 and 1976, with a total of 26 birds seen. The
table summarises the records by months:

Jan.	Feb.	Mar.	Apr.	June	Aug.	Sept.	Oct.	Nov.	Dec.
2	1	1	4	1	3	3	7	7	2

The spring records fell between 16 March and 28 April, and the autumn records between 11 August and 4 December; although there are old spring records up to 8 May, and autumn records from 1 August. The winter records were for 26 December 1959 at Pett Level, 2 January 1965 at the Crumbles, 3 January 1971 at Eastbourne, and 16 February 1975 at Amberley Wildbrooks, found dead. Altogether there are 11 winter records for the county. Although there are three June records altogether, for 1907, 1939, and 1972, there is little evidence that the species has yet bred in Sussex.

Most records since 1947 have been for coastal districts, which perhaps just reflects the distribution of observers at the migration seasons.

MOORHEN—*Gallinula chloropus*

Status.—**Resident. No recent change in status is apparent.**

As breeding birds Moorhens are common, occurring wherever there is water; even ponds of only a few square yards frequently hold breeding pairs. The only recent count of breeding birds over an extensive area recorded 23 pairs along 2.5 miles of the Chichester canal in 1969.

In winter some quite large gatherings have been noted. For example, up to 105 have been seen at Manhood End, 80 at Harting pond, 70 at Swanbourne Lake, 105 in the Arun valley, and 30 at Rodmell, all since 1965.

Although Moorhens are sometimes seen in unusual localities along the coast, definite evidence of migration in Sussex is very scant.

COOT—*Fulica atra*

Status.—Common resident and winter visitor. No recent change in status is apparent.

Very little information on the breeding status of this species is available. Its distribution is certainly more restricted than the Moorhen's, since it requires larger areas of water for breeding. Within this context, however, Coot are believed to be fairly common.

Large flocks winter in the county. Fairly regular counts were made in several areas between 1966 and 1976, and the highest count recorded for each during October to March is shown in the table to indicate the scale of the wintering population.

Counts of Wintering Coot in Sussex, 1966–1976

Thorney Deeps	..	..	380	Weir Wood Reservoir	..	260
Chichester Harbour	..	..	2,335	Darwell Reservoir..	..	410
Pagham Lagoon	..	..	360	Pett Level	..	..	..	500
Chichester gravel pits	..	1,280	Rye Harbour gravel pits	..	1,900
Swanbourne Lake	..	..	260		

Substantial flocks were also recorded elsewhere during the period, for example of 100 or more at Burton ponds, Knepp lake, Barcombe Reservoir, and Piddinghoe pond. It is likely that the records available considerably underestimate winter numbers as the Coot's status on less important areas of water is very imperfectly known.

Winter visitors start to arrive in September, perhaps August in some years, and peak numbers are present in December, after which there is a steady decline through to March and April. But the movements of this species are not well understood and the pattern varies in some areas. For example, at Rye the figures show a marked peak in February, with a secondary peak in December. There is no recent evidence of any passage through the county.

LITTLE BUSTARD—*Otis tetrax*

Status.—**Vagrant.**

There are about 12 records, of which three are undated. Otherwise there are two for January, one for April, and two each for October, November and December. There have been no records since 1914.

GREAT BUSTARD—*Otis tarda*

Status.—**Resident until about 1825. Otherwise two records.**

One was shot near Ripe on 12 January 1876; one was shot on Pett Level on 6 January 1891.

OYSTERCATCHER—*Haematopus ostralegus*

Status.—**A few pairs breed; common non-breeding resident, winter visitor and passage migrant. No recent change in status is apparent, except that some decline in autumn passage may have occurred.**

Breeding is confined to Chichester Harbour, maximum five pairs; Pagham Harbour, maximum 12 pairs; Rye Harbour, maximum 10 pairs; and the Midrips with a maximum of two pairs. Numbers at each site vary annually and the total recorded population has yet to exceed 20–25 pairs. At Pagham Harbour there has been a very sharp increase from one to three pairs up to 1974 to 12 in 1976. The summer population also involves sizable flocks of non-breeding birds, with up to 275 in Chichester Harbour and up to 80 in both Pagham and Rye Harbours in recent summers.

Counts in Chichester and Pagham Harbours, illustrated in Fig. 6, have shown that most Oystercatchers are present in

Sussex during the autumn migration from July to November. Peak numbers were usually present in September or particularly October, but in some years the autumn peak was as late as November. Between September and November the counts recorded flocks totalling 1,000 or more birds almost annually, and the highest count in the period was of 1,670 birds on 22 October 1967. In fact, since 1968 the counts have indicated a decline in the numbers passing through, which may be as high as 20 per cent., despite another very high count of 1,890 on 23 October 1976.

Autumn passage and the arrival of winter visitors obviously overlap, and some movement may occur throughout the winter. However, the counts indicate a wintering population of the order of 800 birds in these Harbours, although the counts from December to February ranged from 400 to 1,450 birds. Elsewhere flocks of 100 to 150 winter regularly near Littlehampton, and flocks of up to 380, but more usually of 100 to 200, do so at Rye Harbour; in both areas rather larger flocks may occur on autumn passage. Complete counts of the Oystercatcher population wintering in Sussex in each January from 1972 to 1976 ranged from 940 to 1,530, and averaged 1,170.

Little passage is recorded in the spring, although there is fairly steady decline in the winter flocks after February. Oystercatchers are rarely noted away from the coast, but have been recorded on occasions on flooded levels as well as at the reservoirs.

LAPWING—*Vanellus vanellus*

Status.—**Common resident, winter visitor and passage migrant. Some decline in the breeding population has occurred recently.**

Although Lapwings still breed in all open habitats in the county, including heathland, numbers have apparently been declining for over 80 years. Walpole-Bond recorded a steady

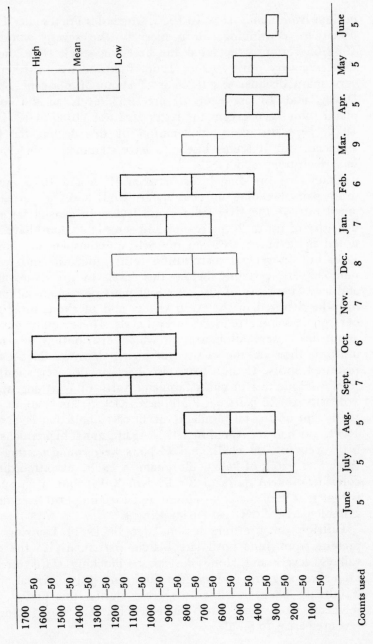

Fig. 6.—OYSTERCATCHER: range and means of monthly counts in Chichester and Pagham Harbours, March 1964 to April 1974

decline from about 1885 to 1937, which des Forges and Harber noted as continuing. More recently the severe winter of 1962/63 seriously depleted the breeding stock. This showed some recovery until 1967 or 1968, followed by a further and very sharp decline, in particular of about 50 per cent. on the Downs and 70 per cent. of pre-1963 levels on the coastal plain; some recovery in the latter area was noted in 1971 and 1972. No satisfactory explanation of this decline has been adduced, but it seems likely to have stemmed from changes in agricultural practice.

Counts of breeding birds between 1965 and 1976 showed most pairs breeding on coastal farmlands and the permanent grasslands of the river valleys and levels. In coastal farmland densities of up to 20 pairs over 250 acres (1 sq. km.) have been noted in favoured areas on the Selsey peninsular and around Rye, but in general distribution is not uniform and overall numbers are certainly below this level. In the river valleys and levels densities of just over four pairs per square kilometre have been noted in the Arun valley, and of about three pairs per square kilometre in Pevensey Levels. These counts covered about 60 square kilometres in which distribution was more uniform than on the coast, but higher densities do occur in favoured spots. Counts have also been made over about 18 square kilometres of chalk farmland north of Worthing, where a density of 22 pairs per 2,500 acres (10 sq. km.), about one-tenth that of coastal farmland, declined to half that level after 1968, but had recovered in 1973. Again, much higher densities may occur on the chalk, and 14 pairs were found nesting in a three-acre patch of kale at Burpham in 1969, an extraordinary concentration. A quirk of the Lapwing's distribution in Sussex is that it is very scarce or absent as a breeding bird from many suitable parts of the East Sussex Downs.

Outside the breeding season large flocks of Lapwings are present from June until late March, particularly in the river valleys, levels and along the coast. Flocking starts directly after breeding, in mid or late June and July. Arrivals have frequently been noted at the coast during this period, and it seems likely that such movements are of birds going to favoured areas to moult.

Counts round Chichester and Pagham Harbours have recorded a steady increase from June to October, high numbers present throughout October to February and a fairly rapid dispersal in March. There is no reason to suppose that this pattern of occurrence is not general in Sussex. But movements occur throughout the winter, particularly if there is even a short spell of hard frost, when spectacular cold-weather movements take place, often involving thousands of birds.

Numerous counts of winter flocks have been recorded in recent years, and gatherings of several thousands have been found regularly in most of the main areas of permanent grassland in the county, and in many coastal areas. Recently the largest winter counts have been made in Pevensey Levels, maximum 15,000 in early 1973, and Glynde Levels, maximum 10,000 in early 1974. In 1976 counts in January, which were very incomplete, recorded a total of 25,500 wintering birds.

GREY PLOVER—*Pluvialis squatarola*

Status.—**A few summer; winter visitor and passage migrant. Some increase in the number wintering recently has occurred.**

A few Grey Plover summer regularly in both Chichester and Pagham Harbours. These birds are nearly always in winter plumage and presumably are immature. Usually about 20 to 40 birds are involved, but there were about 200 in 1964.

In winter this species is also largely confined to these Harbours, where regular counts between 1964 and 1974, illustrated in Fig. 7, fairly consistently recorded flocks totalling 400 to 600 birds between December and March. Flocks of 1,000 to 2,000 were recorded at least once in each month in the period, and are now appearing much more frequently. Elsewhere small flocks usually winter along the coast between Goring and Worthing and at Rye Harbour, but totals do not often exceed about 50 birds. Complete counts of the winter

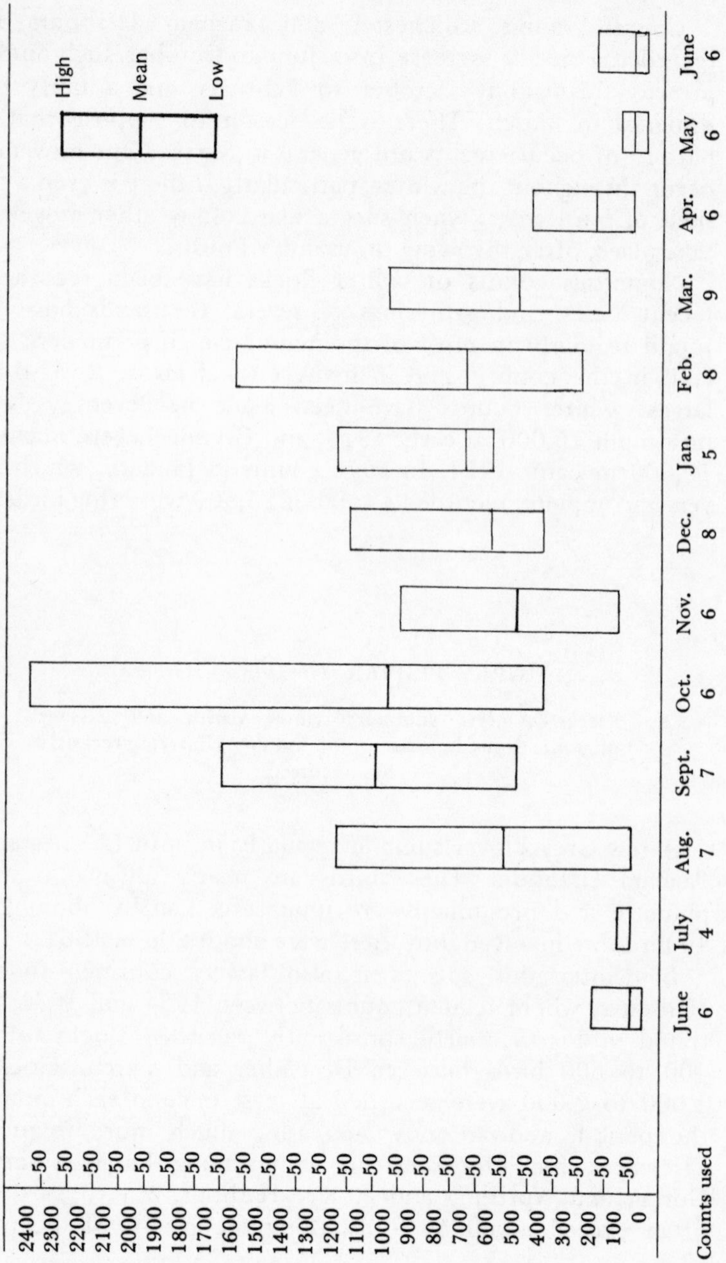

Fig. 7.—GREY PLOVER: range and means of monthly counts in Chichester and Pagham Harbours, March 1964 to April 1974

population were made each January from 1972 to 1976 and recorded a steady increase from 300 in 1972 to 2,175 in 1976.

Winter visitors disperse quite rapidly in April and May, and little through passage in spring is shown by the counts in Fig. 2, except in 1973 and 1974 when a marked movement occurred in the second half of February. Autumn passage may start in July, but most usually does so in August, and peak numbers are most commonly found in September. The highest counts so far recorded are of *c.* 2,400 on 13 October 1973, and 2,480 on 25 September 1976.

Grey Plovers are rarely seen away from the coast in Sussex, but there have been six such records since 1947 in March, April, May, October (three together), November, and December.

GOLDEN PLOVER—*Pluvialis apricaria*

Status.—**Common winter visitor and passage migrant. No recent change in status is apparent.**

In winter most Golden Plover are found on coastal farmland, including the permanent grassland of the levels. In recent years the largest flocks have been fairly consistently noted on the Selsey peninsular, Pevensey Levels, and in the Rye area, with flocks of up to 3,000 occurring in each place. Elsewhere along the coast flocks of up to 500 are regularly found. A few also occur on the Downs and further inland, but usually only in small parties.

Autumn arrival may start in late July, early dates being 21 July 1963 at Chidham, 22 July 1939 at the Midrips, and 22 July 1967 at Thorney. Some always arrive in August and numbers increase steadily thereafter. The largest numbers are present from December to February, but there are sizable flocks throughout the period October to March.

Although quite large flocks may still be present early in the month, winter visitors disperse rapidly in April, and few are seen in May. There are several records for the end of this month, however, and four for June: 21st, 1937, Midrips (three); 16th to 30th, 1954, Hamsey; 9th, 1968, Pagham; and 13th to 21st, 1975, Sidlesham Ferry.

Two races of the Golden Plover are regularly noted in Sussex, *P. a. apricaria* and *P. a. altifrons*. Since these races are only separable in summer plumage most sub-specific records are for April and May, and the extent to which either race occurs in winter is unknown.

RINGED PLOVER—*Charadrius hiaticula*

Status.—Scarce and local breeding species; winter visitor and passage migrant. The number breeding has declined in recent years with the increasing development of the coast.

An incomplete census of the breeding population in 1973 recorded 66–69 pairs, distributed in Chichester Harbour, with 13 pairs; Pagham Harbour, 16 pairs; Chichester gravel pits, eight to 10 pairs; Southwick/Portslade, four to five pairs; Newhaven Tidemills, two pairs; Cuckmere Haven, one pair; Rye Harbour area, including Camber and Northpoint Beach, 22 pairs. In addition, pairs usually breed at Bracklesham Bay, Aldingbourne gravel pits, the Crumbles, and Normans Bay, and up to nine pairs do so at the Midrips. Although the population has shown little change from this level of around 75 pairs since 1965, the figures indicate a decline of 30 per cent., perhaps more, since about 1947, when 40 nesting pairs were noted in the Rye Harbour area alone.

Most birds breed on shingle beaches, where they are increasingly vulnerable to disturbance, so it is fortunate that the two most important localities, at Pagham and Rye Harbours, which hold nearly half the county population, are now statutory Local Nature Reserves administered by the relevant County Councils. Elsewhere, despite disturbance, some young are successfully reared each year, and Ringed Plovers seem to be developing an increasing tolerance of casual disturbance by man of their breeding sites. For example, a successful group now breeds around the power stations at Southwick and Port-slade. In 1972 some birds were also found summering on the Downs, where very stony fields provide apparently suitable nesting sites, and breeding was proved in one such site in 1974.

Counts in Chichester and Pagham Harbours, which are illus-trated in Fig. 8, show that by far the largest numbers of Ringed Plovers are present in Sussex during migration, particularly in the autumn. Peak numbers then occur in August and November and the figures for these two months are extraordinarily similar; prob-ably two distinct populations are involved in these movements.

Surprisingly few remain in winter. Counts in these Harbours of over 200 between early December and March are unusual, and the average of all counts from mid-December to late March is 140. However, Ringed Plovers also winter along much of the county coastline, except the cliffs, and counts have recorded totals of 100–300 birds, mainly between Ferring and the Adur estuary and at Rye Harbour. But it seems unlikely that the county's total wintering population often exceeds some 500 birds, and complete counts made each January from 1972 to 1976 usually recorded smaller numbers, with 165 in 1972, 215 in 1973, 285 in 1974, 490 in 1975; but 761 in 1976.

Winter visitors probably depart in March and there is a very marked spring passage, especially in May, when flocks of over 400 have been noted. This movement may continue into June, but the period has not been defined. On both spring and autumn passage the species frequently appears at inland waters as well as right along the coast.

There have been six records of the race *tundrae,* but none since 1938, presumably as collecting is now illegal.

LITTLE RINGED PLOVER—*Charadrius dubius*
Status.—**Breeds irregularly; scarce but regular passage migrant.**

Although only four birds had ever been recorded before 1948, Little Ringed Plovers have bred in Sussex frequently

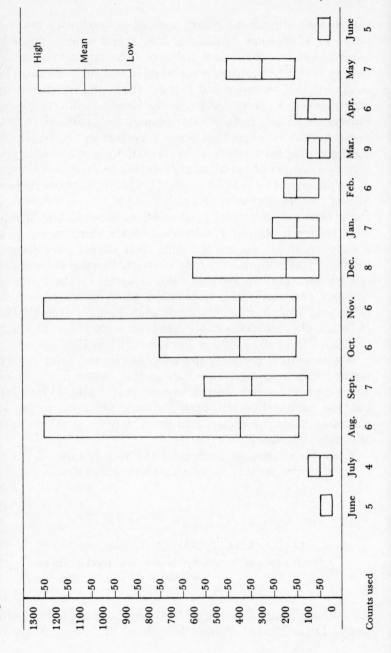

Fig. 8.—RINGED PLOVER: range and means of monthly counts in Chichester and Pagham Harbours, March 1964 to April 1974

since 1950. Up to five pairs were present annually from 1950 to 1960, a single pair bred in 1965 and up to three pairs have been present annually since 1969. Breeding sites have been either reservoirs or gravel pits.

The species occurs regularly on passage. For example, between 1961 and 1976 55 were seen in the spring between 10 March and 16 May, and *c.* 150 in the autumn between 23 June and 3 October. On passage birds are seen on inland waters, particularly the reservoirs, as often as on the coast. Most records are of one or two birds, but seven together were seen at Arlington Reservoir on 6 August 1971 and five on 7 August 1976.

KENTISH PLOVER—*Charadrius alexandrinus*
Status.— **Formerly bred. Rare but possibly regular passage migrant.**

Kentish Plovers bred regularly in East Sussex until about 1920 and between 1949 and 1956; none has bred since 1956. The breeding population was always small, and from 1949 onward consisted of only one or two pairs.

Otherwise des Forges and Harber noted it as occurring on passage in several years between 1947 and 1961, and between 1962 and 1975 about 29 were seen, 18 in spring between 17 March (1969, Newhaven, earliest county record), and 13 May, and nine in autumn between 1 July and 15 September. All records were for the coast.

There were also two in Chichester Harbour in December 1963, and the species has been recorded in late October, November and January in the past.

KILLDEER—*Charadrius vociferus*
Status.—**One record.**

One was seen at Sidlesham Ferry on 30 March 1974.

DOTTEREL—*Eudromias morinellus*

Status.—Irregular passage migrant.

Between 1947 and 1976 there were six spring records comprising 25 birds between 25 April and 24 May, and 21 autumn records comprising 46 birds between 17 August and 22 September. All spring records except one were for the Downs, but all autumn records for the coast. Small parties were as frequent as single birds. The species was more frequent in the 19th century, when extreme dates were 22 March and 11 November, and parties of up to 20 or more were seen.

BLACK-WINGED STILT—*Himantopus himantopus*

Status.—Vagrant.

There are 11 records, comprising about 14 birds. One record is undated, otherwise birds were recorded in May (seven), June (one), August (one), September (three), and December (one); one September bird stayed into October. The most recent records were of single birds at Sidlesham Ferry on 6 and 16 May 1961; possibly, but not certainly, only one bird was involved.

AVOCET—*Recurvirostra avosetta*

Status.—Scarce winter visitor; passage migrant, mainly in spring. A marked increase in the number occurring has been recorded since about 1968, except in the autumn, and the species now winters regularly.

Although des Forges and Harber gave only about 15 winter (November to February) records until 1960, a few birds have wintered regularly since 1964 around Pagham Harbour; what are probably the same individuals have also been seen quite often around Chichester Harbour. Up to 13 birds in one winter have so far been involved, and they usually arrive between mid-December and mid-January, and remain until March or April.

Otherwise Avocets are predominantly spring passage migrants in Sussex; the paucity of autumn records seems remarkable and has always been a feature of the species' occurrence in the county. The numbers recorded each year have shown a large increase, from an average of about nine to 12 per year between 1947 and 1967 to one of about 45 per year between 1968 and 1976. Besides the small wintering population, this increase is confined to the spring migration, as the table of approximate monthly totals for 1947 to 1976 shows:

1947–67

June	July	Aug.	Sept.	Oct.	Nov.	Dec.	Jan.	Feb.	Mar.	Apr.	May
26	2	7	17	23	1	8	4	5	37	25	43

1968–76

June	July	Aug.	Sept.	Oct.	Nov.	Dec.	Jan.	Feb.	Mar.	Apr.	May
44	8	4	0	1	5	36	40	39	62	119	122

A large percentage of recent spring birds have been recorded in parties flying up the Channel during the offshore movements of ducks, waders and terns, which are such a feature of spring migration in Sussex. Parties of up to 23 have been involved and, in general Avocets, are now likely to be met in small parties quite as often as singly in the county. Altogether the timing and pattern of this increase suggests that it is connected with an increase, shift or change in habits of a continental population, rather than the British. In striking contrast to the spring pattern the numbers seen in autumn have, if anything, diminished, although the picture is somewhat distorted by the exceptional occurrence of 21 at Camber on 8 October 1966; there have only been three other October records since 1947. But the eccentric changes in the pattern of this species' occurrence leave little doubt that the increases in winter and spring are genuine increases in numbers, rather than a reflection of increased observation.

Avocets are rare away from the coast in Sussex but, since 1947, there have been ten inland records, comprising 14 birds, and two reports of birds leaving the coast and flying north up the Cuckmere valley, one on 9 May 1968 and six on 16 March 1969.

WHIMBREL—*Numenius phaeopus*

Status.—Occasional in summer and winter. Common passage migrant. No recent change in status is apparent.

Although one or two birds may summer fairly regularly in Chichester or Pagham Harbours, the summer population rarely exceeds about 10 birds; seven summered at Rye Harbour in 1968. There are three winter records of single birds in Pagham Harbour, on 24 January 1965, from January to April 1973, and from 19 January to 8 March 1975.

Most Whimbrel are recorded in Sussex in the spring. The earliest record for spring arrival is of one at Chidham on 23 March 1971, but arrival always starts in the first 10 days of April, and some movement continues to mid-June. Most passage, however, occurs from mid-April to mid-May, when a marked movement along the coast, usually associated with passage of other species such as Bar-tailed Godwits, Scoter, or terns, takes place. Recently such movements have involved up to 960 birds in one spring, and movements of 100 or more in a day are almost annual events; 488 flying east off Beachy Head on 19 April 1976 is the largest single movement noted so far. In addition to these visible movements flocks of 50 to 100 birds are commonly noted during this period in favoured places, such as Chichester, Pagham and Rye Harbours. Small parties are also frequently seen flying over the interior of the county.

Autumn passage starts in July, but visible movements comparable with those of spring have not been observed. At this season by far the largest numbers are found in Chichester and Pagham Harbours, in both of which flocks of 100 or more are of regular occurrence in July and August; the highest count recorded between 1964 and 1976 was a total of 295 on

20 August 1967. The highest numbers usually occur in August, particularly in the first half, and comparatively few Whimbrel are seen in September. Thus the average of all the September counts made in Chichester and Pagham Harbours between 1964 and 1976 was only 15 birds, and the highest count was 41 on 22 September 1968 (mainly on Hayling Island). Stragglers, however, are usually noted into October, and there have been seven November records since 1947, the latest being of one at Thorney Deeps on 25 November 1953.

CURLEW—*Numenius arquata*

Status.—**A few pairs breed. Common winter visitor and passage migrant. No recent change in status is apparent.**

Breeding is confined to Ashdown Forest, where up to six pairs have bred recently, and one area of north-west Sussex, where there are one or two pairs. Some non-breeding birds are present at the coast throughout the year.

Counts in Chichester and Pagham Harbours, illustrated in Fig. 9, have shown Curlews to be most abundant in Sussex during late summer and autumn. Movements or arrivals start in June and large flocks are present from July, with the highest numbers between August and October, when the counts in these Harbours have regularly recorded over 1,000 birds, and over 2,000 have been found. In half the years covered by counts a distinct double peak has been evident during the autumn movements, in August/September, and again between late October and early December.

Numbers appear to drop rapidly in November and early December to the winter level in these Harbours of some 700 to 1,500 birds. There are marked fluctuations in the monthly totals for any one winter, which must partly stem from the species' habit of frequently feeding outside the estuaries during the day, so that birds are missed by the counts.

Substantial flocks are also found between Pett Level and Rye Harbour in the autumn and particularly the winter, when

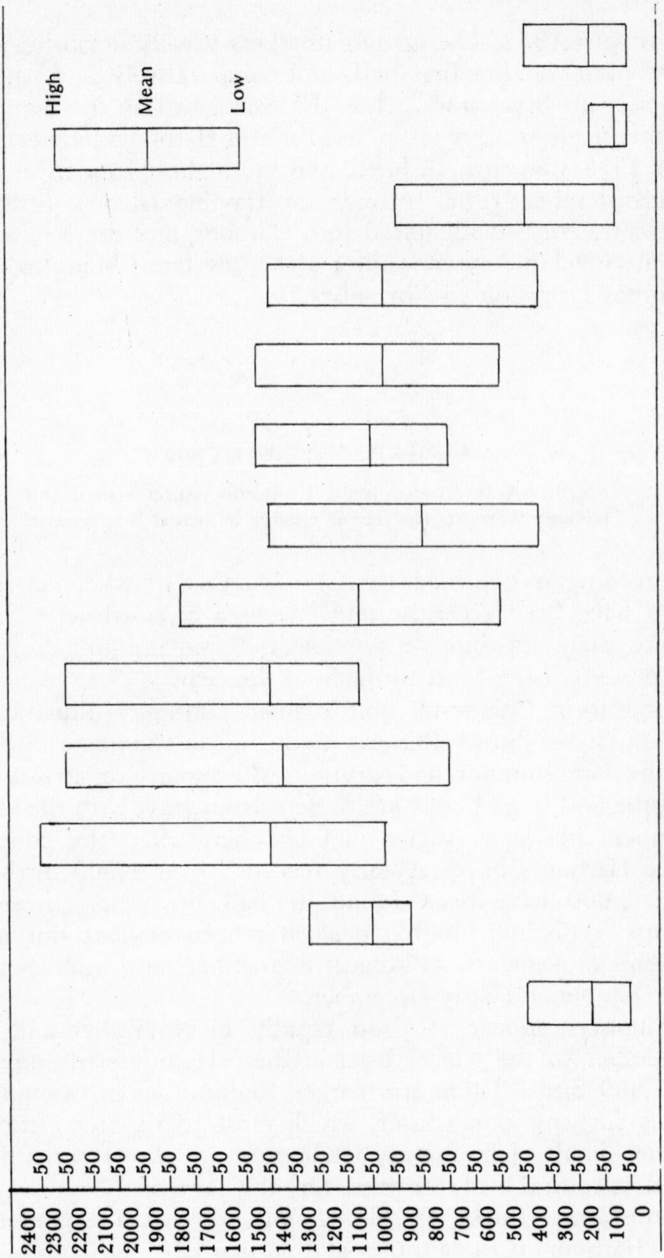

Fig. 9.—CURLEW: range and means of monthly counts in Chichester and Pagham Harbours, March 1964 to April 1974.

up to 800 have been noted. Elsewhere, however, only small parties are found, and Curlews are very infrequent away from the coast or its vicinity in winter. Complete counts of the wintering population were made each January from 1972 to 1976, and ranged between 1,055 in 1973 and 1,830 in 1972, averaging 1,400.

Little spring through passage is recorded, but a rapid drop in the wintering flocks after March, shown by the counts in Fig. 4, indicates the departure of wintering birds. Fewest Curlews are present in the county in May.

BLACK-TAILED GODWIT—*Limosa limosa*

Status.—**A few non-breeding birds summer; winter visitor and passage migrant. No recent change in status is apparent.**

In Sussex this species is largely confined to Chichester and Pagham Harbours, where a few remain to summer in many years, although totals of more than 50 are most unusual.

Counts in these Harbours, however, illustrated in Fig. 10, have regularly recorded sizable flocks from September to April. Interpreting these counts needs care, particularly those for the winter, when very marked fluctuations have been recorded, for, unlike most other waders, the wintering Black-tailed Godwits may move about over the whole of the estuarine complex from Pagham Harbour to Portsmouth Harbour in Hampshire. Thus only counts covering this entire area are likely to give a true indication of winter status. Such counts were made each January from 1972 to 1976 and recorded 760 in 1972 (260 in Sussex), 935 in 1973 (630 in Sussex), 1,050 in 1974 (550 in Sussex), 1,465 in 1975 (950 in Sussex), and 760 in 1976 (310 in Sussex). Larger numbers have been recorded, and the highest winter count so far was of 1,625 on 9 December 1972, of which 1,400 were in Chichester Harbour, the largest winter flock ever recorded in Sussex; higher numbers have been noted during autumn migration.

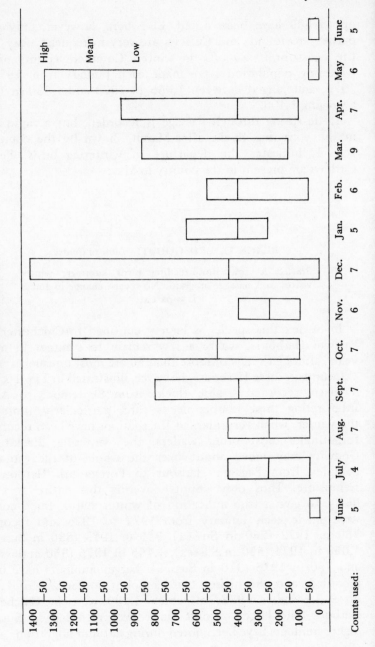

Fig. 10.—BLACK-TAILED GODWIT: range and means of monthly counts in Chichester and Pagham Harbours, March 1964 to April 1974

There is also a considerable passage in spring and autumn. Autumn arrivals start in July and the counts in Chichester and Pagham Harbours have recorded a fairly consistent peak in October. Spring passage is most marked in March and April.

At both seasons flocks totalling 500 or more are common-place, and the highest counts were of totals of 1,210 on 12 October 1969, and 1,430 out of 2,000 in the whole Pagham Harbour to Portsmouth Harbour complex on 19 October 1974; and, in spring, 950 on 15 April 1972, and 1,370 on 29 March 1975.

Away from the western Harbours parties of more than 10 are very unusual in Sussex. However, small groups are noted regularly along the coast and inland on passage. In winter such records are decidedly rare.

BAR-TAILED GODWIT—*Limosa lapponica*

Status.—A few summer; winter visitor and common passage migrant. No recent change in status is apparent.

Except on passage large flocks occur only in Chichester Harbour; even in Pagham Harbour counts of more than 50 birds are very unusual, although it is nearly always present there. A few birds frequently, perhaps always, summer in these Harbours. Since these are nearly always in winter plumage they are presumably immature.

Counts in Chichester and Pagham Harbours, illustrated in Fig. 11, show that most Bar-tailed Godwits are present in Sussex in winter, when there is a very marked peak in January. This usually involves over 1,000 birds, and the highest count so far recorded was of 1,535 in Chichester Harbour on 30 January 1972. However, throughout the period November to February flocks of 500 or more are regularly present, and the average of all counts in this period between 1964 and 1976 was over seven hundred. This is probably the largest wintering flock on the English south coast, and comparisons with des Forges and Harber's account of this bird suggest a large increase in winter

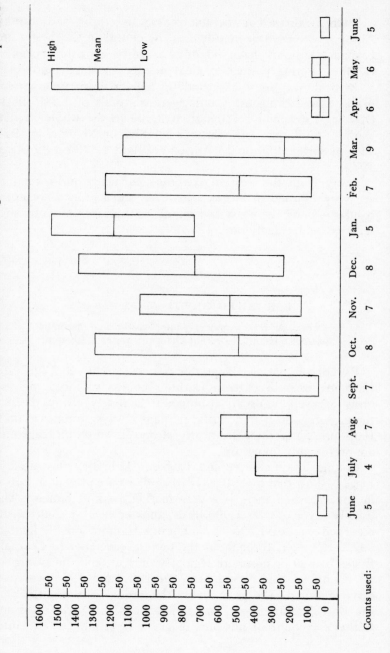

Fig. 11.—BAR-TAILED GODWIT: range and means of monthly counts in Chichester and Pagham Harbours, March 1964 to April 1974

numbers. But this is almost certainly the result of systematic observation in Chichester Harbour.

The arrival of winter visitors clearly overlaps a marked autumn passage. This may start in July and always does so in August. Peak numbers are usually noted in September, when flocks totalling up to 1,600 have been noted in Chichester and Pagham Harbours and flocks of up to 200 have been seen elsewhere along the coast. In marked contrast very little through passage has been noted in the western Harbours in the spring, counts showing only a rapid departure of wintering birds in March and April. However, sea-watching at such sites as Selsey Bill and Beachy Head has recorded a large visible passage in spring. Typically this occurs between mid-April and mid-May, and, as with most such movements, numbers vary considerably. But sometimes they are very large. For example, 6,760 were recorded at Selsey Bill between 23 April and 1 May 1962, 4,310 at Beachy Head between 15 April and 2 June, 1971, and 7,490 there between 25 March and 17 May 1973, and 6,450 between 29 February and 15 May 1976. These are the largest movements so far noted and in some years fewer than 100 birds have been involved. Presumably such marked fluctuations are connected with the prevailing weather conditions.

Bar-tailed Godwits are very rare inland in Sussex, but since 1966 there have been six reports of birds inland on spring migration between 12 April and 3 May, usually in small parties, but 200 together flew north over Arlington Reservoir on 3 May 1971.

SPOTTED REDSHANK—*Tringa erythropus*

Status.—Scarce winter visitor; passage migrant. No recent change in status is apparent.

One or two now winter regularly in Chichester and Pagham Harbours and single birds sometimes do so elsewhere along the coast. It is unusual for more than five birds to be found in any winter, but an exceptional record was of 24 in the lower Rother valley on 13 January 1946.

Spring passage is also quite slight, numbers rarely exceeding about 10 birds in any spring. Passage, however, may extend from March to early June, although most movement is noted in April or May. Many more are seen in the autumn, when arrivals often start as early as late June and always in July. These early parties are nearly always found at Thorney Island and include a high proportion of adults in summer plumage. Possibly they are birds which have failed to breed successfully and have assembled here to moult. The largest numbers are noted in August and September, but the bird is quite common in October and passage sometimes continues into November.

Throughout the autumn the great majority of Spotted Redshanks in Sussex are found at Thorney Island, where flocks of 30 to 60 birds have been an annual occurrence since 1965; the highest count so far was of 69 there on 8 August 1967. Elsewhere single birds or parties of up to five are the general rule, and the species is regularly recorded along the whole coast, and at most of the main areas of gravel pits and the reservoirs during migration.

REDSHANK—*Tringa totanus*

Status.—**Local breeding species; common winter visitor and passage migrant. The breeding population has declined in recent years.**

A survey of the breeding population between 1965 and 1967 recorded about 250 breeding pairs, mainly distributed in coastal marshes and the permanent grasslands of the river valleys and levels, but with some pairs scattered in small areas of marsh in the interior. A fifth of this population was concentrated round Chichester and Pagham Harbours. In the river valleys and levels breeding densities varied from 25 pairs per 2,500 acres (10 sq. km.) in the Arun valley south of Amberley, to about five pairs per 2,500 acres in Pevensey

Levels; this figure may have been too low, and 29 pairs (20 pairs per 2,500 acres) were found in 1976. A full report of this survey was published in SxBR 1967, 53-60.

While little overall change has occurred since 1967, these figures represented a marked decline compared with 1938, when Walpole-Bond's account indicated a population of well over 300 pairs in the main levels, and suggested a wider distribution in small areas of marsh in the interior. This decline is possibly of post-war origin, as in 1949 Thorney Island, the marshes around Pagham Harbour and Selsey, and Rye Harbour still held a total of about 150 pairs compared to about 35 in 1967.

Despite the extensive decline, it is possible that more Redshanks still nest in Sussex today than did in the 19th century. Walpole-Bond noted that few of the early historians of Sussex birds recorded the Redshank as a breeding species, and that there was a marked increase and spread from about 1900. Almost certainly these fluctuations in the breeding population are directly connected with changes in agricultural practice and prosperity, but the recent decline probably stems from the drainage and improvement of large areas of permanent pasture, rather than their loss to arable farming.

Counts in Chichester and Pagham Harbours, illustrated in Fig. 12, show that Redshanks are most numerous during autumn migration. Outside the breeding season they are infrequent inland, and the local breeding stock starts to return to the coast in late June. Substantial arrivals and passage starts in July, and numbers are high throughout the period July to October, all but two of the counts illustrated being of over 1,000 birds, and the mean of all counts in this period being 2,280. The highest numbers of the year occur in September, when flocks totalling 3,000 or more are not unusual in these Harbours; the highest count so far was of 4,200 on 5 September 1971. The pattern of movement shown by these counts is most probably repeated elsewhere along the coast, where this species is a regular and common migrant.

The counts in Fig. 12 show a sharp drop in November, followed in many years by further arrivals in December. But the monthly means from November to February show

Fig. 12.—REDSHANK: range and means of monthly counts in Chichester and Pagham Harbours, March 1964 to April 1974 (June to November).

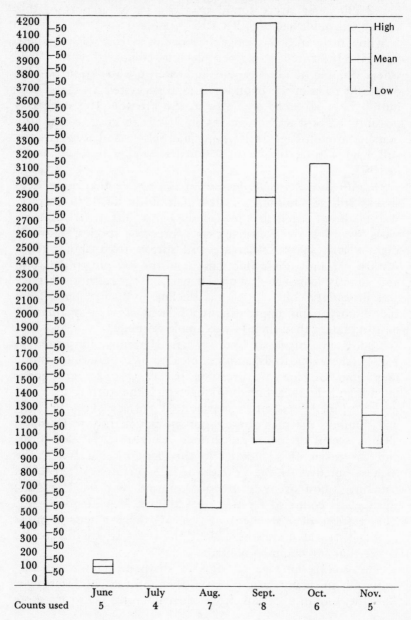

Fig. 12. (cont.)—REDSHANK: range and means of monthly counts in Chichester and
Pagham Harbours, March 1964 to April 1974 (December to June).

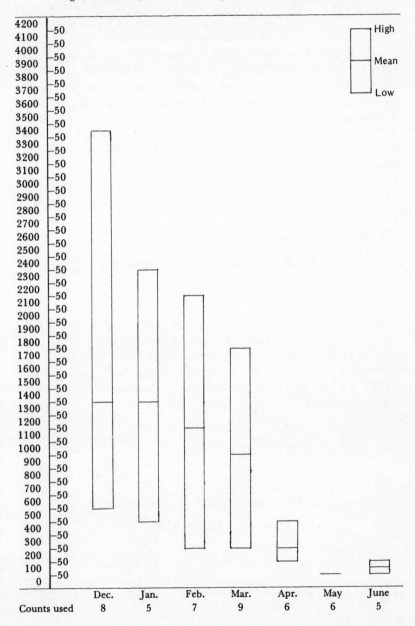

comparatively little variation and indicate an average winter population in the two Harbours of around 1,200 birds; at least some of the fluctuations in the winter counts must arise from the species' regular habit of feeding outside the Harbours in flooded fields, when these are available. Small flocks also winter regularly at Ferring, Shoreham, Newhaven, Cuckmere Haven, and in the Rye area, and complete counts of the wintering population made each January from 1972 to 1976 ranged from 1,190 in 1975 to 1,680 in 1974, averaging 1,380.

Winter visitors depart in late February and March, when our breeding birds also return inland, and the counts in Fig. 12 show very little through passage in the spring.

LESSER YELLOWLEGS—*Tringa flavipes*

Status.—Five records

One was seen at Chichester gravel pits on 15 August 1947; one was seen at Sidlesham Ferry on 13 September 1954; one was seen at Chichester Gravel pits from 16 October to 3 November 1969; one was seen in the Cuckmere valley on 3 and 4 August 1970; and one was seen at Weir Wood Reservoir on 11 and 12 September 1971.

MARSH SANDPIPER—*Tringa stagnatilis*

Status;—Three records.

Two were seen at the Wicks on 26 September 1937. In 1951 one was seen at Thorney Island on 22 April, and another, or perhaps the same bird, in the Cuckmere valley on 29 April.

GREENSHANK—*Tringa nebularia*

Status. —Scarce winter visitor; passage migrant. No recent
change in status is apparent.

Although parties of up to seven have been noted, this species
may not winter every year. Nearly all the winter records recently
have been for Chichester and Pagham Harbours.

Spring arrivals start in late March or April, and movements
continue into June, with a marked peak in May; parties of up
to 10 are not unusual on spring passage.

Greenshanks are common autumn passage migrants in Sussex.
Although arrivals may start in late June, it is less often seen
then than the Spotted Redshank, and movements more usually
start in July. Passage continues into November and there is a
very marked peak in September.

Chichester Harbour is the locality most favoured by Greenshanks in the county and, in autumn, flocks of 50 to 100 are
regularly reported there. Regular counts between 1965 and
1976 have recorded peaks of over 100 in five autumns, with
135 on 5 September 1971, and 130 on 15 September 1974 as
the highest counts. Elsewhere parties of 10 to 20 are often seen
at Pagham Harbour, and the species is widely recorded all along
the coast and inland.

GREEN SANDPIPER—*Tringa ochropus*

Status. —Scarce winter visitor; common passage migrant.
No recent change in status is apparent.

Although a few Green Sandpipers winter regularly in Sussex,
the numbers involved are small, usually five to 10 birds annually.
They are found inland much more frequently than at the
coast, and sewage farms, cress beds, and the dykes in fresh
marshes are the favoured localities.

The movements of winter visitors are obscured by passage
movements in spring and autumn. Spring passage, however,
is usually quite slight and mainly confined to April, while May,

so often an important month for wader passage, is the month in which fewest Green Sandpipers are seen in the county.

Autumn movements or arrival invariably begin in late June, and numbers increase steadily to a peak in August. During the autumn the species occurs all along the coast and widely inland, particularly at gravel pits and reservoirs. Parties of up to 10 birds are regularly seen, and, at Chichester gravel pits, a very favoured locality, flocks of over 20 have been seen in July and August in several recent years. Passage is usually over by mid-October, but certainly continues into November in some years.

WOOD SANDPIPER—*Tringa glareola*

Status.—Once in winter; rather scarce spring passage migrant; regular autumn passage migrant. No recent change in status.

One was seen in the Ouse valley, at Iford, on 11 February 1967, the only winter record for the county, although Hudson (1973) in fact notes this as the earliest spring record for Britain.

Otherwise the pattern and frequency of occurrence of this species has not changed since des Forges and Harber's summary of records until 1961. Most are reported at the coast, but inland records are now regular in autumn from several localities, particularly Chichester gravel pits and Weir Wood Reservoir, as a result of increased observation. Most records are of single birds, but parties of up to nine have been recorded and unusual numbers were seen in the autumn of 1972, when about 60 birds were noted in July and August along the coast.

The records for the years 1970 to 1976 are summarised by months to show the present pattern of occurrence:

Apr.	May	June	July	Aug.	Sept.	Oct.	Nov.
1	6	2	44	113	29	2	1

Apart from the February record, extreme dates for this species are 19 April (1951, Rye, and 1969, Crowhurst), and 3 November (1976, Newhaven).

TEREK SANDPIPER—*Xenus cinereus*

Status.—Two records.

One was seen at the Midrips on 30 May 1951; one was seen in Pagham Harbour on 10 May 1969.

COMMON SANDPIPER—*Actitis hypoleucos*

Status.—Perhaps regular in winter; common passage migrant. No recent change in status is apparent.

Although not recorded every year, it is quite likely that a few Common Sandpipers always winter in Sussex. The numbers involved rarely exceed five birds, although there were 12 in 1950, and sites such as sewage works may be especially favoured.

Most winter visitors seem to leave by March, which is the month in which fewest Common Sandpipers are seen in the county; there were only 10 March records between 1965 and 1976, for example. Spring arrivals and passage begin in April, usually around the middle of the month, and movements continue into early June, with a very marked peak in May. Return movements begin as early as late June, and the species is numerous from July to September; the highest numbers of all occur in August. Comparatively little passage is noted in October, and records for November and December probably refer to wintering birds.

As with most migrants the numbers concerned in these movements vary considerably each year, but typically spring movements have involved some 40 to 50 birds in recent years, and autumn movements some 200 to 300. Particularly in autumn small parties are often seen, and there have been four records of flocks of about 50 birds since 1965.

During both migrations Common Sandpipers are found at suitable inland sites quite as frequently as at the coast.

SPOTTED SANDPIPER—*Actitis macularia*

Status.—Three records.

Two, possibly three, were shot at the Crumbles in October 1866; one was shot at Shoreham on 27 November 1908; one was seen at Weir Wood Reservoir from 11 to 17 August 1974.

TURNSTONE—*Arenaria interpres*

Status.—Winter visitor and passage migrant. No recent change in status is definitely known.

As winter visitors Turnstones are largely confined to Chichester and Pagham Harbours, the open beaches round the Selsey peninsular, and from Pevensey to Rye Harbour. Counts in Chichester and Pagham Harbours, illustrated in Fig. 13, have revealed an interesting pattern in the winter months, with a consistent drop in numbers in December, followed by an arrival of further winter visitors in January, which usually remain until March or April. This pattern has been repeated in counts of the East Sussex population.

From January to March a fairly stable population of 100 to 300 birds has been found in the two western Harbours, and the beaches around the Selsey peninsular regularly attract about fifty. Fairly regular counts from Pevensey to Rye Harbour since 1967 have recorded a wintering population of 200 to 350 birds and the total wintering population of the county, therefore, may be of the order of 300 to 600 birds. But complete counts each January from 1972 to 1976 tended to be rather lower, ranging from 175 in 1973 to 550 in 1976, but averaging 285. Some change in status may therefore be occurring.

The counts illustrated in Fig. 13 also show a fairly marked passage in May, when flocks of up to 300 have been noted, but very few are seen in June, and summering is a rare event. Autumn passage begins in July and peaks consistently occur

Fig. 13—TURNSTONE: range and means of monthly counts in Chichester and Pagham Harbours, March 1964 to April 1974 (June to November).

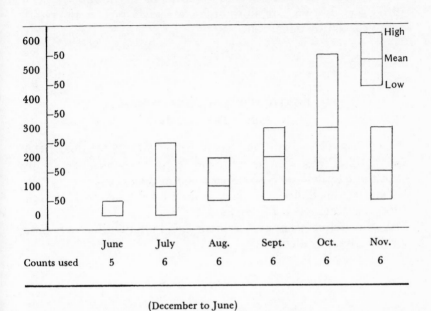

(December to June)

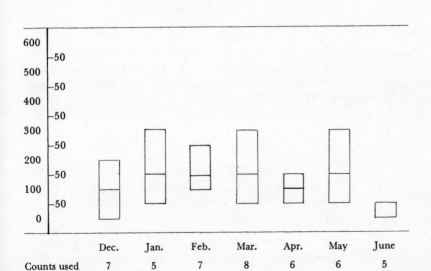

in October, when flocks totalling about 300 are quite frequent. The highest count was of 535 on 3 October 1971.

Although there are about 20 records in all, there have been 1967, one or two are now noted at gravel pits or reservoirs each year during migration.

DOWITCHER—*Limnodromus species*
Status.—Four records.

One was seen at Thorney Island from 15 to 22 October 1950 and another was seen there from 2 to 11 November 1959; both these birds were considered to be *L. scolopaceus.*

One seen at Sidlesham Ferry from 14 February to 15 March 1965 was accepted as *L. griseus.*

A dowitcher seen at Chidham on 4 April 1965 was not specifically identified.

GREAT SNIPE—*Gallinago media*
Status.—Vagrant.

Although there are about 20 records in all, there have been only three in the past 50 years: 30 September 1950 at the Midrips, 10 November 1964 at Pagham, and one shot at Bodiam in September 1976.

SNIPE.—*Gallinago gallinago*
Status.—A local breeding species; common winter visitor and passage migrant. A marked decline has occurred since 1938.

A census of the breeding population was made between 1965 and 1967, which recorded 80 to 100 pairs in the permanent grasslands of the river valleys and levels, and a few pairs in minor patches of marsh and bog in the interior. About 75 per cent. coverage of the river valleys and levels was achieved, and the average breeding density recorded was five pairs per 2,500 acres (10 sq. km.); the highest density was in the Amberley/Pulborough marshes, with 15 pairs per 2,500 acres. The population in minor sites was probably under-recorded and records before and since suggest that nesting Snipe are still quite widely distributed in such sites in Sussex.

These results, however, showed that, although the species' distribution in the breeding season had not greatly changed since 1938, the total population had declined by something approaching 80 per cent., as Walpole-Bond recorded up to 100 pairs 'in some of the largest levels'. Such figures suggest a minimum population of about 500 pairs, and this decline is obviously the result of drainage and considerable pasture improvement in the permanent grasslands. A full report of the census appeared in Sx BR 1967, 53-60.

Although the numbers in winter have almost certainly declined for the same reason, Snipe are still very common winter visitors to Sussex. Counts round Chichester and Pagham Harbours, where the species does not breed, show that autumn arrival starts in July and August, with the main arrival in October. Numbers remain fairly stable from November to March, although influxes occur in hard frost; winter visitors disperse fairly rapidly in April. This pattern probably applies to the whole county. Flocks of 100 or more are commonplace in winter, particularly at Thorney Deeps (maximum count 300), round Pagham Harbour (maximum 350), at the Amberley/Pulborough marshes (maximum 300), Adur Levels (maximum 250), Glynde Levels (maximum 750), Pevensey Levels (maximum 2,000), Wet Level (maximum 160), and Crowhurst Marsh (maximum 400). Smaller parties are regular in many boggy areas throughout the county.

WOODCOCK—*Scolopax rusticola*

Status.—Common resident; perhaps winter visitor;
scarce passage migrant. Some increase in the breeding
population is possible in recent years.

Alexander (1945), during a survey of status in the British
Isles, received 28 reports from Sussex, which showed Woodcock to be widely distributed in the Weald, but absent from
the coastal plain, the Downs, Pevensey Levels, the Rye area,
and the Adur valley. Some breeding densities given were 23
pairs per 2,500 acres (10 sq. km.) around Fernhurst, and
roughly double this density in the Worth/Tilgate/Balcombe
Forest complex.

Latterly S. W. M. Hughes has mapped all the breeding season
records for the years 1966 to 1973 on a tetrad basis. This
map and other recent records leave no doubt that the species
is still as widely distributed and probably as abundant in the
Weald today. It is still particularly numerous in the north of
Sussex, around Midhurst and Fernhurst, and in St. Leonard's,
Worth, Tilgate, Balcombe, and Ashdown Forests. In addition
there has been a marked expansion into the downland forestry
plantations in West Sussex between the Hampshire border
and the river Adur, where Hughes' map shows a notable concentration, and densities of some 20 pairs per 2,500 acres
have been suggested by counts of roding birds. Woodcock are
still largely absent in the breeding season from the coastal plain
of West Sussex, Pevensey Levels, and the Rye area, although
there have been recent records from Old Park Wood at Fishbourne. In addition, Hughes' map shows none breeding on the
Downs east of the river Adur.

The breeding stock is probably resident and, although Woodcock are usually stated to be winter visitors, there is little
concrete evidence that this is so on any scale. Close study of
the movements of the breeding population is needed before
this can be accurately established. Indeed, Alexander (1946)
discussed the movements and winter distribution of this species
in detail and concluded that in many areas, including Sussex,
local movements of the breeding stock, particularly to moult
in early autumn, contributed very largely to the widely-held

belief in a large-scale arrival of winter visitors about October.

However, some movements do occur at the coast in October and November and again in March and April, although the numbers involved are tiny; usually under 10 birds in any year. Influxes are also noted at the coast in severe weather, but many of these birds may be of the resident breeding stock.

JACK SNIPE—*Lymnocryptes minima*

Status.—Scarce winter visitor and passage migrant. No recent change in status is apparent.

The exact status of this species is difficult to define, as it is elusive and easily overlooked. However, fewer than 30 are normally recorded annually, although over 50 were noted in 1968 and 1969, and 1974 and 1975. Jack Snipe may be found in any suitably boggy ground, including quite small sewage works, and nearly always associating with Snipe, but most records are for coastal marshes or the permanent grasslands of the river valleys and levels. Thorney Deeps and Glynde Levels are typical and favourite localities.

Arrival normally begins in late September or October and continues through November; cold weather movements may also occur on a very limited scale. Winter visitors may remain until late April, but most appear to depart in March. Stragglers or late passage birds have been recorded in early May, and the latest spring date is 12 May (1951, Crumbles). There is also a noticeable passage in November and March.

Most records are of single birds, and even where several are present in one haunt they are usually solitary. However, 10–12 were found together at Newhaven Tidemills on 28 November 1968, and 21 were recorded at Thorney Deeps on 1 February 1975; 17 were still present on 1 March.

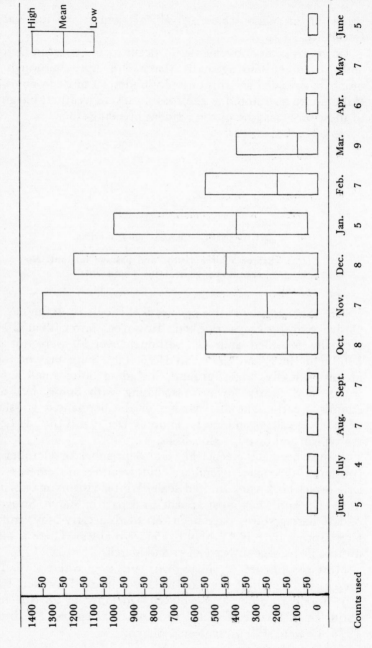

Fig. 14.—KNOT: range and means of monthly counts in Chichester and Pagham Harbours, March 1964 to April 1974

KNOT—*Calidris canutus*

Status.—Winter visitor and passage migrant. Some increase in the number occurring is possible since 1970.

Counts in Chichester and Pagham Harbours, illustrated in Fig. 14, have recorded most Knot in the late autumn and winter. Nearly all these birds have been found in Chichester Harbour, where the main arrival starts in October. The highest numbers are usually present from November to January, and the counts indicate a steady departure from February onwards. Numbers over the period 1964 to 1974 have been very variable and all the counts of over 1,000 birds shown in Fig. 14 have been since 1971. Possibly some genuine increase in the number visiting Sussex has taken place.

Outside Chichester Harbour Knot are quite scarce, but parties of up to 50 sometimes occur along the coast in winter and regularly do so on passage. In fact, on both spring and autumn passage numbers may be quite large; for example, 150 were seen at Rye Harbour on 4 September 1955, and 213 passed east off Beachy Head on 6 May 1971.

There are 10 inland records for the county: in January (three), March (one), April (one), September (four), and December (one). These records comprised 17 birds, and five of them were for 1976.

SANDERLING—*Calidris alba*

Status.—Winter visitor and passage migrant. The numbers occurring in winter may have increased in recent years.

In winter the main Sussex locality for this species is the shore between Middleton-on-Sea and Worthing, where flocks totalling 300 to 600 birds have been found recently. Some increase may have occurred, as des Forges and Harber indicated counts of not more than 250 in this area up to 1961. Elsewhere 100 to 200 Sanderling usually winter in Chichester Harbour, and smaller flocks do so in the Rye area. Complete counts

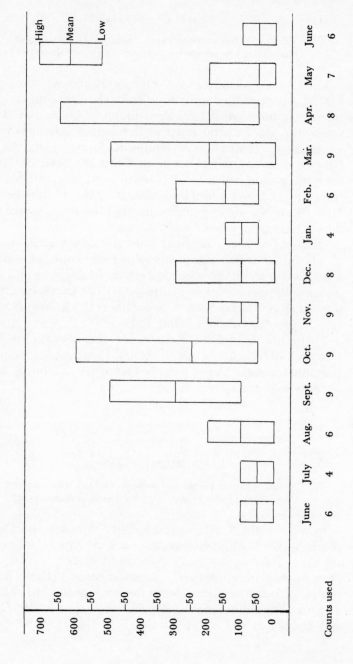

Fig. 15.—SANDERLING: range and means of monthly counts Chichester and Pagham Harbours, March 1964 to April 1974

made of the wintering population in each January from 1972 to 1976 ranged from 460 in 1974 to 825 in 1973, averaging 575.

Counts in Chichester and Pagham Harbours, illustrated in Fig. 15, also show a marked passage through the county in spring and autumn. Spring passage has been most marked in April, but may start as early as February; the low May figures are of interest as there is then a very large passage of this species in other parts of Britain and sometimes a marked visible movement along the Sussex coast (*cf.* Bar-tailed Godwit). Autumn passage may extend from July to October, but is most marked in September and October and the highest numbers may occur in either month. A flock of 560 in Chichester Harbour on 18 October 1970 is the largest yet recorded in the county.

Sanderling are rare away from the coast, but one was seen at Amberley Wildbrooks on 18 February 1963, three together were seen at Chichester gravel pits on 11 May 1969, five on 22 May 1976, and three at Arlington Reservoir on 14 May 1973; and there have been eight autumn records comprising 16 birds inland, between 1 August and 22 September.

LITTLE STINT—*Calidris minuta*

Status.—Rare winter visitor; regular passage migrant. No recent change in status is apparent.

Until 1961 des Forges and Harber recorded only 23 Little Stints in winter, and these included a party of 11 at Thorney Island on 27 December 1960. But since wader counts in Chichester and Pagham Harbours began in March 1964 the species has been found in nine out of 12 winters, usually as single birds associating with the Dunlin flocks. Considering the difficulty of detecting one individual among very large flocks of Dunlin, it seems likely that a few Little Stints winter regularly in Sussex and very probably have always done so.

As passage migrants Little Stints are much more numerous in autumn than in spring, but numbers vary greatly each year.

The records for the years 1970 to 1976 show the present pattern of occurrence well and approximate monthly totals in this period were:

Jan.	Feb.	Mar.	Apr.	May	June	July	Aug.	Sept.	Oct.	Nov.	Dec.
3	7	3	3	26	5	15	103	181	33	6	6

Spring passage was recorded as late as 20 June, but most occurred in the second half of May, and up to 10 birds were seen in one spring; none was seen in one spring. Autumn passage was recorded from 6 July, but usually from the end of this month, and totals varied from 19 to 70 individuals. Most records were for the coast, but the species regularly occurs inland.

In the autumn parties of up to 10 or 15 birds are quite often seen, and in the exceptional influx of 1960, when between 200 and 300 were seen, there were parties of 22 at Manhood End, 31 at Sidlesham Ferry, and up to 70 at the Midrips.

TEMMINCK'S STINT—*Calidris temminckii*

Status.—**Once or twice in winter; rare passage migrant.**

Although only about eight were recorded between 1880 and 1946 (des Forges and Harber), 46 were noted between 1947 and 1976. One wintered at Thorney Deeps in 1975/76, and another was found in Chichester Harbour from 19 March to 9 April 1975 which may also have wintered.

Otherwise 12 were seen in spring, from 1 to 26 May, and 32 in the autumn between 5 July and 21 October, with monthly totals of five in July, 16 in August, and 12 in September, of which one remained at Sidlesham Ferry until 21 October 1975.

Most records were of single birds at the coast or occasionally reservoirs and gravel pits, but there were four reports of two together, and there were three at Sidlesham Ferry on 14 August 1968.

WHITE-RUMPED SANDPIPER—*Calidris fuscicollis*
Status.—Five records.

One was shot at Bexhill on 8 October 1857; one was shot near Eastbourne on 12 November 1870; one was present at the Midrips from 30 August to 19 September 1948; one was seen at Thorney Island from 9 to 28 November 1959; one was seen at Sidlesham Ferry from 24 to 26 August 1974.

BAIRD'S SANDPIPER—*Calidris bairdii*
Status.—Three records.

One was present at the Wicks from 19 to 27 September 1952; one was present at Rye Harbour from 8 to 10 September 1968; one was present at Arlington Reservoir from 11 to 18 September 1973.

PECTORAL SANDPIPER—*Calidris melanotos*
Status.—Rare autumn migrant.

Until 1961 des Forges and Harber gave nine records involving 11 birds, all seen at the coast between 29 August and 20 October. Between 1962 and 1976 11 more were recorded: in July (one), August (one), September (eight), and November (one). Three of these records were for inland localities, at Weir Wood Reservoir from 1 to 7 September 1962, Arlington Reservoir from 3 to 7 September 1972, and Chichester gravel pits on 26 and 27 July 1974.

Fig. 16.—DUNLIN: range and means of monthly counts in Chichester and Pagham Harbours, March 1964 to April 1974 (June to November)

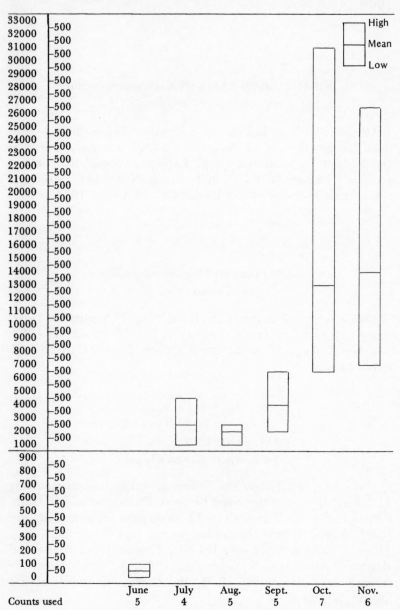

Counts used	June	July	Aug.	Sept.	Oct.	Nov.
	5	4	5	5	7	6

Fig. 16 (cont.)—DUNLIN: range and means of monthly counts in Chichester and Pagham Harbours, March 1964 to April 1974 (December to June)

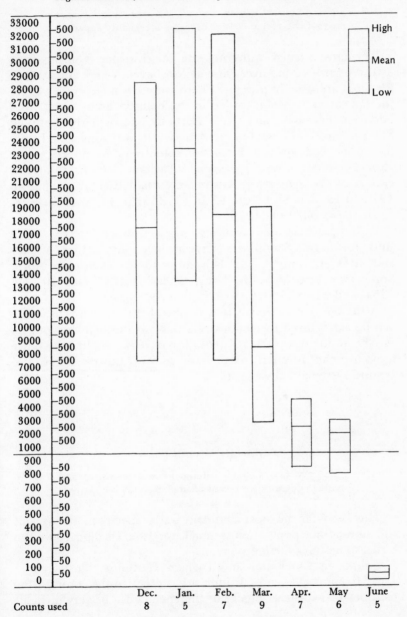

PURPLE SANDPIPER—*Calidris maritima*

Status.—Scarce winter visitor; perhaps also passage migrant. No recent change in status is certainly apparent.

The most regular wintering site for this species in Sussex is at the mouth of the river Ouse at Newhaven, where about 20 to 25 birds are usually present. There were 31 in December 1969, the largest party yet recorded in the county. Some also winter between Pevensey and Rye Harbour, particularly between St. Leonards and Bexhill, and between Worthing and Little-hampton. One or two birds are sometimes found elsewhere along the coast in winter, especially Pagham Harbour. Complete counts of the winter population were made each January from 1972 to 1976 and recorded 27 in 1972, 51 in 1973, 47 in 1974, 63 in 1975, and 49 in 1976.

Although there are records as early as 5 August (1973, Selsey Bill), few Purple Sandpipers arrive in the county before October and most are present from November to March or early April. Some stay into May, the latest dates recently being 20 May 1951, and 21 to 24 May 1974, both at Newhaven.

Although it may occur, it is doubtful if the records available can be safely used to demonstrate passage through the county. As the resident winter population may move about over quite long stretches of coast, particularly in West Sussex, this would require systematic investigation.

DUNLIN—*Calidris alpina*

Status.—A few summer; abundant winter visitor and passage migrant. No recent change in status is apparent.

This is by far the most abundant wader species in Sussex, but the summering population is small, rarely exceeding 100 or so birds; sometimes there is none.

Counts in Chichester and Pagham Harbours, illustrated in Fig. 16, show that most Dunlin are present in the county from October to February. Flocks of this species can be very difficult to count accurately, which must be partly responsible for the marked fluctuations shown in Fig. 16; for example, the January counts have ranged from 13,500 to 32,500. But the means demonstrate the annual pattern of occurrence well, with the first sizable flocks appearing in July and very large arrivals starting in October. Thereafter numbers increase steadily to a peak in January, or sometimes February, after which month the flocks disperse quite quickly.

Chichester Harbour is by far the most important locality in the county for this bird, and the winter peak there was just under 30,000 birds in early 1973, 1974 and 1975, and averaged about 20,000 between 1964 and 1976. Numbers appeared to be exceptionally high from 1973 to 1975. Flocks of 3,000 to 5,000 are regularly found in winter at Pagham Harbour, and flocks of 500 to 1,000 winter between Ferring and Shoreham, with smaller numbers along the coast from Newhaven to Rye. Complete counts of the wintering population were made each January from 1972 to 1976, and ranged from 24,440 in 1976 to 33,095 in 1975, averaging 27,870. In both 1973 and 1974 these counts missed the peak in Chichester Harbour by a fortnight, and this would have added 7,000 and 5,000 to the totals; in both years, therefore, the maximum wintering population of the county probably approached 35,000 birds.

Although it is not evident from the counts in Fig. 16, there is marked through passage in spring and autumn. This is more clearly shown by records of visible passage along the coast in the spring, especially in May when most of the winter flocks have gone, and the frequent inland records in spring and autumn. Inland records are non-existent in summer and rare in winter, when small flocks have occasionally been found on flooded levels.

CURLEW SANDPIPER—*Calidris ferruginea*
Status.—**Rare winter visitor; regular passage migrant. No recent change in status is apparent.**

Until 1960 des Forges and Harber gave about five instances of wintering, and there was one at Pilsey Island on 29 March

1964, which may have wintered. This is the only possibly wintering bird detected in the wintering Dunlin flocks during the regular wader counts in both Chichester and Pagham Harbours (*cf.* Little Stint).

As a passage migrant the Curlew Sandpiper is decidedly scarce in the spring and numbers are very variable in the autumn. The records for the period 1970 to 1976 show the pattern of occurrence well and approximate monthly totals were:

Apr.	May	June	July	Aug.	Sept.	Oct.	Nov.
1	14	1	23	219	187	38	5

In spring up to seven birds were noted, but none was seen in one year. Autumn totals ranged from about 23 to about 85 birds and parties of more than about 20 were most unusual. However, in 1969 there was an exceptional autumn passage, with a total of about 260, including a flock at Sidlesham Ferry which reached a maximum of 180 on 1 September. These are by far the highest numbers ever recorded in Sussex.

Autumn passage in this period fell between 16 July and 15 November, although passage has been noted as early as 27 June (1953). In spring movements were seen between 17 April and 13 June.

Most Curlew Sandpipers are seen at the coast and, although a few are now recorded regularly at inland gravel pits and reservoirs, they seem much scarcer at such sites than Little Stints.

STILT SANDPIPER—*Micropalama himantopus*

Status.—Three records.

One was present at Chichester gravel pits from 1 to 7 September 1962; one was present at Manhood End from 7 to 13 August 1963; one was seen at Sidlesham Ferry on 14 July 1972.

BROAD-BILLED SANDPIPER—*Limicola falcinellus*
Status.—**Five records.**

One was obtained at Shoreham in late October 1845; one was obtained at Rye on 13 August 1887, and another on 2 October 1895; one was seen at the Midrips on 13 September 1934; one was seen at Hove Lagoon on 6 March 1948.

BUFF-BREASTED SANDPIPER—*Tryngites subrufi-collis.*
Status.—**Six records.**

One was obtained at the coast in the autumn before 1843; one was obtained at Rye Harbour on 21 August 1934; one was present at the Midrips from 17 September to 2 October 1955; one was seen at Sidlesham Ferry on 5 September 1970; one was seen at Camber on 6 September 1973; one was seen at Sidlesham Ferry on 9 and 10 September 1974.

RUFF—*Philomachus pugnax*
Status.—**Winter visitor and passage migrant. The numbers occurring have increased in recent years, particularly in winter and on spring migration.**

Although des Forges and Harber noted them as most numerous on autumn migration until 1961, with some 20 to 30 birds reported each autumn, Ruffs are now most numerous in winter or on spring passage, when flocks of 50 to 100 birds are regularly reported. The largest flocks noted so far were of 120 at Bracklesham Bay from 18 February to 17 March 1968, 116 at Chidham on 19 December 1973, and up to 370 on the Selsey peninsular in February and March 1976. Monthly totals from 1965 to 1976 show the present pattern of occurrence well. These were:

June	July	Aug.	Sept.	Oct.	Nov.	Dec.	Jan.	Feb.	Mar.	Apr.	May
26	100	380	504	355	301	455	512	1144	1162	401	83

Thus, there is still apparently a marked autumn passage, with a peak in September, and numbers appear to be greater than those indicated by des Forges and Harber. This is followed by further arrivals from November to January of winter visitors, and there is a very marked movement in February and March. However, some duplication may be involved in the figures given, as flocks may move about over quite large areas, particularly if there is much flood-water in winter. This makes systematic recording difficult.

Although Ruffs are not estuary birds in Sussex, the largest flocks have usually been found near the coast, either in grass marsh or, in winter, wet arable fields.But the species is also widely recorded inland, at gravel pits and reservoirs on passage, and on the permanent grassland of the river valleys and levels when these are wet in winter. I have also recorded the species following the plough on a number of occasions in spring and autumn on the Selsey peninsular.

GREY PHALAROPE—*Phalaropus fulicarius*

Status.—**Rare winter visitor; uncommon passage migrant in autumn. Some decline in the number occurring, particularly in September and October, may have taken place.**

Between 1945 and 1961 des Forges and Harber recorded about one to six annually, except in 1950 when there were 18, and about 60 appeared in Sussex during the exceptional influx into Britain of 1960. Larger numbers apparently occurred in the 19th century after severe gales, for example 250 in 1866.

Between 1962 and 1976 about four were recorded annually, except in 1972 when there were sixteen. This suggests some decrease, and the marked preponderance of November records also indicates change, as des Forges and Harber gave September and October as the peak period. Approximate monthly totals for the period were:

Sept.	Oct.	Nov.	Dec.
6	7	25	2

Records fell between 9 September and 26 December, but there are earlier records for August (earliest, 17 August 1844), and there are records for January (four) and February (three).

Grey Phalaropes usually appear singly, but small parties may be seen, the most recent being of nine off Langney Point on 19 November 1972. The only recent inland records were 18 and 19 September 1957 at Darwell Reservoir, 18 September 1960 at Weir Wood Reservoir, and 3 November 1967 on Glynde Levels.

RED-NECKED PHALAROPE—*Phalaropus lobatus*
Status.—Rare passage migrant.

About 40 were recorded until 1937, and des Forges and Harber gave a further 14 up to 1961. Between 1962 and 1976 only nine were seen. Three of these were in the spring, on 12 and 13 June 1965 at Amberley Wildbrooks, 25 May 1968 at Thorney Island, and 7 and 8 June 1974 at Rye Harbour.

There are now seven spring records for the county and the Amberley record appears to be the only inland report. The remaining records were for July (one), August (three), September (one), and October (one). Surprisingly these are the only August records for Sussex, and it is of interest that des Forges and Harber noted September as the peak month for this species, with records extending into October, and once November. Just possibly some change in the pattern of occurrence has taken place.

WILSON'S PHALAROPE—*Phalaropus tricolor*
Status.—Three records of one bird.

In 1971 one was seen at Arlington Reservoir on 25 September, which moved to the Cuckmere Haven area on the 26th and

27th, and Sidlesham Ferry from the 29 September to 6 October. Although these reports were published as three separate birds by *British Birds* (65, 335), the coincidence of timing makes it almost certain that only one bird was involved. On 6 October it was found shot on the pool it had frequented at Sidlesham Ferry.

STONE CURLEW—*Burhinus oedicnemus*

Status.—**Rare breeding summer visitor; very rare winter visitor and passage migrant. A considerable decline has occurred since 1938.**

A survey of the breeding population was made between 1962 and 1964, which found 12 regular breeding areas along the Downs, holding 15 to 20 pairs, and single pairs breeding or probably breeding sporadically in a further eight sites. The total population was estimated at 20 to 25 pairs, confined to the Downs, except for one pair at the Midrips in 1962. A full report was published in SxBR 1964, 34.

Although breeding has been established since 1964 in two Downland sites missed by this survey, there is little concrete evidence of more recent overall change in numbers, but some observers have reported further local declines. However, 20 to 25 pairs does represent a considerable decline since 1938, when Walpole-Bond estimated a county population of 'quite 60 pairs', although even then the species was patchily distributed and had probably declined in numbers since the turn of the century, when up to 12 pairs were breeding at the Midrips alone.

With the extensive changes in agricultural practice on the Downs since the war, Stone Curlews now have to nest mainly in arable habitats and the 1962–64 survey recorded nests in corn (four), root crops (three), fallows (five), and leys (one); one nest was also found in a young forestry plantation. Even where the downland grassland remains, lack of grazing pressure from sheep or rabbits has allowed it to become too coarse and overgrown to be favoured by Stone Curlews. One result of this change in nesting habitat has been to make the species far more difficult to observe; it is not easy to find any ground-nesting bird in a sea of barley!

Stone Curlews begin to arrive in Sussex about mid-March; in recent years the earliest date was 8 March 1969 at West Chiltington. Walpole-Bond considered that all the Sussex breeding stock had arrived by about 12 April, and subsequent records along the coast may well refer to passage migrants. But these have been very few in recent years, only six such birds being recorded between 1962 and 1976, for the period 16 April to 25 May. In addition there was an exceptional record of 12 together at Mile Oak on 27 April 1973, which seem most likely to have been on migration.

Autumn passage is now equally scant. Thus between 1962 and 1976 there were only eight reports of birds obviously on migration, between 23 August and 10 November, and only three autumn gatherings of any size have been noted since 1947. Formerly these gatherings were a feature of the autumn movements of Stone Curlews in Sussex, and Walpole-Bond implies that assemblies of up to 100 birds were not exceptional. Since 1947, however, the only records have been of a flock of about 50 behind Worthing on 27 September 1955, which increased to about 125 by 1 November, after which they left, and a flock of 27 in the same area on 27 September 1959. On 1 December 1958 there was a flock of 12 at Burpham which may, in fact, have been wintering birds. There is no other recent winter record.

COLLARED PRATINCOLE—*Glareola pratincola*

Status.—**One record.**

One was obtained at Kingston, near Lewes, on 31 August 1840.

BLACK-WINGED PRATINCOLE—*Glareola nordmanni*
Status.—One record.

One was seen at the Midrips on 21 August 1955.

A Pratincole seen at Selsey Bill on 3 September 1975 was not specifically identified.

GREAT SKUA—*Stercorarius skua*

Status.—Occasional in winter; uncommon passage migrant. A marked change in status has been recorded in recent years.

Between 1937 and 1961 des Forges and Harber recorded 26 birds, only six of which were for the spring. Since 1962, however, regular sea-watching has revealed a marked easterly passage in the Channel in spring, and shown that Great Skuas are more numerous off Sussex in the autumn than previously suspected. Clearly greater observer activity has contributed to this revision of status, but, at least in spring, a genuine increase in the numbers occurring may well be involved, perhaps connected with the increase in the British breeding stock.

Approximate monthly totals for the period 1962 to 1976 were:

Jan.	Feb.	Mar.	Apr.	May	June	July	Aug.	Sept.	Oct.	Nov.	Dec.
4	2	4	119	54	5	5	22	23	16	4	2

Four of the six records for January and February were of dead or disabled birds. Spring passage fell between 23 March (1968, earliest spring record) and 29 May, and involved up to 23 birds in one spring; most movement took place in the second half of April.

All the June records were for the last eight days and thus seem likely to refer to early return movements rather than summering birds. Otherwise autumn passage started in July and sometimes continued into early December, but more usually until late October. There was no very clearly marked peak and no more than nine birds were seen in any autumn.

One was found dead at Wiston, near Steyning, on 18 November 1940, otherwise all records are for the coast. Most are seen singly, but two or three sometimes occur together.

POMARINE SKUA—*Stercorarius pomarinus*

Status.—Winter vagrant; scarce passage migrant, mainly in spring. A marked increase in the numbers occurring has been recorded recently, mainly in the spring.

Until 1961 des Forges and Harber recorded a total of about 66 birds, of which five were for the winter, in December (three), January (one), and February (one); there have been no winter records since 1924. Otherwise most records were for the autumn, and five out of the six spring records were for 1961.

Since that year regular sea-watching has revealed that some Pomarine Skuas pass east up the Channel each spring, and the numbers doing so have increased very markedly since 1967. The autumn numbers have shown less change, but sea-watching results have confirmed that the species is of regular occurrence in the Channel.

Approximate monthly totals between 1962 and 1976 were:

Jan.	Feb.	Mar.	Apr.	May	June	July	Aug.	Sept.	Oct.	Nov.	Dec.
0	0	1	78	424	3	0	9	7	9	2	0

Spring passage fell between 10 March (1970, Goring, earliest spring record) and 3 June (1968, Beachy Head, the only June record for the county), but 70 per cent. of the birds were recorded in the first two weeks of May. Numbers varied, but increased from an average of six per spring between 1962 and 1966 to 47 per spring between 1967 and 1976. This increase has been noted at both Selsey Bill and Beachy Head, although the numbers of hours watching at the former site declined considerably in the latter period. This tends to confirm that a genuine increase in numbers of birds passing through is involved. Extraordinary movements occurred in 1971, when over 80 were seen in the first two weeks of May, and in 1976, when 154 were seen between 19 April and 15 May. Up to 23 have been recorded together and such parties seem much more characteristic of this species on migration than of Arctic Skua.

Autumn passage was noted from 13 August until 16 November, although Pomarine Skuas have been noted as early as 5 August (1957, Langney Point). There was no clear peak and little evidence of increase at this season. Seven flying west off Selsey Bill on 15 October 1963 is the largest autumn movement on record. All other autumn records were of single birds. All records are for the coast, except for one caught at Rogate in December 1865.

ARCTIC SKUA—*Stercorarius parasiticus*

Status.—Winter vagrant; common passage migrant. No recent change in status is apparent.

Until 1960 des Forges and Harber recorded eight winter records: four for December, three for January, and one for February. There have been four since, two in December, and one each in January and February.

As passage migrants Arctic Skuas are usually recorded from early April until early November, but the earliest and latest dates are 27 March (1965 and 1967) and 29 November (1970). The numbers recorded annually vary considerably, particularly in the spring when the sighting of large movements depends very largely on the occurrence of southerly or south-east winds. However, between 1962 and 1976 spring totals ranged from 25 to 290 birds, with an average of about 100, and autumn totals ranged from 17 to 135 birds, with an average of about forty-five. Thus the species is now recorded most frequently in the spring (*cf.* des Forges and Harber), but this apparent change in status is, like the increase in the numbers now being reported, almost certainly the result of a very marked increase in spring sea-watching over the period; analysis of the records shows a fairly exact correlation between increased hours of observation and numbers of Arctic Skuas.

Spring passage appears regularly to extend into June, but the peak movements normally occur in late April and particularly the first two weeks of May. Movements of up to 20 to 30 in a day are then frequent and the largest movement so far recorded involved 55 flying east off Beachy Head on 1 May 1972 and another 54 on 7 May.

A few Arctic Skuas may summer off Sussex, accounting for some June and July records, but sea-watching results from Selsey Bill suggest also that return movements may start as early as the second half of June. Thus 16 flew west off Selsey Bill between 21 and 30 June 1969, during a large westerly gull movement. Autumn passage in any case nearly always starts in the second half of July, but movements are smaller than in the spring and there is rarely any clear peak. However, 49 flew west off Langney Point on 14 September 1970, which is the largest autumn movement so far recorded.

Arctic Skuas are usually seen singly, although small groups occur, and there is one record of 20 flying east together off Selsey Bill on 8 May 1960. The species is maritime and the only recent records away from the immediate vicinity of the coast are of single birds at Weir Wood Reservoir on 12 September 1955 and 3 September 1970, Chichester gravel pits on 18 August 1974, and of three flying south-west over the Downs on 10 September 1976. Three other records for the interior were all prior to 1900.

LONG-TAILED SKUA—*Stercorarius longicaudus*

Status. —Vagrant.

Although there have been 11 records, comprising 14 birds altogether, only two have been noted in the last 50 years, one at Cuckmere Haven on 1 June 1942 and one off Selsey Bill on 15 October 1963.

IVORY GULL—*Pagophila eburnea*

Status.—Vagrant.

There are about 11 records; all, except for one in August 1848, for the period November to February. Only three of the records are for the last 50 years; 6 January 1931 at Rye, 19 November 1954 in the lower Cuckmere valley, and 19 November 1961, at Portobello, Brighton.

COMMON GULL—*Larus canus*

Status.—Common non-breeding resident and passage migrant. Has now ceased to breed, but no other recent change in status is apparent.

Although up to 10 pairs apparently bred regularly at the Midrips from 1932 to 1962, none has done so since 1962, when there were two pairs. Little information on non-breeding birds summering in the county is available, but some certainly do so.

In winter this is a numerous species at the coast, and flocks of 200 to 300 occur inland at sites such as Weir Wood Reservoir. At the coast flocks of up to 2,000 have been noted, but few counts are available and larger numbers may occur.

Some very large spring movements have been noted. As with other gulls spring passage extends from mid-February into May, but the largest movements are in April, when movements of 1,000 in a day are not infrequent; 3,000 flew east off Beachy Head on 17 April 1965, and about 10,000 passed through the Rye Harbour area over 10 to 12 April 1971. Return passage starts in July, and apparently peaks in August, although it may continue well into November.

HERRING GULL—*Larus argentatus*

Status.—**Common resident, winter visitor and passage migrant. The breeding population has apparently declined in recent years.**

Two complete counts of the breeding population have been made recently. In 1965 318 nests were counted along the chalk cliffs, 371 along the sandstone cliffs between Hastings and Pett, about 20 in St. Leonards, and 11 at Rye Harbour. The total population was estimated at 790 pairs as not every nest was certainly found, particularly in Hastings and St. Leonards, and surplus adults were present in each area. In 1969 861 to 892 occupied nests were recorded: at Pagham Harbour, one; along the chalk cliffs, 401; in Hastings and St. Leonards, 106 to 131; along the sandstone cliffs between Hastings and Pett, 315; and at Rye Harbour, thirty-eight.

These counts apparently represent a very marked decline, very much against the national trend, since Walpole-Bond, in 1938, estimated that about 2,000 pairs were nesting between Seaford and Beachy Head. Porter *et al.* (SxBR 1965) found only 360 pairs in this area and doubted if nesting sites were available for many more. Quite probably cliff falls have reduced the number of nesting ledges available (*cf.* Razorbill and Guillemot) and it is of interest that Herring Gulls did not breed on the sandstone cliffs between Hastings and Pett before the early 1940s. Perhaps they moved here because of such cliff falls. Breeding on roof-tops in Hastings and St. Leonards was first noted in the early 1950s and noted at Eastbourne from 1972, Brighton and Hove in 1973, 1975 and 1976, and Worthing in 1974. In 1975 seven pairs, of which one certainly bred, were found established on the face of a chalk pit near Lewes, over five miles from the sea, and eight pairs bred in one at Beddingham in 1976.

Very little recent information is available about the winter numbers or passage movements of Herring Gulls in Sussex. However, an extensive easterly passage in the spring has been noted at Selsey Bill, extending from mid-February to early June, with movements of up to 1,000 birds in a day. Return passage starts in late June, and movements of up to 1,600 birds in a day have been noted at Selsey Bill and Beachy Head between late June and early August. As with Lesser Black-backed Gulls, Herring Gull passage apparently continues until early December.

LESSER BLACK-BACKED GULL—*Larus fuscus*

Status.—A few pairs breed and some non-breeding birds summer; scarce winter visitor; common passage migrant. No marked change in status recently is apparent.

Only a very few pairs breed and now perhaps not regularly, although des Forges and Harber recorded up to six pairs breeding regularly between 1946 and 1961. In the most recent census of breeding seabirds in Sussex, in 1969, two pairs were found, one nesting on a Hastings roof-top and one on the cliffs there, where a pair was also present in 1973; in 1975 and 1976 a pair nested in St. Leonards. Accurate information on other summering birds is virtually non-existent, although some non-breeding birds are certainly present.

In winter as many as about 120 have been noted, although numbers are usually much lower. Recently most winter records have been from inland localities and the largest flock noted was one of about 100 birds at a rubbish tip near Christ's Hospital in January 1968. There were also 69 at Weir Wood Reservoir on 1 February 1972.

Spring passage may start in February, but most usually extends from March to the end of May, with the main movement in April. Return movements start in late June, and sea-watching at Selsey Bill recorded some extensive June movements; for example, 1,130 passed west down the Channel in four days between 21 and 30 June 1969. Autumn passage usually peaks in July or August and, in August, counts of up to 600 have been made frequently at Chichester gravel pits. Passage continues until late November or early December.

Two races, *L. f. graellsii* and *L. f. fuscus,* are involved in these movements, but little information on their comparative abundance is recorded.

GREAT BLACK-BACKED GULL—*Larus marinus*
Status.—Non-breeding resident and passage migrant. No recent change in status is apparent.

As with most gull species this bird is probably under-recorded, and, in particular, few counts of the summering population have been made, although at Rye Harbour Local Nature Reserve up to 100 have been noted in recent summers, and similar flocks occur at other favoured coastal sites, such as Shoreham and Sidlesham Ferry. These flocks are largely of immatures.

No complete winter counts have been made, but fairly regular flock counts at coastal sites suggest a minimum wintering population of the order of 2,000 birds. Sometimes many more may be present along the 140 km. or so of Sussex coastline, as 1,400 were counted in 19 km. between Bulverhythe and Rye in December 1971, for example, and individual flocks of up to 600 have been noted at Shoreham, and 800 at Winchelsea and Rye. Otherwise winter flocks are usually of about 50 to 400 birds, and Great Black-backed Gulls are present along the whole coast. Inland in winter they are scarce, but single birds or small parties are noted at such sites as Weir Wood Reservoir.

Little information is available on this species' movements, but most spring passage undoubtedly occurs in March, when up to 40 per hour have been noted passing east up the Channel. Return movements begin in July and counts at Rye Harbour have suggested steady movements in August and September, although sea-watching at Selsey Bill has indicated that most movement occurs in November and December.

One found dead at the Midrips on 12 February 1972 had been ringed at Great Ainov Island, U.S.S.R., in July 1965.

ICELAND GULL—*Larus glaucoides*
Status.—Winter vagrant; rare spring passage migrant.

Until 1961 des Forges and Harber recorded a total of 26, of which 19 were noted after 1947 as follows: one remained at Shoreham from 24 January 1958 to 22 January 1961; 13 on spring passage between 13 March and 18 May; one each in June and August, and the rest for November to January. Between 1962 and 1976 only six were seen, in March (two), April (two), June (one), and November/December (one). A decline in the number occurring in Sussex is possible.

All records have been for the coast, except for one near Tunbridge Wells on 8 and 9 December 1958.

GLAUCOUS GULL—*Larus hyperboreus*

Status.—Scarce winter visitor and passage migrant. No change in status is apparent.

Until 1961 des Forges and Harber recorded a total of over 50 birds, numbers varying from none to seven annually after 1946. Between 1962 and 1976 a further 67 birds were seen, up to seven being noted annually, except in 1972 when there were fourteen. There were records for every month except June.

Besides birds occasionally doing so elsewhere along the coast, one or two have wintered each year since 1967 between Worthing and Brighton, usually at Hove. Wintering birds usually arrive in October and remain until March or April, but in 1967 one arrived at Hove on 5 July and remained until the following February; 30 April is the latest date for a wintering bird.

Regular sea-watching has also revealed a small spring passage in March, April and May, these birds usually being noted during movements of other gulls. About half the spring passage records are for March, which is now the month in which most Glaucous Gulls are seen in Sussex. But there were nine May records (up to the 18th) between 1962 and 1976, compared with one only until 1961. In the autumn about twice as many are seen in December as any other month, but otherwise no regular pattern of movement has been observed.

All records are for the coast and for single birds, although two individuals are sometimes present in one area at the same time.

GREAT BLACK-HEADED GULL—*Larus ichthyaetus*
Status.—Two records.

One was seen near Telscombe Cliffs on 4 January 1910; one was seen at Hove on 9 August 1932.

LAUGHING GULL—*Larus atricilla*
Status.—One record.

One was seen at the Crumbles from 2 to 9 July 1923. This was the first record for Britain.

FRANKLIN'S GULL—*Larus pipixcan.*
Status.—One record.

An adult in summer plumage was seen at Arlington Reservoir on 4 July 1970. This was the second record for Europe.

MEDITERRANEAN GULL—*Larus melanocephalus*
Status.—Scarce winter visitor and passage migrant, which has increased steadily since 1950.

There were no acceptable records before 1950, but since 1950 about 145 have been recorded and the records are summarised by five-year periods in the table on page 188.

The monthly totals in this table include duplications where birds have made prolonged stays, for example in winter; the total number of birds involved is shown separately.

During the period numbers have not only increased, but the pattern of occurrence has changed. Thus, until about 1963

Mediterranean Gulls in Sussex, 1948 to 1976

	June	July	Aug.	Sept.	Oct.	Nov.	Dec.	Jan.	Feb.	Mar.	Apr.	May	Total Birds involved	Adults
1948–52				1	1	1							3	1
1953–57		3	3					1	3	5	1		11	8
1958–62	3	7	7	4	6	1	2		2	1	3	2	27	18
Total	3	10	10	5	7	2	2	1	5	6	4	2		
1963–67	4	5	4	3	5	7	7	7	4	9	7	6	49	30
1968–72	1	2	4	3	3	6	6	6	7	10	7	4	46	37
1973–76		3	4	5	2	5	4	8	5	1	12	5	43	29
Total	5	10	12	11	10	18	17	21	16	20	26	15		
Grand total	8	20	22	16	17	20	19	22	21	26	30	17	179	123

nearly all records were for birds on passage, in spring from mid-February to late May, but particularly in February and March, and in autumn from July to October, sometimes November/December, with a peak in July/August. These are fairly typical patterns for gull passage, and more were seen in the autumn than in the spring. Since 1963 the pattern has changed, with most now seen in winter and on spring passage; it is not really clear whether this change is related to changes in observer activity. An exceptional movement occurred in April 1976 when eleven birds were seen. One or two have wintered each year since 1963, mainly in the Pagham/Selsey area, and between Shoreham and Hove. Wintering birds arrive in October, or more usually November, and stay until February or March.

All records are for the coast and usually of single birds, although two have been seen together. Adults predominate as the table shows, but some immatures may well be overlooked in large flocks of mixed gull species.

BLACK-HEADED GULL—*Larus ridibundus*

Status.—**Common resident, winter visitor and passage migrant. The breeding population has increased since 1961, but no other change in status is apparent.**

The only breeding colonies are in Chichester Harbour, with four pairs in 1971, 33 pairs in 1973, and over 400 in 1976, and at Rye Harbour Local Nature Reserve, where over 200 pairs have bred since 1965. There were 315 pairs in 1971, when steps to control numbers were started in the interests of the nesting terns; numbers had declined to 25 pairs in 1974. Between 1948 and 1961 des Forges and Harber recorded only 100 to 150 pairs at this colony and none elsewhere. Thus some increase in the breeding population has occurred.

This species is a recent colonist in Sussex. Some bred at the Midrips/Wicks and Pett for a few years prior to 1948, and 200 pairs bred at the former site in 1947; almost certainly the present Rye colony derives from these birds. An isolated instance at the Wicks in 1932 is the only other breeding record for the county since the 17th century.

From July to April Black-headed Gulls are the commonest gulls in the county. Flocks of up to 5,000 are of common occurrence at the coast and inland, where, for example, up to 4,600 have been counted at Weir Wood Reservoir. Larger winter flocks have been noted at Pagham Harbour, up to 10,000; Shoreham, up to 7,000; and around Roedean, up to 12,000; very incomplete counts since 1967 suggest a minimal winter population along the coast of some 40,000 birds. But numbers may be much larger; for example, about 30,000 were estimated on Shoreham airfield alone on 9 February 1974.

Spring passage probably begins in February, and most of our wintering birds leave in March and April, although passage continues into May when small parties often pass up the Channel with parties of terns. Return movements start in July, sometimes late June, and continue until at least October. Of the local breeding stock some young of the year leave the county for the winter, and two juveniles ringed at Rye in 1958 were recovered in Wales in October and Portugal in December of that year.

SLENDER-BILLED GULL—*Larus genei*

Status.—Two records.

A first summer bird was seen at Langney Point between 19 June and 10 July 1960; a first-year bird was seen at Rye Harbour gravel pits on 28 April 1963. These were the first records for Britain.

BONAPARTE'S GULL—*Larus philadelphia*
Status.—Four records.

One was shot at St. Leonards in early November 1870; one was seen at Newhaven on 14 November 1949; one was seen at Langney Point on 24 June 1951; one was seen at Portobello, Brighton, on 20 June 1961.

LITTLE GULL—*Larus minutus*
Status.—Scarce summer and winter visitor; passage migrant. The numbers occurring have increased markedly since about 1967, particularly in the spring.

Apart from a bird which summered at Pett Level in 1969, summering by this species is a very recent phenomenon. One or two apparently summered in the Rye area in 1972, and a few did so annually here and at Chichester Harbour or gravel pits up to 1975. These birds were immatures, and no more than 10 appear to have been involved in any year so far. The number seen in winter (January to March) has not exceeded about five birds in any year since 1948.

The table on page 192 gives approximate monthly totals by five year periods from 1948 to 1972 and for 1973 to 1975.

As the table shows most birds are recorded on spring and autumn passage. Spring passage extends from early April, possibly February or March in some years, into June, but most pass through in April and May. The numbers involved have increased very sharply since about 1967; a total of under 50 birds was noted in these two months from 1948 to 1967, compared with well over 200 from 1968 to 1972, and nearly 570 from 1973 to 1975. This increase, which continued in 1976, cannot be accounted for by changes in observer activity. Many of these birds are recorded during spring sea-watches and observations often correlate with southerly or south-east winds; the largest movement so far noted involved 206 birds off Beachy Head between 3 and 19 May 1974, and 349 between 21 April and 16 May 1976, including 115 on 1 May. Small

Little Gulls in Sussex, 1948–1975

	June	July	Aug.	Sept.	Oct.	Nov.	Dec.	Jan.	Feb.	Mar.	Apr.	May	June
1948–52	0	0	1	0	14	15	6	0	1	2	6	3	0
1953–57	4	1	10	18	9	17	6	4	3	3	3	6	4
1958–62	3	4	17	20	40	37	20	6	4	4	7	5	3
1963–67	3	5	18	43	20	11	14	2	0	0	6	4	3
1968–72	15	9	29	231	111	38	6	4	7	6	101	133	15
1973–75	34	19	27	68	12	6	0	0	5	3	147	421	34
Total	59	38	102	380	206	124	52	16	20	18	267	572	59

parties now often occur and records include one of 19 at Arlington Reservoir on 29 April 1972, after a severe gale.

Return movements may start as early as the second half of June, although usually not until the end of July. Most birds are now seen in September, although formerly October and November were the peak autumn months. Passage still regularly continues into November and sometimes December. An extra-ordinary movement was seen in 1972, mainly off Beachy Head where a flock of 40 was noted on 17 September, 70 flew east on the 19th, and 45 on 1 October. These are by far the largest autumn counts noted in the county.

Very few inland records were noted by des Forges and Harber, but Little Gulls are now recorded annually at the main gravel pits and reservoirs in Sussex. As these continue to increase it is probable that the species will become more wide-spread inland.

SABINE'S GULL—*Larus sabini*
Status.—Vagrant.

Until 1961 des Forges and Harber recorded 15, all for the coast or nearby. Between 1962 and 1976 a further six were seen, three of them on 13 September 1970 at Selsey Bill, Newhaven Harbour, and Langney Point.

One record is undated, otherwise records are for January (one), August (one), September (eight), October (eight), and December (two).

KITTIWAKE—*Rissa tridactyla*
Status.—Bred in 1976; non-breeding summer visitor; winter visitor; passage migrant. No recent change in status is apparent.

Although recorded in every month, winter numbers are comparatively small, rarely exceeding 20 to 40 birds on any date.

More are seen in the summer and June is undoubtedly the month in which most Kittiwakes are seen in Sussex. Flocks of 100 or more are then regularly noted at well-watched coastal sites, and flocks of 500 or more sometimes occur. These flocks are sometimes obviously forced inshore by rough weather, but this is not always so, and a considerable population probably summers in this part of the Channel. In 1976 four or five nests were found, and at least two young were hatched.

Spring movements are now most usually noted in April and May, coinciding with movements of other gulls and terns; movements of up to 300 in a day have been noted recently. Autumn movements are noted until early December and there is often no clear pattern. Substantial movements, particularly in late autumn, often correlate with rough weather, and counts of up to 600 have been noted frequently.

Nearly all Kittiwakes are seen at the coast, but single birds are found inland in most winters, usually at large reservoirs. On 13 November 1972 100 appeared briefly at Arlington Reservoir after a severe south-west gale.

WHISKERED TERN—*Chlidonias hybrida*
Status.—Three records.

One was seen at Darwell Reservoir on 3 September 1963; one was seen in Chichester Harbour on 11 September 1967; one was seen at Chichester gravel pits from 14 to 21 May 1970.

WHITE-WINGED BLACK TERN—*Chlidonias leucopterus*
Status.—Vagrant.

Until 1961 des Forges and Harber recorded 12, three of them in 1959, and between 1962 and 1976 13 were seen. Altogether records have been for April (two), May (eight), June (two), August (nine, all since 1964), and September (two). Most records were for the coast, Chichester gravel pits, or Rye Harbour, but the species has also been recorded at Warnham Mill Pond, near Horsham, and Arlington Reservoir.

BLACK TERN—*Chlidonias niger*
Status.—Common passage migrant. No recent change in status is apparent.

The numbers recorded each year vary considerably. Thus since 1947 the totals noted annually have ranged from as few as six to as many as 1,100.

Extreme dates for spring passage are 4 April (1957, Chichester gravel pits), and 16 June (1971, Rye Harbour), but most movement occurs in late April and May. Movements of 20 to 30 in a day and flocks of similar size are commonplace, and much larger movements are sometimes seen. The largest yet noted involved about 850 birds on 1 May 1965, mainly in the afternoon. The birds passed through on a front stretching from Selsey Bill to Chichester gravel pits, and many moved north-east inland, as few were noted further east along the coast. Spring passage continues very late in some years and was noted into June in eight springs between 1962 and 1976.

Autumn passage commonly begins in July, sometimes in the first week, and usually extends to late September or early October. There were records for the second half of October in six years between 1962 and 1976, and there have been four November records; three in 1967, on 5 November at Chichester gravel pits, the 10th at Thorney Deeps, and the 12th at Glynde Levels, and in 1954 there was one in the Cuckmere from the 13th to 21st. Total numbers in the autumn are often higher than in the spring, but very large movements have not been recorded. Thus 42 flying west off Langney Point on 20 August 1971 was the largest autumn movement noted between 1962 and 1976.

Most birds are seen at the coast, but Black Terns are often seen at gravel pits and reservoirs and other sizable inland waters.

GULL-BILLED TERN—*Gelochelidon nilotica*

Status.—Perhaps rare non-breeding summer visitor; rare passage migrant, although only two have been seen since 1967.

Until 1937 seven had been obtained, but between 1950 and 1967 a total of 54 was noted; there have been only two since 1967. Monthly totals were:

Jan.	Feb.	Mar.	Apr.	May	June	July	Aug.	Sept.	Oct.	Nov.	Dec.
0	0	0	6	18	11	13	6	3	0	0	0

Extreme dates were 19 April (1964, Selsey Bill) and 17 September (1950, Shoreham), but there is also a record for 31 March 1852 from Selsey Bill. Most records have been of single birds, but small parties have been seen, the largest being of six off Langney Point on 26 June 1952. Numbers between 1950 and 1967 varied from one to 10 in a year, but none was seen in 1954 and 1957.

All records have been for the coast.

CASPIAN TERN—*Hydroprogne caspia*
Status.—Vagrant.

There are 12 records, all since 1960, falling between 30 April (1969, Worthing) and 13 September (1964, Langney Point). Records are for April (one), May (three), June (one), July (five), and September (two). All records have been for the coast except for two at Chichester gravel pits during July 1966.

COMMON TERN—*Sterna hirundo*
Status.—Scarce breeding summer visitor; common passage migrant. The breeding population has declined in recent years.

There are two breeding colonies, in Chichester Harbour and at Rye Harbour gravel pits. During a complete census of breeding seabirds in Sussex in 1969 there were 32 pairs in Chichester Harbour and 118 pairs in two groups at Rye. In 1976 there were *c.* 40 pairs in Chichester Harbour and 32 pairs at Rye. One or two pairs have also bred at Chichester gravel pits in recent years, but with varying success, and a pair probably bred at Pagham Harbour in 1974.

This population represents a considerable decline since the 1950s, when up to 300 pairs bred at Rye, up to 20 pairs did so at the Crumbles, near Eastbourne, and up to 10 at the Midrips. Common Terns bred at the Crumbles and the Midrips before 1938, but the Rye colony was founded in 1945 and probably derived from Dungeness, where a colony was broken up by military activities during 1939 to 1945. The birds apparently moved first to Pett Level then to Rye (des Forges and Harber). The Chichester Harbour colony was first reported in 1961.

The decline of this species as a breeding bird in Sussex is probably mainly due to human predation and disturbance. Thus, in 1961, vandals shot at least 50 adults at the Rye colony in the first two weeks of June, and despite wardening, something similar appears to have happened in 1973, while every clutch was stolen in 1976.

For a discussion of passage movements *see under* Arctic Tern.

ARCTIC TERN—*Sterna paradisaea*

Status.—**Common passage migrant.**

The definition of status given is an assumption. Although there are records for this species every year, they give no idea of its true status; it is virtually impossible to separate Common and Arctic Terns in the field, except under the most favourable conditions, particularly over the sea. In fact, even over inland waters, where parties often occur on passage, most observers are content to describe them as Common/Arctic Terns. Passage movements of both species are therefore dealt with under this heading. *Common/Arctic Terns* have been recorded between 25 March (1972, Beachy Head and Roedean) and 23 November

(1963, Selsey Bill), but the main movements in spring and autumn take place in comparatively restricted periods, in spring between about 16 April and 16 May, and in autumn between about 20 August and 7 September. The numbers involved vary considerably; between 1960 and 1976 up to 10,000 have been noted in one spring, when movements of 500 to 1,000 in a day are an annual occurrence, and up to 2,000 not infrequent. Larger movements are sometimes seen. Thus, between 8 and 15 May 1960 4,900 passed Selsey Bill, on 1 May 1965 4,180 passed Beachy Head, 2,400 likewise on 9 May 1968, 3,000 on 10 May 1975, and 3,365 on 5 May 1976. Large spring movements of these birds almost invariably coincide with southerly or south-east winds, sometimes of gale force.

Autumn movements of this scale are much rarer, although movements of up to 1,500 in a day have been noted, and feeding flocks of 1,000 to 2,000 birds are sometimes seen offshore. Overall, however, numbers are very similar to the spring and the peak of autumn passage occurs remarkably consistently in the last 10 days of August.

On 30 and 31 December 1966 an Arctic Tern was present in Pagham Harbour.

ROSEATE TERN—*Sterna dougallii*

Status.—Scarce non-breeding summer visitor and passage migrant. The number occurring appears to have increased since about 1964.

Until 1961 des Forges and Harber recorded 44, all but four of them after 1950. Between 1962 and 1976 a further 106 birds were noted, with a sharp increase evident since 1964. Up to 12 have been seen in one year, and approximate monthly totals were:

Apr.	May	June	July	Aug	Sept.
7	44	11	26	10	9

Extreme dates were 17 April (1968, Beachy Head, earliest county record) and 30 September (1965, Langney Point, latest county record). Most May records occur during passage of other tern species, but many June and July reports suggest clearly that a few non-breeding Roseate Terns summer off our coast. Small parties are often seen, the largest being of seven flying east off Selsey Bill on 14 May 1967.

All records have been for the coast.

SOOTY TERN—*Sterna fuscata*

Status.—**One record.**

One was obtained at Brighton on 24 April 1911.

LITTLE TERN—*Sterna albifrons*

Status.—**Scarce breeding summer visitor; passage migrant. The breeding population has fluctuated markedly since 1938, but overall numbers show surprisingly little change.**

There are breeding colonies in four localities, and an annual total of up to 150 pairs has bred since 1965. Complete counts made in 1967, 1969 and 1971 are tabulated.

Breeding Little Terns in Sussex

		Chichester Harbour		Pagham Harbour		Rye Harbour		Midrips/ Wicks	
		Colonies	Pairs	Colonies	Pairs	Colonies	Pairs	Colonies	Pairs
1967	..	1	15	1	44	3	19	1	9
1969	..	2	52	1	35	4	55	1	5
1971	..	1	30	1	30	3	10	1	26

In addition a pair was present at Chichester gravel pits each year and four pairs bred at the Crumbles, near Eastbourne, in

1970. In 1976 there were 100 pairs in Chichester Harbour and 75 in Pagham Harbour, but only eight pairs at Rye Harbour.

Breeding success has been very poor at all these colonies, except one in Chichester Harbour, because of constant human harassment and predation. Breeding sites at Chichester, Pagham and Rye Harbours are now within Local Nature Reserves and it is hoped that this protection will improve the species' success. The largest and most successful colony is very inaccessibly placed in Chichester Harbour, and it is now one of the largest in Britain.

The present population shows remarkably little change since 1938, a demonstration of the Little Tern's resilience; is anything there has been some increase. Until 1938 about 40 to 50 pairs bred at Pagham Harbour and a similar number did so from Rye to the Wicks. Total protection during 1939 to 1945 enabled this population to double, but by 1954 constant human disturbance had reduced the Pagham colony to about seven pairs, and the Rye/Wicks population to less than 20 pairs.

Extreme dates for Little Terns are 4 April (1976, Pagham Harbour), and 20 October (1963, Pagham Harbour), but most breeding birds arrive in the second half of April and early May, and have nearly all departed by mid-September. Some through passage occurs, mainly in early May, but movements of more than 40 to 50 birds in a day are uncommon in spring and autumn; 107 flying east off Beachy Head on 30 April 1973 appear to be the largest single movement ever recorded in the county.

The species only occasionally appears on inland waters, but these records include a bird at Weir Wood Reservoir on the late date of 15 October 1967.

SANDWICH TERN—*Sterna sandvicensis*

Status.—Winter vagrant; scarce non-breeding summer visitor which has bred since 1975; common passage migrant.

Although a small summering population has been noted along the Sussex coast since 1948, breeding was not noted until 1975 when 20 pairs bred in Chichester Harbour; there were 35 pairs in 1976. Otherwise about 30 to 50 non-breeding birds are usually present, but up to 100 together have been recorded after a summer gale.

There are four winter records, 19 December 1953 at Winchelsea, and 20 December 1972, 1 and 19 January 1974, and 18 December 1975 at Hove/Southwick. There are also two February records, on the 13th, 1971, at Southwick, and the 23rd, 1958, at West Wittering, but these records may refer to very early spring passage.

Otherwise the earliest date for spring arrival is 8 March (1975, Selsey Bill), and a few always arrive by the end of this month. Passage continues to late May but, as with other terns, the main movement occurs between mid-April and mid-May and nearly always correlates with periods of south or south-east winds. Up to 4,500 have been noted in one spring, and movements of between 300 and 600 in a day are noted nearly every spring. The largest single movement recorded so far was during 1968, when a total of 3,140 flew east off Beachy Head between 13 and 21 April, including 1,080 on the 18 April.

Autumn passage tends to be smaller, although movements of up to 300 in a day are noted, and flocks of up to 1,000 are very occasionally noted feeding offshore. Most passage takes place between mid-August and mid-September, but stragglers are regularly noted in late October or early November, up to the 7th. The species is only rarely seen inland.

LITTLE AUK—*Alle alle*

Status.—Perhaps regular winter visitor. No recent change in status is apparent.

Between 1949 and 1960 des Forges and Harber recorded 43, up to 16 being seen in one year and records falling between 23 October and the end of February. Between 1961 and 1976

32 more were seen: in November (25), December (five), January (two), February (one), and March (one); the March bird was found dead on 1 March 1969 at Rye. The only later record for the county is of one at Shoreham on 9 March 1900.

Many records of this bird are associated with periods of severe gales, which sometimes blow them some way inland where they may be found in very unlikely places. For example, one was killed on the A.27 at Fontwell on 6 November 1971.

RAZORBILL—*Alca torda*
Status.—Non-breeding summer visitor; winter visitor; passage migrant.

Razorbills once bred at Beachy Head, Belle Tout and perhaps Seaford Head, but there has been no record of breeding since 1878. Today the species is present offshore throughout the year, but status is difficult to define accurately as a high proportion of the auks observed cannot be specifically identified.

However, in winter Razorbills are probably less common than Guillemots, for of 520 auks picked up oiled along the Sussex coast between 1968 and 1972, only 26 per cent. were Razorbills. But sea-watching results from Selsey Bill recorded little difference in abundance between this species and Guillemot, and, at Beachy Head, Razorbills have been identified about twice as often as Guillemots in the migration seasons.

A more detailed discussion of auk movements off Sussex is given under Guillemot.

GUILLEMOT—*Uria aalge*
Status.—Non-breeding summer visitor; winter visitor; passage migrant.

Guillemots bred at several places along the chalk cliffs, including Beachy Head, until 1853, when cliff falls destroyed the nesting ledges. A few pairs remained until about 1879, but there is no reliable record since.

Today the status of this species is very similar to that of the Razorbill, but it is apparently more common offshore in winter, as 74 per cent. of 520 auks picked up oiled along the Sussex coast between 1968 and 1972 were Guillemots.

Between 1960 and 1969 fairly detailed records of auk movements were kept at Selsey Bill, and the monthly totals recorded were:

Jan.	Feb.	Mar.	Apr.	May	June	July	Aug.	Sept.	Oct.	Nov.	Dec.
50	30	80	300	1230	85	45	50	135	475	140	515

These totals include all identified Razorbills and Guillemots, and it is assumed that the bulk of these records refer to these two species, as other auks are so infrequently identified. Undoubtedly the table reflects the pattern of observer activity to some extent, but a marked movement in April, and particularly May, and again in late autumn, was consistently noted each year. October is usually the peak autumn month, but large movements may occur in December.

Records from other localities suggest that these birds may be more numerous off East Sussex than West Sussex in winter, so that a similar exercise in the former might produce a different pattern.

Two races of the Guillemot occur off Sussex, *Uria a. aalge* and *Uria a. albionis*. The comparative abundance of these forms is poorly documented, but records of oiled birds in winter show both to be present offshore and that they are possibly equally numerous.

BLACK GUILLEMOT—*Cepphus grylle*
Status.—**Vagrant**.

Until 1961 des Forges and Harber recorded nine, four of them during the autumn of 1961. Between 1962 and 1976 a further three were seen, on 20 April 1965 at Selsey Bill (the only spring record for the county), and two in 1969 at Beachy Head on 5 July and 26 August.

PUFFIN—*Fratercula arctica*
Status.—Rare visitor.

Between 1946 and 1960 des Forges and Harber recorded only 13, between 18 July and 9 May; six were dead or dying.

Between 1961 and 1976 a total of 27 was recorded: in January (one), March (three), April (three), May (seven), June (four), October (six), November (two), and December (one). The records for December to March were for oiled birds picked up along the shore.

Puffins have been found as far inland as Haslemere after severe gales.

PALLAS'S SANDGROUSE—*Syrrhaptes paradoxus*
Status.—Recorded in the irruptions of 1863 and 1888.

During the irruption of 1863 three were obtained and others seen between late May and July. During the irruption of 1888 the species was recorded in the same months; in addition Walpole-Bond recorded single birds shot at Shoreham on 8 November, and Itchenor in February 1889, which he presumed to be stragglers from this invasion. Numbers in 1888 were much greater than in 1863, with several parties of 10 to 30 birds noted.

One was shot at Balcombe in 1863, and a party of 20 to 30 was seen at Warnham, near Horsham, in 1888. Otherwise all records were for the coast.

STOCK DOVE—*Columba oenas*
Status.—Common resident, but the population has fluctuated markedly in recent years.

The Stock Dove was noted as a common species by des Forges and Harber, with breeding colonies of up to two or three dozen pairs. But a marked decline was evident in the early 1960s, particularly, for example, in the arable farmlands of south-west Sussex. However, the species is still widespread, particularly north of the Downs in areas of old scattered timber, and in farmland with old buildings; some still breed along the cliffs. There has recently been a marked recovery in south-west Sussex and probably elsewhere, as several observers have reported increases since 1967. However, not until 1971 were there any records to suggest colonies of the size indicated by des Forges and Harber.

Winter flocks may be a simpler and more reliable guide to changes in this species' status. Up to 1961 des Forges and Harber noted flocks of up to 200 occurring, and such flocks were certainly regular in the Selsey peninsular until about 1960. Between 1965 and 1970, however, only four flocks of 100 or more were reported in Sussex, the largest being of 175 birds at Rye Harbour on 2 January 1965. Since 1970 there has been an obvious improvement, with flocks of 200 to 400 noted in several areas.

WOODPIGEON—*Columba palumbus*

Status.—**Abundant resident and probably also winter visitor and passage migrant. No recent change in status is apparent.**

Very few counts of breeding birds have been made, but figures from local Pest Control officers, working in the Harting area, recorded 572 nests destroyed in 1962 and 398 in 1963. This species is said to have declined in many parts of Britain in recent years, but this does not appear to be so in Sussex, at least in the south-west of the county.

Movements are often noted at the coast. In spring birds have been observed arriving and departing in the period March to May and quite extensive movements occur in the autumn, nearly always in late October or November; this again is a two-way traffic, although departures predominate. Movements have involved up to 10,000 birds in one day (27 October 1973).

In 1975 an exceptional passage at Beachy Head involved *c*. 70,000 birds between 19 October and 5 November, and included 30,000 flying south-east out to sea on 2 November.

These movements were thought by des Forges and Harber to arise largely from the Woodpigeon's frequent habit of flying out to sea and then returning. Such movements are not annual, however, and their scale and very consistent timing in a limited period of October and November suggest that this explanation is not correct. Certainly some Sussex birds emigrate, as two nestlings ringed at Sidlesham in July 1957 were recovered in France in December 1957.

TURTLE DOVE—*Streptopelia turtur*

Status.—**Common summer visitor to breed; winter vagrant; common passage migrant. No recent change in status is apparent.**

Comparatively few breeding season records are received but the species is known to be widespread in the breeding season. In the Woodland Survey, see page 17, it was recorded in nearly every area visited, but, although it averaged only 1.4 per cent. of the total bird populations recorded, it was much more numerous in some old coppice woodlands and forestry plantations at the thicket stage, particularly in the Weald and near the coast. Turtle Doves are also reasonably common breeding birds in farmland, the few common bird census counts available suggesting a density of about 50 pairs per 2,500 acres (10 sq. km.), although numbers vary greatly with the amount of cover available and possibly cropping programmes.

There are four winter records as follows; Denton, February 1847; Horsham, 8 February 1898; Patcham, 5 and 8 February 1969; Bexhill, December 1969. Both the last two birds were found with Collared Doves.

Turtle Doves usually start to arrive in the second half of April or early May, although the earliest date for Sussex is

22 March (1966, Plumpton). Arrivals may continue until early June. Autumn movements begin in July and quite large flocks, of up to 50 and sometimes more (once 200), may be seen in late July and early August; des Forges and Harber noted that emigration started in August. Movement continues throughout September, but after the beginning of October only stragglers are seen. However, there have been eight November records up to the 11th (1967, Beachy Head).

COLLARED DOVE—*Streptopelia decaocto*

Status.—**A recently established and increasing resident.**

The first county record was for West Wittering in 1958, and breeding was first definitely proved at Selsey and St. Leonards in 1960. By 1966 the population had increased to some 1,400 birds, and they were present or had been seen in 61 localities. By 1969 a further increase of the order of 380 per cent. had taken place, resulting in a minimum population of 5,300 birds, and the species was present or had been recorded in 107 localities. It was recorded in about 40 new localities between 1970 and 1976. The colonisation of Sussex by Collared Doves is described by Porter (1966, 1969).

In Sussex this is very much a bird of built-up areas and farmlands and steadings, and its main numbers are still along the coast, with by far the largest breeding concentration around Bexhill, where 360 pairs were counted in about eight square miles (about 20 sq. km.) in 1967. No other area approaches this breeding density, but counts of up to 25 pairs have been made at other coastal towns; for example, Selsey.

Winter flocks of 50 to 300 birds are noted each year, particularly in coastal localities, but now increasingly inland. In recent winters maize stubbles, a spreading feature of the arable farming scene in Sussex, have proved especially attractive feeding areas for these flocks, and a further spread of maize-growing may have a significant effect on this species' status.

Spring arrivals at the coast are still often noted; for example, there six such records at Beachy Head between 15 and 23 April 1972. In addition one ringed in Belgium on 19 October 1968 was caught at Seaford on 1 June 1969. Thus fresh colonists still appear to be arriving in the county.

GREAT SPOTTED CUCKOO—*Clamator glandarius*
Status.—One record.

One was picked up dead at Shripney, near Bognor, on 4 August 1967.

CUCKOO—*Cuculus canorus*
Status.—**Common summer visitor to breed; passage migrant. No recent change in status is apparent.**

Although this is one of our most familiar summer visitors, surprisingly little detailed information about its status is available. However, comparing the records from 1965 to 1976 with Walpole-Bond's account in 1938 suggests very little change, and it is quite clearly a generally distributed species which can be found in every habitat in the county.

Although there are a few records for March, the earliest being 15 March 1936 at Fairlight, and 23rd, 1967, at Harting, arrival does not usually take place before early to mid-April; it continues through May and, at least in some years, into early June. Birds are quite often recorded coming in off the sea, but large 'falls' never occur; for example, the largest daily count at Beachy Head to date was seven on 17 May 1968. Autumn departure is noted in July, August, and the first half of September, after which the species is not often seen. However, there are six records for October and two for November, the latest being of one at Goodwood on 11 November 1928.

YELLOW—BILLED CUCKOO—*Coccyzus americanus*
Status.—Two records.

One was picked up dead at Eastbourne on 4 November 1952; one was picked up dead at Middleton-on-Sea on 14 December 1960.

BARN OWL—*Tyto alba*
Status.—Uncommon resident. Numbers have shown quite marked fluctuations in recent years.

Although uncommon, Barn Owls are widely distributed in Sussex, being found in or adjacent to most areas of open country. Numbers, however, appear to have fluctuated since 1947. Thus Prestt (1965) reported a moderate decline between 1953 and 1963, and that the species was sparsely distributed in 1963. This opinion was apparently based largely on records of hunting birds, which may not necessarily be a reliable guide to the species' status, and few records of breeding sites for the period are available today.

However, most experienced ornithologists in the county agreed, and some recovery has been evident since 1964, as the table shows:

Annual totals of Barn Owls recorded in Sussex, 1964 to 1973, and in 1975

	Pairs proved to breed	Pairs or birds present in breeding season	Other birds recorded	Total bird/sites
1964	6	11	0	17
1965	6	2	10	18
1966	3	12	23	38
1967	7	9	31	47
1968	6	17	23	46
1969	3	18	23	44
1970	5	16	38	59
1971	14	33	31	78
1972	10	10	50	70
1973	6	14	40	60
1975	7	17	40	64

Although more observer activity has contributed to the rise in records a genuine increase in numbers certainly occurred in the period, as many records came from well-watched areas of west and central Sussex, in which the species was searched for in most years.

Some figures indicating breeding densities were recorded. Thus, five to seven pairs were found in 1967 and 1970 in about six square miles (about 15 sq. km.) of coastal farmland centred on Sidlesham; there were nine pairs in 1969/70 in about 23 square miles (about 58 sq. km.) to the west of Horsham including three or four pairs in Slinfold parish; and there were eight occupied territories in 30 square miles (about 77 sq. km.) enclosed by Pulborough, Bury, Bignor, and Byworth in 1970.

Little definite information about the causes of the population fluctuations of this species is available. Parslow (1973) noted a long-term decline in Britain, on which a sharp decline in the late 1950s was superimposed. Comparing more recent records with Walpole-Bond's account leaves little doubt that this pattern has occurred in Sussex, and a major cause may be the real decline in the number of thatched or decrepit farm buildings in the county, as Walpole-Bond estimated that 65 per cent. of Sussex Barn Owls bred in farm steadings, usually barns. The provision of nest-boxes will often mitigate the effects of this change. Barn Owls are also fond of hunting road verges where they may be killed by fast-moving traffic; between 1970 and 1976 a total of 16 such casualties were reported. There is no evidence that the use of farm chemicals has been a major cause of change in Sussex, but changes in general agricultural practice are bound to affect this species, which, like the Kestrel, may be at a disadvantage in areas where permanent grassland is converted to arable for cereals.

Both Walpole-Bond and des Forges and Harber recorded an influx in winter, more marked in some years, but there is no evidence that such an influx occurs today. The breeding stock is of the race *T. a. alba,* but about nine birds showing the characters of the race *guttata* have been noted, most recently at the Midrips/Wicks from 3 December 1938 to mid-February 1939.

EAGLE OWL—*Bubo bubo*
Status.—Two records.

One was shot at Herstmonceux on either 29 December 1782 or at some time in 1784; one was shot near Cuckfield on 13 January 1939.

SNOWY OWL—*Nyctea scandiaca*
Status.—One record.

One was seen at Seaford Head and in the Cuckmere valley on 8 November 1968.

LITTLE OWL—*Athene noctua*
Status.—An introduced and common resident which has declined in numbers in recent years.

It is not known when Little Owls were first introduced into Sussex, but Walpole-Bond recorded two pairs being released at Knepp in November 1876, which were possibly found dead later, and in about 1874 some were released at Edenbridge, just in Kent, which became established. By 1904 Walpole-Bond found the species well established in the Horsham area, and by 1938 he described it as abundant and generally distributed.

A similar status was recorded by des Forges and Harber until 1961, but a decline has been apparent since about 1963, and it is probably no longer the commonest owl in the county, as stated by des Forges and Harber. It is still generally distributed, however, being present in all habitats, including suburban areas and sea-cliffs. It is probably most numerous in farmland.

Between 1968 and 1976 between 50 and 90 sites occupied by at least one bird were reported annually, and counts recorded included 15 pairs in about six square miles (about

15 sq. km.) of coastal farmland centred on Sidlesham in 1967, eight occupied territories in a circle of two miles radius (about 32 sq. km.) centred on Blackdown, and at least five pairs in Slinfold parish in 1969, and 13 occupied territories in about 26 square miles (about 65 sq. km.) of downland north of Worthing in the period. These are higher densities than recorded for the Barn Owl.

During 1968 and 1973 three observers recorded declines in a local Little Owl population, in the Rye area, in the Cuckmere valley, and south of Chichester. In addition numbers apparently dropped very sharply in the Singleton/Cocking/East Dean area between 1963 and 1967. The cause of these changes is not known, but it is possibly of interest that, among the few reports of breeding success in the period, there were no records of failed breeding attempts. Habitat changes therefore seem the most likely cause.

TAWNY OWL—*Strix aluco*
Status.—Common resident. No recent change in status is apparent.

Without much doubt this is the commonest owl in Sussex, and it is found wherever there are trees, including hedgerow trees in otherwise open country. It is also well established in the centres of large towns, for example, Southwick, Brighton, Eastbourne (six pairs in 1975), Horsham, and Crawley.

In the more heavily-wooded parts of the county Tawny Owls are quite numerous. Thus in the large blocks of forest on the Downs north of Chilgrove, Singleton, East Dean, Eartham and Arundel, at least 50 occupied territories were known between 1966 and 1971, and over 40 were located in an area of 21 square miles (about 54 sq. km.) centred on Horsham in the same period. There were also 18 occupied territories in a circle of two miles radius (about 32 sq. km.) centred on Blackdown in 1969.

These figures indicate breeding densities of about 12 to 15 pairs per 2,500 acres (10 sq. km.), but densities of up to two or three pairs per square kilometre (250 acres) have been noted in some very favoured areas in central Sussex, although these figures may be distorted by the limited size of the samples involved.

Some information on breeding success has been recorded, which shows remarkably little variation since 1965. About 58 broods were reported, averaging just over two young per brood, and only in 1972, when an average brood size of 1.3 was noted, was there any significant variation from the average.

LONG-EARED OWL—*Asio otus*

Status.—Scarce resident and passage migrant. A marked decline has occurred in recent years.

Walpole-Bond described this species as moderately common in 1938, although its distribution was largely controlled by the distribution of mature conifers. However, it was sufficiently numerous for a few pairs even to breed in overgrown hedgerows on Pevensey Levels.

A considerable decline has occurred since he wrote, and the species has now become a very scarce breeding bird. Thus between 1962 and 1976 it was recorded as breeding in only six sites, with birds present and probably breeding in eight more; 10 winter records came from areas suitable for breeding. Very probably this much understates its true status, as Long-eared Owls are notably inconspicuous, but the records since 1947 leave no doubt that they had become very difficult to find and had vanished from a number of known breeding sites, for example behind Brighton and in Friston forest, in the 1950s.

As a passage migrant the species is now equally scarce, although Walpole-Bond's account indicates it was once quite numerous, at least in some years, either on passage or as a winter visitor; flocks of 15 to 20 sometimes occurred. However, since 1962 there have only been 14 records from the coast indicating migration, all of single birds, in September (six), October (one), November (one), March (three), and April (four). One present at Pagham Harbour on 9 February 1975 may have been a winter visitor.

SHORT-EARED OWL—*Asio flammeus*

Status.—**Has bred. Regular winter visitor and passage migrant. No recent change in status is apparent.**

Perhaps as many as 10 pairs (Walpole-Bond) bred on Pevensey Levels in 1921, and a pair did so in 1922. These are the only breeding records for Sussex.

Otherwise Short-eared Owls are regularly recorded from September to April, with occasional reports in August and May. Birds are fairly regularly encountered in most extensive open habitats in the county, and parties, sometimes of as many as 12 birds, are often found in favoured localities, particularly around Rye Harbour, at the Midrips, in certain areas of the Downs, and the coastal farmland around Chichester and Pagham Harbours. The numbers recorded annually vary, ranging between 1962 and 1976 from about 15 to about 80 birds per year. Approximate monthly totals in this period were:

Aug.	Sept.	Oct.	Nov.	Dec.	Jan.	Feb.	Mar.	Apr.	May
6	37	137	161	172	153	150	142	59	13

Except for breeding birds extreme dates are 8 August (1956, Pevensey Levels) and 21 May (1955, Pevensey Levels), but most winter visitors arrive in October and November and depart in March. The records suggest that many September records and some for March, April and May relate to passage birds, rather than arrivals or departures of our winter visitors, and birds are often noted arriving or departing at the coast in both autumn and spring.

NIGHTJAR—*Caprimulgus europaeus*

Status.—**Locally distributed summer visitor to breed. No recent change in status is definitely apparent.**

In common with most other nocturnal or crepuscular species, Nightjars are probably under-recorded. However, much attention has been paid to this species in Sussex since 1966 in an attempt to assess how many breed, and in the period 1966 to 1973 breeding season (mid-June to end August) records, involving a total of 240 pairs or territorial males, were received from 109 localities. Of the latter just over half, containing about 65 per cent. of the total population, were found occupied in at least two years, and are probably regular sites. Numbers evidently vary annually and the amount of time devoted to searching for Nightjars also varied each year, so that more sites may be regularly occupied than the present records show. Thus population trends are difficult to detect.

S. W. M. Hughes has mapped all these records on a tetrad basis, and this map shows a very marked correlation between the Nightjar's breeding distribution and sandy or chalk soils. Thus the downland forestry plantations, the greensand heaths and woods, and the forest ridges of the north of the county emerge as the most important areas for the species, and about three-quarters of the regular breeding sites discovered and total population counted were found in such sites. In forestry plantations nests have been found on the stumps of old felled trees. A fresh census was made in 1977.

Few Nightjars are noted on migration. Extreme dates are 8 April 1912 at Pulborough, and 5 November 1961 at Worthing, but the species is not often seen before May or after the second half of September.

ALPINE SWIFT—*Apus melba*

Status.—**Vagrant.**

There have been 11 records, all but two since 1964. Records have been for May (two), June (one), August (four), September (two), and October (two). The October records include one at Church Norton on 30 October 1972, an exceptionally late date.

SWIFT—*Apus apus*
Status.—**Summer visitor and passage migrant. No recent change in status is apparent.**

In June 1970 a survey involving about 85 per cent. coverage of the towns, villages and hamlets of the county revealed a summer population of about 4,000 Swifts, and the results of a longer survey during 1968 to 1970 suggested a breeding season population of about 4,500 birds. A full account of this survey was published in SxBR 1970, 61–69.

Very large numbers also pass through the county during migration and the regular mid-summer movements which take place. Spring arrivals normally start in the second half of April, although 14 April (1956, Normans Bay) is the earliest date yet recorded, and continue until early June. Numbers noted arriving at the coast are usually quite small, but concentrations of up to 1,000 birds may be noted inland, particularly over large areas of water such as Chichester gravel pits; 1,500 were noted at Arlington Reservoir on 16 May 1975, when 915 also arrived from the south at Beachy Head, an exceptional movement in spring. Extensive and complicated mid-summer movements, sometimes involving many hundreds of birds, occur annually.

Autumn departures begin in the first half of July, with the peak autumn movement at the end of this month or in early August. Few are noted after the middle of this month, although very small numbers are quite regular up to mid-September, and stragglers may be noted into October; there were nine October records in 1976, a high number. The latest date recorded is 2 and 3 November (1975, Sidlesham).

KINGFISHER—*Alcedo atthis*

Status.—**Uncommon resident. Some decline has probably occurred in recent years.**

Kingfishers suffer considerable losses in very severe winters, but since the last, in 1962/63, the population has made a substantial recovery. Thus between 1964 and 1973 there were breeding season reports from about 100 sites, in 35 of which breeding was proved.

Study of the records suggests that these figures represent over half the county population and the species is clearly widely distributed throughout the Weald. Few pairs breed along the coast, however, and there are no suitable nesting sites on the Downs. Apart from the effects of severe winter weather numbers appear very stable, with many sites consistently recorded as holding birds each year.

Most breeding pairs are now noted on the many mill and hammer ponds or other artificial waters scattered throughout the Weald and the streams which serve them, or the numerous feeder streams of the main rivers. W. Merritt, who has examined the Sussex river systems in great detail in searching for Grey Wagtails, has noted that few pairs of Kingfishers now breed along the main rivers, perhaps owing to pollution. Thus some change in the species' habits is likely, as Walpole-Bond noted comparatively few pairs as nesting at ponds, compared with the rivers. Possibly, however, this represents a decline in numbers rather than a change in habits.

Although rarely breeding there Kingfishers are quite numerous along the coast from August to March. Walpole-Bond remarked that many of these were first-year birds and believed that they were mostly of Sussex origin, noting a decline in numbers inland in winter. No recent investigation of this point has been made, but· a Belgian ringed bird was recovered at Buxted in March 1975, indicating that long-distance movement occurs.

BEE-EATER—*Merops apiaster*
Status.—**Vagrant, which has bred once.**

In 1955 three pairs nested in Streat sandpit, near Plumpton, two of which successfully reared a total of seven young; a single bird was noted in another locality in June. In 1957 a single bird summered there.

Otherwise there have been nine records: in May (three), June (two), August (one), and September (one); two records are undated. The most recent report was of one seen at Beachy Head on 5 June 1969.

ROLLER—*Coracias garrulus*

Status.—**Vagrant.**

There have been 14 records, but only two of them since 1947. Two records are undated. Otherwise Rollers have been seen in May (one), June (four), July (four), August (two), and September (two). The most recent records are of one which stayed around Weir Wood Reservoir from 28 June to 4 July 1970, and one at Charleston Bottom on 12 July 1976.

HOOPOE—*Upupa epops*

Status.—**Has bred. Scarce passage migrant. No recent change in status is apparent.**

Hoopoes have been proved to breed in Sussex six times as follows: Park End, Chichester about 1835; Southwick, a few years before 1849; Oving, near Chichester, in 1868 or 1869; near Eastbourne in 1895; Asham, near Iford, before 1908; and a pair bred in 1976. In addition two birds summered at Storrington in 1921 and at Uckfield in 1932, which may have attempted to breed; one did so at Robertsbridge in 1968, and a second locality in 1976.

Otherwise the species occurs annually on spring passage and slightly less regularly on autumn passage. Until 1960 des Forges and Harber recorded about 385 birds, 125 of them between 1947 and 1960, of which almost half were seen in April. Between 1961 and 1976 another 145 were seen, with records every year and annual totals varying from four to 32 (in 1968). Approximate monthly totals were:

Mar.	Apr.	May	June	July	Aug.	Sept.	Oct.	Nov.	Dec.
1	76	41	8	3	12	14	2	2	1

Although there are older records for the first week of March, extreme dates in this period for spring passage were 31 March and 18 June. A record for 4 July may refer to a summering bird, and autumn records otherwise fell between 20 July and 6 December (1970, Climping). However, the species is rarely seen after September, and there are only three November and two December records in all. The latest record for Sussex is of one at Hartfield on 14 December 1897.

Nearly all records are of single birds which may appear anywhere, although gardens near the coast are very favoured spots. However, two together were noted on seven occasions between 1961 and 1976, and three were seen together at Coombes on 15 April 1966.

WRYNECK—*Jynx torquilla*

*Status.—*Formerly bred. Scarce passage migrant, of which the numbers occurring are possibly increasing.

Although a common summer visitor to breed until 1920, Wrynecks had ceased to nest in Sussex by 1944, possibly earlier as a regular occurrence. Apparently unmated birds have, however, summered three times since 1965.

As passage migrants Wrynecks had also become quite rare by the 1940s, and des Forges and Harber recorded only 30 between 1947 and 1960, equally divided between spring and autumn. Considerably larger numbers have been seen since 1961, and a very marked increase has been apparent since about 1968, as the average number recorded per year increased from two to four between 1947 and 1967 to about 27 between 1968 and 1976. This increase is confined to the autumn passage.

Approximate monthly totals between 1961 and 1976 were:

Apr.	May	June	July	Aug.	Sept.	Oct.
15	10	2	3	55	190	20

Annual totals varied from four to 59 (in 1976), and spring records fell between 12 April and 31 May, with autumn records between 28 July and 28 October (1969, Bexhill). There is one November record, for 5 November 1947, at the Crumbles. Most records are of single birds, but two together are not very uncommon. The majority of present-day records come from the immediate vicinity of the coast, particularly Beachy Head.

GREEN WOODPECKER—*Picus viridis*

Status.—**Common resident. No marked change in status is apparent.**

Perhaps as late as 1962 this was our most abundant and widespread woodpecker, breeding wherever there were mature trees (Walpole-Bond and des Forges and Harber). The severe winter of 1962/63 greatly depleted the breeding stock, however, and the species has never re-colonised parts of its former range, such as the coastal plain of south-west Sussex. It is once again widespread in the interior and, for example, in the three years 1971 to 1973 there were breeding season records from at least 140 localities involving approximately 230 pairs or birds.

The records available indicate that it is now rather less common than the Great Spotted Woodpecker, at present the most numerous Sussex woodpecker (*cf.* Walpole-Bond and des Forges and Harber). This is confirmed by the more detailed records of the Woodland Survey (see page 17), which showed the Great Spotted Woodpecker to be slightly more numerous, but, interestingly, revealed no clear population trend for either species. The population of Green Woodpeckers now seems very stable, and it is unlikely that any very significant long-term change in status has occurred.

GREAT SPOTTED WOODPECKER—*Dendrocopos*
major

Status.—**Common resident; possibly winter visitor and passage migrant. Some increase has occurred since at least 1938.**

Both the Woodland Survey (see page 17) and the other records available suggest that this is now the most numerous woodpecker in Sussex, although as late as 1961 des Forges and Harber considered it to be less common than the Green Woodpecker. Great Spotted Woodpeckers are widespread in wooded areas throughout the interior of Sussex, and have started to colonise coastal areas, where they were formerly only occasional winter visitors. During the period 1971 to 1973 the species was recorded in the breeding season in about 100 localities, involving a total of 180 pairs or birds. It should be noted that this is a less conspicuous bird than the Green Woodpecker.

Parslow (1973) noted a marked increase in southern England since about 1920, but stated that it was not known whether this continued. In Sussex the woodland survey counts revealed no clear population trend since 1964, and, apart from the colonisation of coastal districts noted, the population now appears to be very stable. It seems likely, therefore, that the increase which has certainly occurred was most marked in the 1940s and 1950s.

There are very occasional records of migration at the coast, usually in April or October/November, and wandering birds often appear there in the autumn and winter. The source of these birds is not known, but as only two birds of the northern race *major* have ever been recorded, at Brede on 9 November 1903, and Ninfield on 24 November 1910, they seem most likely to be wandering British birds.

LESSER SPOTTED WOODPECKER— *Dendrocopos minor*
Status.—**Resident.**

While this species is the least numerous woodpecker nesting in Sussex, it is also a much less conspicuous bird than either

Green or Great Spotted Woodpeckers, so that it is probably under recorded.

In the Woodland Survey (see page 17) Lesser Spotted Woodpeckers were recorded in only five out of the 23 areas visited, and the counts suggested it to be about three to five times less numerous than the other woodpeckers. The counts also recorded it most frequently on the greensand and forest ridges in the north of the county. However, this distribution must be viewed against the species' known inconspicuousness, and the general records of the Society for the period 1971 to 1973 note it in a total of 64 sites, with a fairly general distribution in woodland north of the Downs. Both sources of information confirm that the species is comparatively much scarcer on the chalk and absent from many areas along the coast in the breeding season, although it may occur more frequently there in the winter. In 1975 and 1976 both spotted woodpeckers started to appear much more frequently on the coastal plain, probably attracted by the number of dead elm trees.

WHITE-WINGED LARK—*Melanocorypha leucoptera*
Status.—Three records.

One was caught near Brighton on 22 November 1869; three were seen on Hove seafront on 15 November 1917; one was seen between Rye and Camber on 19 August 1933.

SHORT-TOED LARK—*Calandrella cinerea*
Status.—Five records.

One was caught near Brighton on 26 September 1854; one was caught at Amberley on 18 July 1888; one was caught near Brighton on 16 November 1909; two were seen at Pagham on 29 April 1951; four were seen at Beachy Head on 2 October 1972.

CRESTED LARK—*Galerida cristata*
Status.—Four records.

One was obtained at Littlehampton prior to 1845; one was caught near Shoreham on 20 October 1863; one was shot near Worthing in the spring of 1879; one was caught at Portslade on 10 October 1881.

WOODLARK—*Lullula arborea*
Status.—Rare breeding resident; occasional winter visitor; scarce passage migrant. The breeding population has suffered a catastrophic decline recently.

A survey of the breeding population made between 1967 and 1969 revealed only about 10 pairs breeding annually. This represented a decline of some 90 to 95 per cent. compared with the period 1946 to 1955, for which the records available indicated a population of 50 to 100 pairs. The decline has probably continued and none was found breeding from 1972 to 1976, despite some search of potential breeding areas. The Sussex population of this species has fluctuated considerably during the past 100 years, and a detailed summary of these changes was published in SxBR 1969.

Both Walpole-Bond and des Forges and Harber indicated that parties of up to 20 birds were regular in winter, with larger numbers appearing in severe weather, but, with the virtual disappearance of the breeding stock, Woodlarks are now rarely seen. However, influxes may still occur in severe cold, and at least 35 were noted along the coast between Seaford and Eastbourne in a hard frost in January 1966.

Small numbers still occur on passage, when some movement may occur every year in October and November. A very few also move through Sussex in spring, particularly in March, but again numbers may have declined, as the table suggests.

Approximate monthly totals of winter visitors and passage migrants between 1962 and 1976 were:

	Aug.	Sept.	Oct.	Nov.	Dec.	Jan.	Feb.	Mar.	Apr.
1962-68	0	2	16	14	3	41	6	16	6
1969-76	6	6	6	2	1	0	0	2	1

SKYLARK—*Alauda arvensis*

Status.—**Common breeding resident, winter visitor and passage migrant. No recent change in status is apparent.**

Skylarks breed commonly in all open habitat types in the county. Recent counts suggest that they are most numerous on the coastal plain, where densities of up to 175 pairs per 2,500 acres (10 sq. km.) have been noted. Elsewhere densities varying from 35 to 100 pairs per 2,500 acres have been noted recently on the Downs, 60 pairs per 2,500 acres in the permanent grassland of the river valleys, and about 85 pairs per 2,500 acres on wealden farmland. In addition 57 pairs were counted on about 4,500 acres (*c.* 17.5 sq. km.) of heathland in Ashdown Forest in 1971.

Very little information is available about winter status, although large winter flocks occur regularly, for example on the coastal plain. Numbers are considerably increased in severe weather, when very large movements may occur. These may include arrivals from the Continent; for example, 2,000 flew in from the south at Selsey Bill in very hard frost on 16 January 1966.

Substantial passage movements are also recorded, with immigration and emigration being noted in both spring and autumn. Most spring passage is noted in March, although some movement probably takes places from February to the end of April. In autumn passage probably continues from September to early December, but most occurs in October and November, when some very large flocks involving several thousand birds have been noted, particularly at Beachy Head. Quinn and Clement (1971) noted that these late autumn flocks were the result of a steady build-up rather than a sudden influx.

SHORE LARK—*Eremophila alpestris*

Status.—Rare winter visitor and passage migrant. No recent change in status is apparent.

Until 1960 des Forges and Harber recorded a total of over 100, records falling between 28 September (1946) and 22 April (1885); most records were for November to January.

Between 1961 and 1976 a total of 48 was noted, but the species was not annual. Monthly totals were:

Oct.	Nov.	Dec.	Jan.	Feb.	Mar.	Apr.
13	12	13	14	10	9	5

Of these birds three wintered at the Midrips in 1962/63, five did so at Crowlink in 1969/70, remaining until 16 April 1970, at least one did so at Camber in 1970/71, and another at Pagham Harbour in 1972/73. Otherwise the records relate to passage, and over half were for 1972, when an exceptional total of 23 was seen, including flocks of 11 at Beachy Head on 15 October and six at Cuckmere Haven on 10 December.

All records are for the coast.

SAND MARTIN—*Riparia riparia*

Status.—Locally common breeding summer visitor; common passage migrant. Some decline has possibly occurred recently in the breeding population.

Because of habitat restrictions Sand Martins are the least widespread of the hirundines in Sussex. However, counts between 1965 and 1972 recorded a maximum total of just under 4,000 pairs. Well over half this total was located in the sandpits in the Sullington and Washington area, where there were 2,980 pairs in 25 colonies in 1967, and 1,550 in 12 in 1969. No reason for this sharp decline was noted, nor is there evidence that a decline of this scale has occurred in the county as a whole, but by 1974 only 148 occupied nest-holes could be found by the same observer, and a survey of the whole

county is needed to establish trends in this bird's breeding
population. Nearly all the known colonies are in sandpits in
which changes in management are probably bound to affect
numbers, perhaps only temporarily. Breeding has also been
recorded in chalk pits, on the cliffs, in holes in masonry, and
once in a pile of salt used for defrosting roads. It has even been
noted in river banks!

The earliest date for arrival is 7 March 1886, and other early
dates are 11 March 1950 at Cuckmere Haven and 12 March
1966 at Chichester gravel pits. Some Sand Martins probably
always arrive in the second half of March and the main arrival
takes place in April, particularly in the second half. Autumn
passage starts earlier than with the other hirundines, with quite
extensive movements in late July and peak passage in the
second half of August or first half of September. Movements
tend to be smaller than for either Swallow or House Martin.
However, counts of up to 40,000 Sand Martins have been made
at reed-bed roosts and movements of several thousand in a
day are not infrequent. Few Sand Martins are seen after
mid-October, but there have been seven November records
since 1966, between the 3rd and 19th, and the latest county
record is for 5 December 1911.

SWALLOW—*Hirundo rustica*

Status.—**Common breeding summer visitor and passage
migrant. No recent change in status is apparent.**

Although very little recent information is available on the
numbers involved, this species is clearly a widespread and
common breeding bird and the possible decline noted by des
Forges and Harber does not appear to have been confirmed
more recently.

Swallows have been seen in Sussex in every month except
January. The earliest record is of one at Langney Point on
4 February 1967, and other very early dates are 12 February
1914 at Playden, Rye, 3 March 1969 at Pebsham, 5 March 1972

at Rottingdean, and 6 March 1960 at Ashburnham. Otherwise spring arrival usually starts in late March or early April, with the main movement fairly consistently occurring in the first half of May.

Very large movements are noted in autumn, when passage continues from August to early November. The main passage period is from mid-August to mid-October, with a fairly consistent peak in the middle two weeks of September, when movements of 10,000 to 30,000 birds in a day are seen annually. The largest single movement on record involved about 55,000 birds at Beachy Head over 13 and 14 September 1971; a further 15,000 were recorded there five days later. A few birds are regularly noted in the second half of November and early December records are not very unusual. The latest date for Sussex is 28 December 1974 at Church Norton, and other very late dates are 23 December 1894 at Chichester, 25 December 1966 at Eastbourne, and 26 December 1960 at Pagham. In 1974 there were, in fact, an unusual number of December records, comprising some 18 birds in seven localities, with records throughout the month until the 28th.

RED-RUMPED SWALLOW—*Hirundo daurica*
Status.—**Three records, all since 1967.**

Single birds were seen at Beachy Head on 23 April 1967 and 18 April 1970; one was seen at Litlington on 4 May 1971.

HOUSE MARTIN—*Delichon urbica*
Status.—**Common breeding summer visitor and passage migrant. No recent change in status is apparent.**

During counts of breeding colonies organised between 1967 and 1972 a total of 2,700 nests was recorded at 53 localities. Many counts covered complete villages or parishes, but the census was incomplete, although providing useful comparative data. The largest groups recorded were 345 nests at Plumpton, including 240 on the Agricultural College in 1971, 250 nests at Ditchling, one colony of 182 nests at Icklesham, 178 nests at Ringmer, 119 nests at Nyewood, and 93 nests at Rye. In addition counts of over 50 nests, and totalling at least 720 were made at Horsham, Pevensey, Billingshurst, Arundel, Crowborough, Lewes, Uckfield, Winchelsea, Battle, Ripe, and Chailey Heritage. Cliff-nesting was noted at Saltdean and Seaford. No clear trend emerged to support the possible decline reported by des Forges and Harber, but numbers at individual colonies showed much annual variation. The species is clearly widespread and, as it can colonise new building estates fairly quickly, its distribution is likely to change even if overall numbers do not.

The earliest date for arrival is 13 March 1966 at Chichester gravel pits, and other early dates are 19 March 1939 at Cuckmere Haven and 22 March 1963 at Chichester gravel pits. However, few House Martins normally arrive before mid-April and the main arrival usually occurs in the first half of May. As with the other hirundines spring movements are rarely large.

Large autumn movements occur regularly, however, mainly in the peak passage month of September, when movements of several thousands in a day are noted every year. The largest movement on record involved a total of about 45,000 birds at Selsey Bill and Beachy Head on 19 September 1970. Some passage always continues into November, but December records seem rather less frequent than for Swallow. The latest date for House Martins is 22 December 1894 at Fishbourne, and other late dates are 12 December 1966 at Alfriston, and 16 December 1972 at Camber, 1974 at Arundel, and 1976 at Seaford.

One seen near Petworth on 1 February 1975 may either have wintered or been a freak migrant.

YELLOW WAGTAIL—*Motacilla flava*

Status.—Local summer visitor to breed; winter vagrant; common passage migrant. The numbers breeding and possibly those on passage have declined in recent years.

A breeding survey made from 1965 to 1967 recorded between 150 and 270 pairs. The species was widely distributed in the permanent grassland of the river valleys and levels and around Rye Harbour, and a few pairs bred around Chichester Harbour. Breeding densities varied from 6.5 to 43 pairs per 2,500 acres (10 sq. km.), but numbers fluctuated annually and the distribution was uneven. Thus over half the population was found in the Amberley/Pulborough marshes, with about 32 pairs per 2,500 acres, Pevensey Levels, with about 22 pairs per 2,500 acres, and the Rother Levels, with about 43 pairs per 2,500 acres. A density of about 20 pairs per 2,500 acres was found in the Adur Levels, but elsewhere densities were all between four and nine pairs per 2,500 acres. The Pevensey figures may have been low, as the whole area was not covered, and 127 pairs, giving a density of 35 pairs per 2,500 acres, were recorded in 1972, and 165 pairs in 1976; some increase in this area is also possible. Otherwise little change has been noted since 1967. A detailed account of the survey was published in SxBR 1967, 53–60.

In 1961 des Forges and Harber noted that a decline, which started in 1939, was apparently still continuing. Study of the county files suggests that this was particularly marked between 1947 and 1956, when the population may have halved, but the situation may now be more stable. Without doubt Yellow Wagtails have, like Snipe and Redshank, been adversely affected by draining and improving many areas of wet grassland in Sussex.

There are four winter records. One wintered at Sidlesham Ferry in 1960/61; one was seen at West Wittering on 19 January 1947; one was seen at Glynde on 7 and 13 January 1973, and one was seen in the Cuckmere valley on 12 February 1967.

Otherwise extreme dates for this species are 23 March (1957 and 1971), and 21 November (1926). Some nearly always arrive in the first week of April, and spring passage usually continues until mid-May, although arrivals have been noted as late as 8 June. In recent years numbers seen arriving at the coast have been very small. Autumn passage is much larger and extends from early August to early October, with stragglers until the middle of that month in many years; there are also

six November records. Most passage, however, occurs in a
fairly restricted period from mid-August into the first 10 days
of September. In this period counts of up to 300 to 500 are
fairly regular in favoured areas such as the Selsey peninsular
or Rye Harbour, and sometimes Beachy Head. Larger numbers
have been recorded in the past; for example, about 2,000 were
roosting at Camber on 1 September 1949.

Five races of the Yellow Wagtail have been recorded in
Sussex. The breeding population is of the race *flavissima,* but
birds showing the characters of the nominate race, *flava,* bred
regularly until 1948 and may still do so very rarely. One or two
such birds are still seen annually on spring passage, but are
rarely identified in autumn. Birds showing the characters of
the race *thunbergi* have occurred three times as follows: one
shot near Lancing on either 24 April 1870 or 28 May 1869;
one seen at Selsey Bill on 18 September 1960; and one seen
at Pagham Harbour on 4 June 1970. A bird showing the
characters of the race *cinereocapilla* was seen at Beachy Head
on 28 April 1968, and one showing the characters of the race
feldegg was seen at Thorney Island on 23 July 1974.

GREY WAGTAIL—*Motacilla cinerea*

Status.—Resident and passage migrant. A marked
increase has occurred since 1938.

Between 1967 and 1969 Merritt, Bonham and Greenhalf
made a detailed study of the status and distribution of this
species, an account of which was published in SxBR 1969,
68-80. Tables A and B, and Fig. 17, taken with permission from
this paper, summarise the breeding position recorded. In calcu-
lating breeding densities they defined potential breeding
habitat as all the one-km. square on the one inch Ordnance
Survey maps containing a non-tidal river, stream or a lake,
and breeding distribution in Fig. 17 is shown on this basis. An

interesting feature of the survey was the extent to which Grey Wagtails were dependent on human artefacts for nesting localities, which were largely at the outfalls of Hammer or other man-made ponds (48 per cent.), bridges (26 per cent.), or weirs (18 per cent.).

The total of 193 occupied territories located represents an increase compared with 1938, when Walpole-Bond estimated 60 to 70 pairs nesting annually in the county, a trend which has been evident throughout southern England during this century (Parslow, 1973). Merritt *et al.*, however, compared their records with sites listed by Walpole-Bond and found that 83 per cent. of the latter were still occupied in 1967–69, and, lacking details of the extent of his coverage, concluded that the scale of increase could not be determined.

Fig.18 maps all the wintering sites of Grey Wagtails Merritt *et al.* found in the same survey period. Once again the dependence of the species on human artefacts in Sussex is marked; of the 147 sites mapped, holding some 240 birds, 111 are sewage works, with 14 at ponds, gravel pits or reservoirs, 11 streams or marshes, four cress beds, and the remainder farmyards, pumping stations, and a rubbish tip. They concluded that the Sussex breeding population was largely sedentary, simply making small local movements between the breeding site and wintering site, most usually the nearest sewage works. They suggest that the species' present success stems from its exploitation of these works as a source of winter food; they rarely freeze.

Some movement always occurs at the coast in the autumn, and sometimes in the spring, although the source of these birds is not known. The Beachy Head records show peak movements in early September, but passage extends until late October. Most movement is along the coast, but some emigration is noted; up to 25 birds in a day are now recorded. The 1962/63 winter caused a marked reduction in passage birds, but numbers recovered by 1968. Spring passage is always very small, but a few have been recorded arriving at the coast, and what passage there is extends from late March to early May.

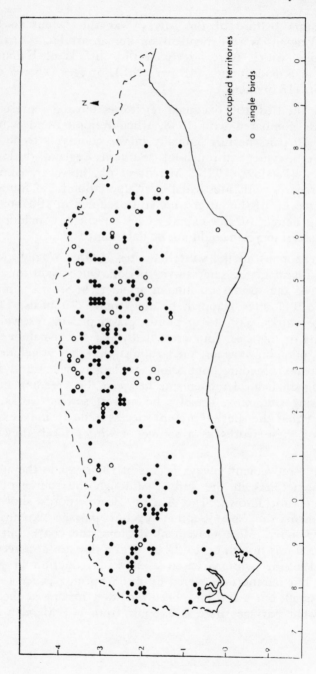

Fig. 17.—Distribution and Total Number of Occupied Territories of Breeding
Grey Wagtails in Sussex, 1967 to 1969

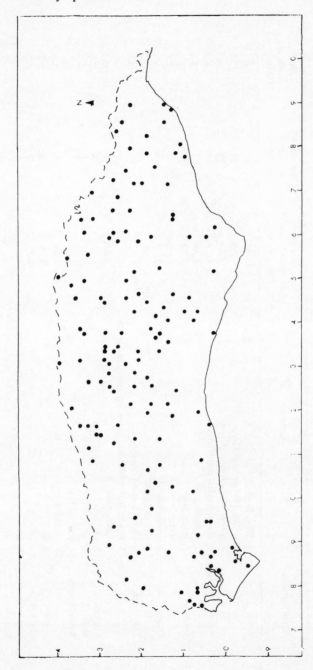

Fig. 18.—The Distribution and Total Number of Wintering Sites found Occupied by Grey Wagtails in Sussex, 1967 to 1969

Table A — The Breeding Density of Grey Wagtails in Sussex, 1967–69

River System	Region	Area of potential habitat* (100 sq. km.)	Number of occupied territories	Density (pairs per 100 sq. km.)
Arun	1 West Rother	2.03	40	20
	2 below Wisborough Green	1.46	11	7.5
	3 above Wisborough Green	2.30	13	5.7
Adur	4 Great Betley tributaries	1.58	10	6.3
	5 remainder	1.88	3	1.6
Medway	6 main river	1.97	28	14
	7 Teise	0.55	2	3.6
Ouse	8 above Isfield	2.93	45	15
	9 below Isfield	1.83	5	2.7
East Rother	10 above Robertsbridge	1.82	12	6.6
	11 below Robertsbridge, including rivers Brede and Tillingham	2.81	1	0.4
Cuckmere	12 all	1.05	3	2.9
Mole	13 all	0.82	5	6.1
Ashburnham	14 old sea	1.06	—	—
	15 remainder	0.61	3	4.9
Asten	16 all	0.53	3	5.7
Chichester	17 all	1.32	7	5.3
Wey	18 all	—	1	—
Eden	19 all	—	1	—
Totals		26.55	193	7.3

*Note.—Potential breeding habitat is defined on page 230.

Table B — Breeding Densities of Grey Wagtails on the Principal Geological Strata occurring in Sussex, 1967–69
(Based on study areas)

Area*	Surface geological strata	Area of potential habitat (100 sq. km.)	Number of occupied territories	Density (pairs per 100 sq. km.)
A	Lower Greensand, Gault, Upper Greensand	1.20	37	30.8
B	Ashdown Sandstone	1.60	29	18.1
C	Tunbridge Wells Sandstone	1.87	32	17.1
D	Brickearth valley gravel	0.79	7	8.9
E	Weald Clay	2.13	8	3.8

*Note.—The location of these areas is shown in the original paper.

PIED WAGTAIL—*Motacilla alba*

Status.—Common resident and perhaps winter visitor;
passage migrant. Some recent decline of this species is
possible.

Little information on breeding status has been recorded
lately. Although stated by des Forges and Harber to nest commonly throughout the county, H. A. R. Cawkell, in Parslow
(1973), noted that nesting numbers had declined by about half
in East Sussex in 30 years. A breeding study of this species
would be worthwhile, and my own experience suggests that
it should show Pied Wagtails to be less numerous and widespread than generally thought.

Some substantial autumn/winter roosts of this species,
however, have been recorded. In most cases it is not established
if these are occupied every year, but, since 1965, roosts holding
more than 100 birds during the autumn or winter were found
at Rewell Wood (maximum 200), Redgate Mill sewage farm
(maximum 250), Tunbridge Wells sewage farm (maximum 300),
Litlington reed bed (maximum 350), Scaynes Hill sewage farm
(maximum 600), Itchenor Quay (maximum 140), Thakeham
(maximum 1,000), Streat (maximum 150), Arundel (maximum
270), Fishbourne (maximum 300), Crawley (maximum 100),
High Hurstwood (maximum 200), and Worthing (maximum
200). Somewhat bizarre roosting sites are characteristic of this
species and, in Sussex, roosts have been recorded at Brighton
railway station, trees in well-lit town roads, glasshouses at
Thakeham, and the hold of a disused barge at Itchenor; reed
bed roosts are commonplace. The extent to which the birds
using these roosts are our own breeding stock or visitors to the
county is not known.

Regular passage movements are noted at the coast in autumn,
extending from August into November. The Beachy Head
records show a clear peak in the last week of September or the
first half of October, and suggest a recent decline in numbers,
which Quinn and Clement (1971) in fact suggest may be the
result of a local autumn roost being broken up. Most movement
there is of coasting birds, but further west at Selsey Bill nearly
half the autumn movements noted from 1963 to 1969 involved
emigration. Numbers are quite small at both stations, not

often exceeding 100 or 200 birds annually. Small return movements are noted from February into May.

Two races of this species occur in Sussex. Our breeding birds are nearly all of the race *yarrellii*, but birds showing the characters of the nominate race, *alba*, have bred occasionally, most recently in the Cuckmere valley in 1974. Similar birds occur regularly on migration, especially in spring, but it is doubtful if the records give a very accurate picture of numbers.

RICHARD'S PIPIT—*Anthus novaeseelandiae*
Status.—Vagrant.

Until 1961 des Forges and Harber recorded about 33, mostly for the 19th century. Between 1962 and 1976 19 more were noted, all but one since 1967. Of the old records many are not accurately dated, but one is for 12 March (1869, Clayton Hill), three or four are for December or January, and the remainder for September to November. Since 1947 birds have been seen in March (26th 1974, Beachy Head), September (five), October (15), and January (one). Four birds first seen late in October stayed into early November. Nearly all records have been for the coast.

The Sussex records for the species make an interesting pattern, as 73 per cent. of the total of *c.* 52 birds were seen or obtained between 1865 and 1869 (20 birds), and between 1967 and 1972 (18 birds). The spate of records for the 1865-69 period is of particular interest in view of our recent experience of this bird in Britain as a whole.

TAWNY PIPIT—*Anthus campestris*
Status.—Rare but regular autumn passage migrant; twice in spring. No recent change in status is apparent.

Until 1961 des Forges and Harber recorded about 60, and between then and 1976 another 67 were noted. Nearly all records are for the coast, where systematic recording of migration leaves no doubt that Tawny Pipits are regular autumn migrants in Sussex, particularly in September.

The two spring records were of one at Beachy Head on 24 May 1969, and one at Pevensey Levels on 30 April 1975. Autumn records fall between 6 August (1973, Arlington reservoir) and 8 November (1874, Eastbourne). Altogether there are 20 records for August, *c.* 81 for September, 19 for October, and one for November. Usually only one or two are seen each year, but six were seen in 1968 and 1969, eight in 1960, nine in 1973, and 10 in 1970; up to three have been seen together.

TREE PIPIT—*Anthus trivialis*

Status.—Local breeding summer visitor; passage migrant. Although a major habitat change appears to have occurred in recent years, little overall change in status has resulted.

A breeding survey made from 1967 to 1970 recorded 449 occupied territories, which were distributed over much of the northern half of the county. Breeding densities were uneven, which Figs. 19 and 20, showing the known breeding densities in each 10-km. square (25,000 acres) of the county, demonstrate. Ashdown Forest is clearly the most important area for the species in Sussex, but there is also a substantial population in the north-west of the county. About 70 per cent. of the county was searched for the species, and calculations suggested a total county population of about 600 pairs. A detailed account of the survey appears in SxBR 1971, 68–79.

Comparatively little change in general distribution or numbers compared with Walpole-Bond's account in 1938 was revealed by the survey. But a major change in nesting habitat was found, with about half the population breeding in young forestry plantations, which Walpole-Bond does not mention as a breeding habitat. This change has probably enabled Tree Pipits to increase their range in Sussex, but will result in marked local variations in abundance, as they rapidly leave individual

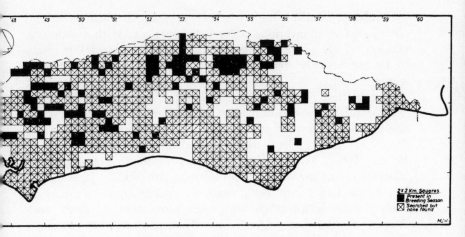

Fig. 19.—The Breeding Distribution of the Tree Pipit in Sussex (1967-1970).

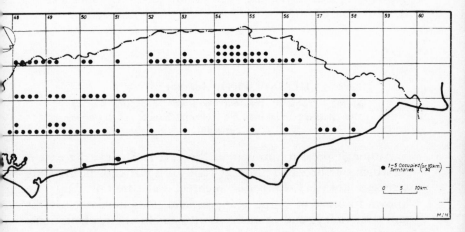

g. 20.—Distribution and total number of occupied Tree Pipit territories (1967-1970).

plantations at the thicket stage; in fact the survey found changes after plantations were five years old. With continuing erosion of its more traditional habitats, this species is likely to be increasingly dependent on forestry for nesting in Sussex in the future.

The earliest date for spring arrival is 27 March (1967, Sidlesham), but arrivals usually start in the first half of April, often the first week. Spring passage is quite small. For example, 15 to 20 on 21 April 1968 is the highest daily count so far noted at Beachy Head. The Beachy Head records show a clear peak in late April, but arrivals may continue as late as early June. There is a much larger autumn passage extending from late July to early October, although the main movement is from mid-August to mid-September. The Beachy Head records show the second half of August to be the peak period, and counts of 50 to 100 in a day are then frequent; 250 on 18 August 1968 is the highest count there so far. Few Tree Pipits are seen after September, but there are records up to 24 October (1971, Beachy Head).

MEADOW PIPIT—*Anthus pratensis*

Status.—**Probably resident; common breeding species and passage migrant. No recent change in status is apparent.**

Although present throughout the year in Sussex, the extent to which our breeding birds are resident is not known. Breeding status is not very fully documented, but Meadow Pipits are known to breed in permanent grassland along the coast, Downs and river valleys and on many heaths and in young plantations. Counts recorded densities of 40 to 60 pairs per 2,500 acres (10 sq. km.) in the Arun valley in 1967 and 1970, and the Rother Levels in 1966, and in 1976 118 pairs were located on Pevensey Levels. On downland much greater variations have been found, with densities as high as 200 pairs per 2,500 acres in very favourable areas such as Beachy Head, and as low as 13 pairs per 2,500 acres in predominantly farmland regions;

the average is probably well below 100 pairs. A complete count recorded 49 males holding territory on Ashdown Forest in 1971.

Virtually nothing is known of the species' status in winter other than that some individuals, at least, are present, and small movements are often noted in severe weather. Numbers are probably always small from December to February.

There are extensive movements. in both spring and autumn. Arrivals and departures are observed at the coast in both seasons, but arrivals predominate in spring and departures in autumn. Spring passage may extend from early March into May, but arrivals fairly consistently peak at the end of March or in the first week of April, when arrivals of 300 to over 1,000 in a day have been noted regularly. There is a similar clearly-defined peak in the autumn, when movements may extend throughout much of September and October, but the main movement is consistently recorded in the second half of September, regularly involving departures or westerly movements of 500 to 1,000 birds in a day; *c.* 2,000 were noted at Beachy Head on 29 September 1975.

RED-THROATED PIPIT—*Anthus cervinus*
Status.—Three records.

One was seen at Beachy Head on 19 and 20 October 1969; one was seen at Arlington reservoir from 13 to 15 October 1970; one was seen at Beachy Head on 6 October 1973.

ROCK PIPIT—*Anthus spinoletta*
Status.—Local resident; winter visitor; passage migrant.
No recent change in status is apparent.

Breeding pairs are confined to the chalk and sandstone cliffs. A complete census in 1965 recorded 42 territorial males along

the chalk cliffs, of which 23 were found between Birling Gap
and Holywell, Eastbourne, and three along the sandstone cliffs
between Hastings and Pett, apparently the first breeding birds
ever found there. Walpole-Bond noted that although Rock
Pipits bred regularly in Sussex up to 1891, there were no
breeding birds from then until 1932, after which colonisation
of the chalk cliffs was rapid, and he estimated 30 pairs there
in 1938. No reason for this pattern is known. A modest increase
occurred after 1938, but there has been little change for the
past 15 years.

As far as is known our breeding birds are resident. In addition
winter visitors are found along the whole coast, including the
estuaries, from October to March. Numbers have not been very
accurately assessed, but may be quite substantial. For example,
a total of about 50 wintered around Thorney Island and the
Chidham shore in 1965/66, and 30 from Bracklesham Bay to
Church Norton in 1968/69. Gatherings of up to *c.* 10 have
been noted quite regularly elsewhere along the coast, for
example at Ferring, Shoreham Beach, Brighton seafront, the
Cuckmere estuary, and Eastbourne, and winter counts of up
to 30 have been made at Rye Harbour.

The movements of Rock Pipits in Sussex have been little
studied, but arrival of winter visitors most usually starts in late
September or early October (early date 5 August 1974, Arlington Reservoir), and some movement has been recorded into
November. There is quite a marked return passage in March
and early April, and wintering birds have probably all left by
late April.

Three races of this species occur in Sussex. The breeding
birds and probably most of the winter visitors belong to the
race *petrosus*. The nominate race, *spinoletta* (Water Pipit),
also winters occasionally and occurs regularly as a passage
migrant. Up to 1976 there were about 125 records of this
form, about 51 being for September to November, about
27 for December to February, probably wintering, and 47
for March and April. In addition one was identified at Beachy
Head on 28 May 1967. At present most records are for March
and ˙April, although about half the records up to 1961 were
for the autumn period. The race *littoralis* (Scandinavian

Rock Pipit) also occurs on spring passage and was identified 21 times between 1947 and 1976, between 1 February (1975), and 4 April (1965).

At all seasons Rock Pipits are largely confined to the coast, but since 1961 there have been seven inland records of *spinoletta,* five on spring passage and two in autumn, all at reservoirs or gravel pits.

RED-BACKED SHRIKE—*Lanius collurio*

Status.— Formerly summer visitor to breed; now rare passage migrant. A very marked decline has thus occurred.

Although the numbers breeding were never large, Red-backed Shrikes were said to be increasing in parts of Sussex in 1949. Unfortunately, virtually no nesting records have been retained in the county files for the period 1947 to 1958, and by 1960 only three pairs were known to be present. Regular breeding ceased by 1963, after which single pairs in 1964 and 1968 have been the only breeding records.

Otherwise during the period 1962 to 1976 49 birds were recorded: in May (four), June (two), July (one), August (11), September (20), October (10), and November (one). The November record was of a bird at Pebsham, Bexhill, from 26 October to 6 November 1968, the latest date for the county; the earliest date is 20 April (1958, Selsey Bill).

RED-TAILED SHRIKE—*Lanius collurio*

*Status.—*One record.

A bird showing the characters of one of the *isabellinus* group of red-railed races of the Red-backed Shrike was seen at Sidlesham Ferry from 1 March to 20 April 1975. Because of the extraordinary date *British Birds* (69, 353) considered this bird to be an escape, but, unfortunately, did not amplify this statement, although England (1974) does not suggest this bird as a very likely candidate for the category.

LESSER GREY SHRIKE—*Lanius minor*

Status.—Four records.

One was shot at Bosham on 14 October 1905; one was seen at Sidlesham on 1 and 2 July 1962; one was seen at Beachy Head on 25 May 1969; one was seen at Sidlesham on 6 September 1973.

GREAT GREY SHRIKE—*Lanius excubitor*

Status.—Winter visitor and passage migrant. Some increase in the number occurring is possible since about 1966.

Between 1946 and 1961 des Forges and Harber noted that Great Grey Shrikes were of almost annual occurrence. Two or three were seen each year, with totals of 10 for October/November, 16 for December to February, and 10 for March to May; little change from previous years was indicated. Between 1962 and 1976 about 135 were recorded, with a very noticeable increase from the average of about two or three noted by des Forges and Harber to about 12 per winter since 1966/67. While greater observer activity during the period has doubtless contributed to this increase, the records leave little doubt that more Great Grey Shrikes now winter in Sussex.

Autumn arrival begins in October, the earliest date recently being 3 October (1961 and 1974), and rather more birds are noted in October and November than in any other month, as the table of monthly totals shows:

Oct.	Nov.	Dec.	Jan.	Feb.	Mar.	Apr.
46	45	41	39	37	40	10

However, this table also suggests that a high proportion of the birds recorded now winter, staying into February or March, or sometimes April. Some spring passage also occurs, usually in March. In recent years the latest date was 27 April 1976. But among older records there is one for September (7th, 1899, Crumbles), and one for May (14th, 1950, Rye Harbour), and five comprising six birds for June and July, the most recent being at Lewes in July 1935.

Most records are of single birds, but records of two or three in one locality are no longer rare, another indication of increased numbers. On passage birds may be seen anywhere, and one or two have wintered at least once on a municipal rubbish tip; but most birds are seen on heathland, downland or extensive areas of wet grassland. Surprisingly few are recorded from large areas of forestry plantation, perhaps reflecting a lack of observer activity in such areas in winter.

WOODCHAT SHRIKE—*Lanius senator*
Status.—Vagrant.

Until 1961 des Forges and Harber recorded about 17, and there were six more up to 1976. Records have been for April (one), May (nine), June (five), August (one), September (four), and October (three).

WAXWING—*Bombycilla garrulus*
Status.—Irregular winter visitor. No recent change in status is apparent.

Between 1962 and 1976 a total of about 410 Waxwings was recorded in 10 winters. Of these birds over 300 were seen in 1965/66 and about 70 in 1970/71. A party of 130 was seen in 1965/66, when over 200 were present in early December. Otherwise records were for single birds or parties of up to about fifty. Most birds were recorded in east and north Sussex and suburban or village gardens with berry-bearing trees or shrubs were the most usual habitat.

The earliest record was for 14 November, and most birds were seen in November and December, with declining numbers in January and February and a few remaining into March. In both 1965/66 and 1970/71 the last record was for 5 April. There is one other April record for Sussex, of a party of 20 on the Downs near Bramber on 20 April 1941, and the earliest autumn record is of one shot at Littlehampton in October 1898.

A comparison of this account with those of des Forges and Harber and Walpole-Bond leaves little doubt that the pattern of occurrence of Waxwings in Sussex has hardly changed in 200 years.

DIPPER—*Cinclus cinclus*
Status.—Vagrant.

There have been six records comprising seven birds. Three records comprising four birds are undated, except that they occurred about 1821, 1870 (two together), and 1871; otherwise there has been one each for September, November and December. The most recent record was of one near Heathfield on 29 December 1962.

WREN—*Troglodytes troglodytes*
Status.—Abundant resident; probably also passage migrant and winter visitor. No change in status recently is certain, but some increase is possible.

The status of this bird in the past decade was strongly influenced by the winter of 1962/63, which drastically reduced the population. The Woodland Survey (see page 17) then showed a fivefold increase between 1963 and 1974, the population rising steadily throughout the period. The distribution in woodlands suggested by the counts was fairly uniform except on the Downs, where numbers were lower, perhaps reflecting a slower recovery from the 1962/63 winter; the effects of this were in any case uneven. On average during the period of the counts, Wrens comprised from four to eight per cent. of the total populations recorded and were encountered from twice to nine times an hour. It was thus among the 10 most numerous birds recorded and, in fact, counts after 1968 suggested that it may have become our most abundant woodland bird, as it then comprised about 13 per cent. of the total population recorded and was encountered about 12 times hourly.

Outside woodland this is also an abundant and generally distributed species, breeding wherever there is suitable nesting cover. Thus on the few farmland counts available a density of 140 pairs per 2,500 acres (10 sq. km.) was recorded before 1968, and is probably higher today. No statistics are available for other habitats.

Much movement occurs at the coast in the autumn. The Beachy Head records show a regular build-up during September and October, usually to about three times the level of the local population, sometimes more; the highest daily count was 130 on 21 October 1967. The origin of these birds is obscure but, as with some tit species, the bulk of these movements may be of local birds, since there is little evidence of any spring movement, and there are few ringing recoveries; out of 735 Wrens ringed by the Beachy Head Ringing Station up to 1971 the only recovery was of a bird ringed on 7 October 1970 found dead at Aldeburgh, Suffolk, on 6 June 1971. The only other recoveries since 1947 appear to have been of birds ringed in Sussex and recovered in Surrey, Wiltshire, and Warwickshire.

ALPINE ACCENTOR—*Prunella collaris*

Status.—**Four records comprising five birds.**

Two were shot near Lewes about 26 December 1857; one was seen at Seaford Head from 7 to 20 April 1921; one was seen at Rottingdean on 16 March 1922; one was seen on Telscombe Cliffs on 24 April 1955.

DUNNOCK OR HEDGE SPARROW—*Prunella modularis*

Status.—**Abundant resident; perhaps passage migrant. No recent change in status is apparent.**

The Hedge Sparrow is one of our most universally distributed birds, happy to breed almost anywhere with a suitable bush in which to construct a nest. In the Woodland Survey (see page 17) the species was recorded in every site visited and, over the period of the survey, was the tenth most numerous bird noted, comprising on average just over three per cent. of the total bird populations recorded, and being encountered on average about twice hourly. There were marked fluctuations between areas and years, which perhaps stemmed partly from the bird's unobtrusive habits, but the counts also clearly suggest that fewer Hedge Sparrows breed in woodlands on the lighter sandy soils of the greensand and forest ridges than elsewhere.

In farmland it is also a widespread bird, and our few Common Birds Census counts have indicated breeding densities of some 250 pairs per 2,500 acres (10 sq. km.). Very few figures from other habitats are available, but some information on breeding success has been recorded from Sidlesham and Bognor from 1963 to 1965, and Plumpton from 1968 to 1972. At Plumpton in the later period the average brood size in successful nests was 23 per cent. higher, but nest losses through desertion and predation were also much higher at 61 per cent., compared with 20 per cent. at Sidlesham and Bognor. Altogether 124 nests were investigated which produced 185 young, an average production of 1.49 young per nest. Only 51 per cent. of all nests checked were successful, giving an average brood size of 3.08 young per successful nest; average clutch size in 30 nests was 3.65.

Both Walpole-Bond and des Forges and Harber state that this species is a passage migrant in Sussex, particularly in autumn, but more recent records suggest that some, at least, of this passage takes the form of excited jumping up and down near the sea rather than convincing migration, and the true scale of this movement has yet to be determined.

RUFOUS BUSHCHAT—*Cercotrichas galactotes*
Status.—Two records.

One was shot at Plumpton on 16 September 1854. One was seen at the Wicks on 12 September 1951. This record was omitted by des Forges and Harber, but is accepted by Hollom in the *Popular Handbook of Rarer British Birds,* and the B.O.U. Check List for 1968 as a Kent/Sussex record.

ROBIN—*Erithacus rubecula*
Status.—Abundant resident; perhaps winter visitor; partial and passage migrant. Some recent increase of the breeding population is possible.

Robins are abundant and widespread breeding birds in Sussex, nesting wherever there are trees, including urban gardens. The Woodland Survey (see page 17) showed this to be the most numerous woodland bird in Sussex over the period of the survey, being slightly more numerous overall than Blackbirds, except on the chalk, with a rather similar distribution pattern. Thus Robins were, like Blackbirds, more numerous on the heavier soils of the Weald and coastal plain than elsewhere. After 1968 Wrens probably displaced Robins as the most abundant woodland birds, despite a marked increase of Robins, which was apparent between 1969 and 1974.

On farmland this species is far less numerous than either Blackbird or Song Thrush, which suggests a much greater dependence on trees, as opposed to scrub. The few counts available suggest a breeding density of about 145 pairs per 2,500 acres (10 sq. km.).

Although Robins were stated by des Forges and Harber to be winter visitors, it is difficult, in common with many other resident species, to say if this is so on any scale. Ringing recoveries certainly do not suggest it.

There is, however, a good deal of movement. Ringing recoveries suggest that a proportion of Sussex birds may winter abroad. Thus of 13 long-distance recoveries between 1962 and 1975 five birds, including one adult and two juveniles, ringed in Sussex between 21 July and 10 August, were recovered between mid-December and March in France (three), Spain and Portugal. In view of the ringing dates it seems quite likely that these were Sussex birds. Otherwise passage is noted regularly along the coast from September to about mid-November, with most probably moving in October, and spring passage in March particularly, and April. Records from Beachy Head show influxes of up to 100, but more usually 50 to 60, in autumn and up to 45 in spring. Birds showing the characters of the continental race *rubecula* are often identified in these movements.

NIGHTINGALE—*Luscinia megarhynchos*

Status.—Summer visitor to breed; passage migrant. No recent change in status is definitely known, largely because comparative data are lacking, but many observers suspect a decrease.

Although Nightingales breed fairly widely in Sussex, they are not very numerous. Thus between 1968 and 1974 the records suggest a population not exceeding about 500 pairs, and more usually of the order of 300. However, a census in 1976 recorded a total of 664 singing males between 5 May and 6 June in 244 out of *c*. 960 tetrads (2 x 2 km. squares) in the county. About 25 per cent. of this population was found in two of the county's 10km. squares, TQ 02 and TQ 71.

W. Merritt, who has studied the bird in detail, has suggested that distribution may be partly governed by altitude, as the greatest breeding densities occur below 75 metres and very few pairs have been recorded above 120 metres. In addition the 1974 records, involving a total of 217 pairs, showed about 64 per cent. of pairs in deciduous woodland, nearly always neglected and so with a heavy shrub layer, and 36 per cent. in thorn thickets and similar scrub habitats. Another frequent breeding site is on river, stream or pond banks, which are often fenced from livestock, allowing a good growth of scrub to develop.

Very few Nightingales are recorded on passage, when the species is most inconspicuous. Thus at Beachy Head eight in a day is the highest total yet recorded, although the records there show a small spring peak in late April and a similar autumn peak in the second half of August. Extreme dates for Sussex are 2 April (1966, Milton Hide) and 10 October (1947, Handcross).

BLUETHROAT—*Luscinia svecica*

Status.—Scarce passage migrant, regular in autumn but not in spring. No recent change in status is likely.

Although des Forges and Harber only recorded about 34 up to 1961, six in spring and about 28 in autumn, they considered that Bluethroats were possibly regular autumn migrants. Observations at the coast, particularly Beachy Head, have since confirmed this, and between 1962 and 1976 60 were recorded, in April (three), May (two), August (seven), September (39), October (eight), and November (one).

Spring records have been between 1 April (1958, Pett Level) and 27 May, and autumn records between 24 August and

3 November (1968, Selsey Bill). Nearly all records are for the coast, but there are occasional inland records and the species is possibly more regular inland than these reports indicate. Birds are most often seen singly, but up to six have been recorded in one area in a day (20 September 1969, Beachy Head).

Usually Bluethroats cannot be subspecifically identified in Sussex, but males showing the characters of the race *svecica* were obtained near Brighton on 1 October 1862, and at Pett on 11 September 1903, and seen at Beachy Head on 18 May 1975; and three birds showing the characters of the race *cyanecula* have been recorded in April, all in 1958, and four in September, up to the 14th.

BLACK REDSTART—*Phoenicurus ochruros*

Status.—A few pairs breed; winter visitor and passage migrant. No definite change in status recently is apparent.

Although breeding was first proved on the cliffs between Hastings and Fairlight Glen between 1923 and 1925, most pairs now breed in urban areas, so that the population may be under-recorded. However, des Forges and Harber recorded regular breeding after 1945 in Eastbourne, Bexhill, St. Leonards, and Hastings, which may continue, and since 1962 breeding has also been proved at Worthing, Southwick, Brighton, Newhaven, and Beachy Head. Not every site is recorded as occupied annually, and the total population may not be more than 10 to 20 pairs; a total of up to six pairs has been found in the Bexhill and Hastings districts.

A few birds, probably less than 20, also winter along the coastline, but particularly from Shoreham to Newhaven, where as many as seven have been found recently, including four together at Shoreham in 1968/69.

There is a marked movement in spring and autumn. Although recorded all along the coast and sometimes inland, it is best illustrated by the records from Beachy Head, where most are seen. These show marked peaks in late March and mid-October, with a strong secondary autumn peak in early November. Spring passage may continue until mid-May and autumn passage from early September to early November. Recently peak counts of 10 to 20 birds have been made at Beachy Head in both seasons, and 25 were counted there on 19 October 1960. Numbers are usually, but not always, higher in autumn than in spring.

REDSTART—*Phoenicurus phoenicurus*

Status.—Scarce summer visitor to breed; passage migrant.
Numbers have declined steadily since 1965.

An incomplete survey of the breeding population between 1967 and 1969 recorded about 40 to 60 pairs in 1967 and 1968 and showed Redstarts to be thinly distributed along the whole of the northern half of the county. Most breeding pairs were found on the commons from Midhurst north and west to the county boundary, in the forest complexes between Horsham and Worth Priory, and from Ashdown Forest to the county boundary north of Wadhurst. A few pairs may breed occasionally in downland woods. A considerable decline was noted in 1969·when only 22 pairs were found, and the species has not recovered since.

Walpole-Bond's account suggests that regular breeding north and west of Midhurst represents an increase and extension of range since 1938, when he noted Cowdray Park as the only regular nesting site west of Horsham. Numbers in 1976, however, are almost certainly below the 1938 level and the distribution may once again be as he described it. This decline has also been shown in the ringing returns from Beachy Head, which recorded a decline of about 75 per cent. between 1965 and 1974.

Redstarts are still reasonably common passage migrants, however. Spring arrivals usually start in the first half of April, but records for late March are not unusual; the earliest county record is for 18 March (1972, Church Norton). Numbers in spring are usually quite small, daily totals at Beachy Head rarely exceeding 10 to 20 birds. Movement may continue into early June, but the peak occurs in early May. Autumn passage is larger and lasts from early August until mid-October. The Beachy Head records show most movement in late August until mid-September. During this period peak counts of 25 to 50 in a day are regular, although 25 to 30 have been more usual recently; 85 on 12 September 1965 is the highest count so far recorded. Stragglers are often noted in the second half of October, and there are seven November records, up to the 23rd (1968, St. Leonards).

WHINCHAT—*Saxicola rubetra*

Status.—Breeds occasionally; common passage migrant.
Some decline in the number breeding has occurred since
1938.

Walpole-Bond, in 1938, noted a few regular breeding sites on the south side of the Downs between Worthing and Eastbourne, on rough ground near Chichester, and in Ashdown Forest. Since 1947, however, there have been reports of proved breeding in only five years, involving a total of about 10 pairs; there were four pairs in 1949 and possibly three in 1967.

Spring passage usually starts in mid- to late April, records from Beachy Head showing a very consistent first arrival around the 25th. But there are a few records for early April, and the earliest date for Sussex is 17 March (1968, Weir Wood Reservoir). Passage may continue until early June, but numbers are never very large; for example, daily totals of more than 10 are unusual at Beachy Head, and counts of 27 at the Cuckmere on 29 April 1948, 25 at Beachy Head on 9 May 1965, and 38 at Sidlesham on 1 May 1972 were quite exceptional.

In autumn Whinchats are far more numerous. Return movements may start as early as the first week of July and continue until mid-October, with stragglers occasionally as late as mid-November; 17 November (1967, Rustington and 1976 Ovingdean) are the latest county records. Records from Beachy Head show a very marked peak from late August to mid-September, and numbers then may be large. For example, 250 were counted on 30 August 1970 and 300 on 17 August 1971. These figures may be exceptional, but counts of 40 to 100 are annual there and frequent elsewhere along the coast in the same period.

STONECHAT—*Saxicola torquata*

Status.—Scarce resident; perhaps winter visitor; passage migrant. The breeding population has fluctuated in recent years and a long-term decline is likely.

Detailed records of this species' breeding status were gathered almost every year between 1962 and 1975, when annual totals of between 31 and 57 pairs were found. A sharp decrease was recorded after the 1961/62 and 1962/63 winters, followed by a steady increase to 54 pairs in 1969; after this, numbers fluctuated around 45 pairs until 1974, when about 57 pairs were found, and 1975, when nearly 50 pairs were found, but no census of Ashdown Forest was made, indicating a total of over 70 pairs. The main breeding concentrations are now in the Beachy Head area, with up to 20 pairs, and Ashdown Forest, with up to 27 pairs. Otherwise the species is distributed in scattered pairs on gorse brakes on the greensand heaths and East Sussex Downs, and about seven pairs have been found nesting in coniferous plantations, mainly in the St. Leonards/ Worth Forest complex.

Although the Stonechat's breeding distribution in Sussex has thus changed little, the numbers involved have declined considerably since 1938, when Walpole-Bond described it as locally abundant and noted several areas on the Downs as containing 'semi-colonies', one of which was of over 20 pairs. In addition, Alexander (1974) noted a sizable population, possibly as high as 50 to 60 pairs, in the Ashdown Forest area between

1908 and 1916. Breeding in coniferous plantations was not recorded before 1962. Although severe winters have caused marked population fluctuations and may have been the main cause of the decline in Ashdown Forest (where Alexander noted them as more or less resident), there is little doubt that agricultural improvement on the Downs and the afforestation of many commons are the main cause of this long-term decline. A detailed discussion of this species' present status was published in SxBR 1973, 50-56.

The extent to which our breeding birds are resident is not known, but records from Beachy Head show that only about 15 per cent. of the Stonechats nesting there remain to winter and it is unlikely that the proportion is higher elsewhere. A scattered but possibly fairly substantial population winters in open country along the whole coastline, however, and some of these birds may be of our breeding stock.

Some passage also occurs, and passage birds or winter visitors first appear at the coast in September. At Beachy Head regular counts have shown a peak in early October, but this is usually quite small, involving well under 50 birds including local residents; an influx of 60 on 15 October 1971 was quite unusual. Some return passage is often visible at the coast in March.

WHEATEAR—*Oenanthe oenanthe*

Status.—Rare breeding summer visitor; winter vagrant; common passage migrant. The breeding population has declined drastically in recent years and some decline in passage numbers is also likely.

During a survey of the breeding population between 1962 and 1964 only 11 pairs were found on the Downs, while there were about 20 on the shingle areas from Rye Harbour to the Midrips, four on the Crumbles, near Eastbourne, and single pairs at Shoreham Beach and Newhaven Tidemills. None was found elsewhere. Between 1970 and 1972 numbers were rather lower, with up to 15 from Rye Harbour to the Midrips, three on the Crumbles, occasional breeding season records from several other coastal areas, and six pairs on the Downs; the last were nearly all found in 1972, and it is probable that breeding is now only sporadic anywhere on the chalk.

These figures represent a catastrophic decline since 1938, when Walpole-Bond recorded it as one of the typical summer birds of the Downs and quite widely distributed along the coast. Undoubtedly the ploughing-up of most of the Downs coupled with the lack of heavy grazing pressure by sheep and rabbits, which have largely disappeared, and the development of most of the Sussex coast have caused this decline.

A bird wintered at Northpoint Beach, Rye, in 1960/61 and records for 26 December 1948, 30 December 1969, 6 January 1912, and 22 January 1969 seem likely to have been of wintering birds; four February records, up to the 26th, may refer to either wintering birds or very early spring arrivals.

The pattern of migration is well illustrated by the Beachy Head records. These show a marked spring peak in late March, with secondary peaks in late April or early May which are possibly of birds of the Greenland form, *O. o. leucorrhoa*. Spring numbers are never very large, the highest daily count from Beachy Head being about 50 birds, although 70 to 80 have been noted at Selsey Bill in late March or early April. Some spring passage may continue into the first week of June.

Autumn passage is more extensive. The Beachy Head records show movement continuing from the beginning of August until early November. Passage is heavy from mid-August throughout September, with peak numbers in the second half of August. Counts of 100 or more in a day are not unusual in the main period at Beachy Head, and the highest count there so far involved 500 on 17 August 1971, with another 250 on the 23rd. Elsewhere in coastal and downland localities counts of 30 to 100 are regularly made during the main passage, but north of the Downs Wheatears are always comparatively scarce. A few stragglers may occur in the second half of November, and there have been four records for early December, up to the 10th, since 1960.

DESERT WHEATEAR—*Oenanthe deserti*
Status.—Two records.

One was seen at Selsey Bill from 28 October to 8 November 1960; one was seen at Beachy Head from 17 to 21 April 1966.

WHITE'S THRUSH—*Zoothera dauma*
Status.—One record.

One was found dead in a Hove garden on 26 September 1898, after being present there for two or three weeks.

RING OUZEL—*Turdus torquatus*
Status.—Winter vagrant; regular passage migrant. No recent change in status is apparent.

In Sussex most Ring Ouzels are recorded at Beachy Head, where up to 200 have been recorded in a day in early October. Elsewhere it is unusual to see more than one or two together, although parties of up to 20 are sometimes recorded, and there were 100 at the Crumbles on 2 October 1951, and 40 at Bexhill on 22 October 1969. Nearly all records are for the Downs or the coast.

Spring passage is usually small, rarely involving more than about 20 birds in any year. A total of 40 in the spring of 1967 was most exceptional. Most spring passage occurs in April, but movement sometimes starts in late March and continues into early May. Extreme dates are 5 March (1967, Beachy Head) and 29 May (1957, Wicks).

The much larger autumn passage usually starts in late August or early September (earliest date 16 August 1964, Beachy Head) and continues into early November. There are a few records for the second half of this month, and one was seen at Beachy Head on 8 December 1968; several other very late summer visitors were recorded in this autumn. Most autumn passage occurs in September and October, with a fairly well-defined peak in the first half of October. Counts of 30 to 50 in a day are regularly recorded in these months at Beachy Head, and more sometimes occur; the largest counts there so far were of 150 on 2 October 1965, and 200 on 9 October 1966.

There are three winter records of Ring Ouzels: on 2 February 1905 at Mannings Heath, shot; 24 December 1926 at Horsham and 21 December 1969 at Exceat.

BLACKBIRD—*Turdus merula*

Status.—**Abundant resident; common winter visitor and passage migrant. Some recent increase in the breeding population is possible.**

This is perhaps the most abundant and widespread breeding bird in Sussex. In the Woodland Survey (see page 17) it was the second most numerous species over the period of the counts, comprising on average about eight to 12 per cent. of the total bird populations recorded, and noted between four and 11 times an hour; there was a rather wider variation between individual areas and years. The counts suggested very strongly that the species was much more numerous on the heavier soils of the Weald and coastal plain than on the Downs or sand or greensand areas. In areas for which there were three or more counts available a marked overall increase was also noted, mainly between 1968 and 1974.

Elsewhere few data on breeding numbers are available, although some farmland counts suggest a breeding density of about 350 pairs per 2,500 acres (10 sq. km.). But some records of breeding success have been recorded from Sidlesham and Bognor (1963-65) and Plumpton (1968-72). Although the proportion of successful nests was 19 per cent. higher in the first two areas, there was little variation in the average brood size in successful nests. Altogether 439 nests were investigated, which produced 483 young, an average production of 1.1 young per nest (1.75 at Sidlesham and Bognor, and 0.96 at Plumpton). Nest predation and desertion was very high, and only 34 per cent. of nests checked were successful, giving an average brood size in successful nests of 3.2; average clutch size in 76 nests was 3.5. For a comparison between this species and Song Thrush, *see under* that species.

Ringing recoveries show that some Blackbirds are winter visitors to Sussex, for birds ringed in Sussex in late December or January have been recovered in the breeding season in Norway, Sweden and Germany.

There is also a strong autumn passage, which is most marked in October and early November. Visible movements at Beachy Head have often been smaller than those of Song Thrushes, but counts of 150 to 250 Blackbirds in a day have been made in several autumns. A number of breeding season recoveries of migrants ringed in Sussex show these movements to derive from a wide arc of northern and western Europe from Finland to northern France. Return movements are noted in March.

BLACK-THROATED THRUSH—*Turdus ruficollis atrogularis*

Status.—One record.

One was shot near Lewes on 23 December 1868.

FIELDFARE—*Turdus pilaris*

Status.—Common winter visitor and passage migrant. No recent change in status is apparent.

The number of Fieldfares seen always varies annually, and the records show the population to be very mobile. In general, however, more Fieldfares are found in winter (late November to late February) than Redwings, and some measure of abundance may be given by the number of winter flocks of 100 or more reported; between 1967 and 1976 a total of 75 such flocks of Fieldfares were reported, of which 17 were of 500 or more birds, and the largest of 5,000 birds. A preference for open country in the interior was noted by des Forges and Harber, and the permanent pasture of the river valleys and levels is perhaps a particularly favoured habitat.

In severe cold very large numbers are regularly noted, usually moving west along the coast. Movements of 1,000 to 3,000 in a day in such conditions are commonplace; 15,000 moved west over Beachy Head in a snowstorm on 16 February 1969.

Autumn arrival and passage most usually starts in October, although individual Fieldfares are not uncommon in September and there are three August records: 27th 1972 at Littlehampton; 28th 1972 at Southwick; and 30th 1965 on Pevensey Levels. The main movement takes place in October and the first half of November, and movements of up to 500 in a day are an annual event. Curiously, however, the autumn passage is usually smaller than that of Redwings. Spring passage seems less well documented in Sussex, but a marked movement of Fieldfares does occur in March and April, when 1,000 or more have been noted in a day. The latest date for the county is 22 May 1966 on Thorney Island.

REDWING—*Turdus iliacus*

Status.—Common winter visitor and passage migrant. No recent change in status is apparent.

As with Fieldfares, Redwing numbers vary annually and the population is very mobile. In general, however, the winter (late November to late February) population is smaller than that of Fieldfares, with only 33 flocks of 100 or more Redwings noted in this period between 1967 and 1976; although the largest was of 3,000 birds, only six were of more than five hundred. A preference for more enclosed country in the interior was noted by des Forges and Harber, which probably contributes to the disparity between these two species. Certainly I have seen very large numbers of Redwings flushed from dense yew woods on the West Sussex Downs during December.

Very large movements occur in severe cold, usually associated with those of Fieldfares. Movements of 1,000 to 4,000 in a day are then commonplace, and 40,000 Redwings were counted flying west in a snowstorm at Beachy Head on 16 February 1969, and 7,000 in similar circumstances at Eastbourne on 31 January 1972.

The autumn passage of Redwings follows a very similar pattern to that of Fieldfares, although the earliest date is 5 September 1933. Numbers are often much higher than those of Fieldfares, however, with movements of 1,000 or more in a day not infrequent. The largest movements noted so far were of 5,000 at Beachy Head on 19 October 1968, 10,000 there on 12 October 1972, and 4,000 at Brighton on 11 October 1973. Spring passage is much less obvious than with Fieldfares, although movements occur in March and April. The latest date for spring passage is 24 May 1959 at Rye Harbour, but dead Redwings have twice been found in June.

SONG THRUSH—*Turdus philomelos*

Status.—**Common resident, winter visitor and passage migrant. No marked recent change in status is apparent, but some increase in the breeding population is possible.**

Song Thrushes are common breeding birds throughout the county whevever there is suitably bushy nesting cover. The Woodland Survey (see page 17) suggested a gentle increase throughout the period 1963 to 1974, but to some extent this was recovery from the 1962/63 winter. With the present series of unusually mild winters (there was no serious cold spell between 1963 and 1975) some further increase was, perhaps, to be expected; Parslow (1973) linked a decline of this species after 1940 with the increased incidence of severe winters. The distribution in Sussex woodlands indicated by the survey was fairly even but there was a clear suggestion of higher numbers near the coast, which possibly reflects the generally milder climate south of the Downs. There was much individual variation between areas and years, but on average Song Thrushes comprised over five per cent. of the bird population recorded near the coast, and 2.5 to 3.5 per cent. further inland. Altogether the species was about three times scarcer than Blackbird.

Elsewhere the very few farmland counts available indicate a breeding density of about 235 pairs per 2,500 acres (10 sq. km.), and the species is again scarcer than Blackbird, in the ratio of two Song Thrushes to three Blackbirds. Few counts for other habitats are available, but some figures for breeding success have been recorded for Sidlesham and Bognor between 1962 and 1965, and Plumpton between 1968 and 1972. These show very little variation between either the localities or periods covered. Altogether 295 Song Thrushes' nests were examined, which produced a total of 323 young, an average production of 1.09 young per nest. Average clutch size in 40 nests was 3.5, and a very high rate of desertion or predation was recorded, with only 34 per cent. of the nests successful, giving an average brood size in successful nests of 3.2.

There is little information about the numbers which visit the county in winter, although some undoubtedly do so, and marked movements occur in severe weather. But it is interesting that all the ringing recoveries since 1960 indicate either emigration of first-year birds bred in Sussex, or through passage rather than movements of winter visitors, compared with those of Blackbird, which indicate that some birds from northern Europe winter in Sussex.

A very marked movement of Song Thrushes occurs in the autumn, and some return passage is noted in spring. The Beachy Head records show that autumn movements start in late September and are most marked in October and sometimes November; influxes of up to 250 in a day have been noted there in mid-October. It has also been noted there that flocks arriving in November often winter. Spring passage is much smaller and is most often seen in March, when influxes of up to 50 birds in a day have been recorded at Beachy Head.

MISTLE THRUSH—*Turdus viscivorus*

Status.—A widely distributed resident; perhaps winter
visitor and passage migrant. No recent change in status
is apparent.

Although this is a widely distributed species, nesting where-
ever there are suitable trees, and occasionally on such bizarre
places as telegraph poles, it is not particularly abundant. Pairs
breeding in open habitats such as farmland may hold very large
territories—I have records of pairs regularly gathering food
for young over distances of half to three-quarters of a mile
from the nest, suggesting territories of over 250 acres. This
may well lead to over-estimating numbers. In the Woodland
Survey (see page 17) it was by far the scarcest *Turdus* species,
being about three times scarcer than Song Thrush and 10 times
scarcer than Blackbird. Mistle Thrushes were found in every
site visited except one, however, and were fairly evenly distributed, although there was some indication that they were
less numerous on the clay soils of the Weald than elsewhere.
Altogether they comprised on average about 0.5 to 1.5 per
cent., very occasionally up to three per cent., of the total
populations recorded. No change in abundance was suggested
by the counts between 1963 and 1974.

Some movement is recorded at the coast. The Beachy Head
records show two clear peaks. The first, in late July and August,
is probably mainly of birds of the year, as also noted along the
coast by des Forges and Harber; some quite large flocks have
been noted at this time, of which 250 at Cissbury on 28 August
1965 seems to be the largest. At Beachy Head there is a much
larger peak usually in October, sometimes in November, which
has involved influxes of up to 100 birds in a day. At the same
time a few are regularly noted arriving or departing right along
the coast. A similar, but smaller, movement has been noted
in spring, up to early May. There are two foreign ringing
recoveries of birds ringed in Sussex, of a nestling ringed in 1919
recovered in Normandy, France, the following December, and a
juvenile ringed at Marley on 3 August 1962 recovered at Olonne-
sur-Mere, France, on 2 February 1963.

CETTI'S WARBLER—*Cettia cetti*

Status.—Uncertain, but perhaps now a rare resident.

This species is still colonising southern England, including Sussex, and its status is liable to change rapidly. Up to 1976 one pair had definitely bred in West Sussex and breeding may have occurred in another area. Reports that the species is also resident in a third area have yet to be properly substantiated. Otherwise there have been nine records, all since 1962: in May (one), September (three), October (four), and December (one).

SAVI'S WARBLER—*Locustella luscinioides*

Status.—Three records.

One was seen at Selsey Bill from 10 to 18 April 1961; one was seen at the Devil's Dyke, near Brighton on 26 April 1968; one was seen at Beachy Head from 7 to 10 May 1972.

GRASSHOPPER WARBLER—*Locustella naevia*

Status.—Locally common summer visitor to breed; passage migrant. There have probably been marked fluctuations in the breeding population in recent years.

The main breeding habitat of Grasshopper Warblers in Sussex is young forestry plantations, where the species is now widespread. The largest numbers may occur on the West Sussex Downs, where densities of 300 pairs per 2,500 acres (10 sq. km.) of plantation have been recorded. But numbers and distribution in this habitat fluctuate and change as young plantations mature and old ones are felled and replanted. Colonisation of new plantations is quite rapid. A few pairs still breed in gorse brakes on the Downs and similar areas of scrub and common elsewhere, but many such areas are still vanishing to agricultural and other development.

Comparing modern records with Walpole-Bond's account, however, suggests that the species may now be more numerous as a breeding bird than in 1938 and distribution has certainly changed, as Walpole-Bond makes no mention of plantations as breeding habitat and stresses that the East Sussex Downs were the major breeding area; this is no longer so.

Extreme dates are 4 April (1965, Beachy Head) and 1 November (1969, Beachy Head). Movements by this very skulking bird are hard to assess, but records at Beachy Head show larger movements in spring than autumn. Although Quinn and Clement (1971) suggest this is because singing birds are conspicuous in spring, Walpole-Bond's account suggests a similar pattern. In fact he recorded several spring arrivals running into hundreds of birds, including a personal record of about 600 in an 80-acre patch of scrub near Newhaven on 21 April 1922. Most spring passage occurs from mid-April to mid-May and autumn passage from late August to mid-September, but the highest daily count recorded at Beachy Head between 1960 and 1973 was 30 on 30 April 1970.

AQUATIC WARBLER—*Acrocephalus paludicola*

Status.—**Vagrant.**

Until 1961 des Forges and Harber recorded about 11, and between 1962 and 1976 another 11 were reported, nearly all trapped and ringed. All records are for the autumn: in August (eight), September (11), and October (three). Extreme dates are 7 August (1969, Litlington) and 19 October (1853, Brighton).

SEDGE WARBLER—*Acrocephalus schoenobaenus*

Status.—Local summer visitor to breed; passage migrant.
A marked decline in the breeding population recently
is probable.

The breeding distribution of Sedge Warblers in Sussex is very
similar to that of Reed Warblers, but Sedge Warblers are less
tied to *Phragmites* reeds and have recently been colonising dry
habitats such as hedgerows or scrubby areas in arable farmland,
where they may compete with Whitethroats. Breeding season
counts in 1974 in the same areas of West Sussex surveyed for
Reed Warblers (q.v.) recorded about 130 singing Sedge
Warblers, and 196 were counted in Pevensey Levels in 1976
and 80 in the Filsham/Crowhurst area in 1969.

The 1974 counts suggested a catastrophic decline in the
Arun valley since 1966, when 165 singing males were counted
between Burpham and Houghton Bridge, compared with
seven in 1974; there were 26 pairs here in 1976, indicating some
recovery. Although this species can be surprisingly inconspicuous at certain stages in the breeding cycle, it seems likely
that a major decline has occurred here and the ringing returns
from Beachy Head also record a serious decline, of about
60 per cent. since 1971 (Cooper, 1974). The reasons for this
decline are unclear, but there seems little doubt that changes
in the breeding habitat have contributed.

The earliest date for spring arrival is 29 March (1968,
Chichester gravel pits) and a few always arrive in the first half
of April. The Beachy Head records show passage continuing
to late May, with a very marked peak in the first half of that
month, when the bulk of our breeding birds probably arrive.
Autumn passage lasts from early August into early October,
but the Beachy Head records have shown no very clear peak,
although most passage tends to be between mid-August and
mid-September. But numbers seen at such coastal sites are not
large, and probably much under-estimate the scale of passage.
Sedge Warblers are, for example, very numerous in fields of
standing corn near the coast in August, which I have not
observed to be so on my own farm with other common
migrant warblers. At Chichester gravel pits a consistent total

of about 1,100 birds was ringed each autumn from 1965 to 1971, except 1969. Sedge Warblers are not infrequent up to mid-October, and one at Pett Level on 29 October 1961 is the latest for Sussex.

MARSH WARBLER—*Acrocephalus palustris*
Status.—Breeds irregularly; rare passage migrant.

Up to 20 pairs bred annually from 1920 to 1939 but none did so after 1947, until 1966 when four pairs were found in one locality. One or two pairs have bred in the same area since, but not every year.

These records apart, only seven were reported between 1947 and 1976, all on late spring passage between 28 May and 25 June. All these records were supported by details of the characteristic song.

REED WARBLER—*Acrocephalus scirpaceus*
Status.—Local summer visitor to breed; passage migrant. Some recent decline in the breeding population is possible.

The main breeding colonies are near the coast and in the main river valleys and Levels, with a few scattered colonies elsewhere in the interior, mainly at ponds with good emergent vegetation. Breeding season counts in 1974, covering much of West Sussex east to the A24 road, recorded a total of 328 singing males in 30 localities. The main concentrations were found round Chichester and Pagham Harbours and Chichester gravel pits, with a total of 133 singing males, and in the Arun valley north to Greatham Bridge, with 148 singing males. Elsewhere significant counts recently have been made in the Filsham/Crowhurst area, with *c.* 60 pairs in 1969, Pevensey

Levels, with at least 74 pairs in 1976, and between Shoreham and Beeding cement works, with 67 pairs in 1976.

Some recent decline in the breeding population is possible. For example, a total of 93 singing males were found between Burpham and Houghton Bridge in the Arun Valley in 1966, compared with 52 in 1974. Perhaps this reflects a not unusual fluctuation, but this species is very vulnerable to drainage operations and agricultural improvements, which have been actively pursued in many Sussex marsh areas in the past decade. Ringing returns at Beachy Head recorded a marked decline from 1971 to 1973, but some recovery in 1974.

The earliest date for spring arrival is 9 April (1966, Selsey Bill), and a few nearly always arrive in the second half of April. The main arrival, however, is in May, usually in the first half for our breeding birds, but the Beachy Head records show a peak at the end of the month. Passage continues into early June. Autumn passage extends from early August until early October, with a few stragglers into the second half of October quite regularly since 1966; the latest county record is for 2 November (1963, Pagham Harbour). Most movement is from mid-August to mid-September, but numbers seen at coastal watching sites are usually quite small, the highest count recorded at Beachy Head, for example, being 40 birds, compared to about 300 trapped at Chichester gravel pits in one autumn.

GREAT REED WARBLER—*Acrocephalus arundinaceus*

Status.—**Vagrant.**

There are seven records altogether. The first was seen near Rye from 24 May to 28 July 1951. Otherwise there have been three records for May and three for June.

ICTERINE WARBLER—*Hippolais icterina*

Status.—Vagrant or perhaps rare autumn passage migrant.

There have been nine records comprising 10 birds, all since 1965. Two have been recorded in spring, at Church Norton on 7 May 1968, and Beachy Head on 28 May 1967. Otherwise birds have been recorded in August (six) and September (two). All the autumn records except one have been from Beachy Head, where the species may prove to be a more regular passage migrant than the records so far show.

MELODIOUS WARBLER—*Hippolais polyglotta*

Status.—Vagrant.

About 20 have been recorded, all between 1957 and 1976; about five were seen in 1962. One was seen at Beachy Head on 27 and 28 May 1968, otherwise all records are for the autumn, in August (nine), September (nine), and October (one). Extreme dates are 1 August (1973, Beachy Head) and 4 October (1969, Beachy Head).

BARRED WARBLER—*Sylvia nisoria*

Status.—Vagrant in autumn.

Altogether 18 Barred Warblers have been recorded in Sussex, all since 1959, and all but two at Beachy Head. All records are for the autumn between 29 August (1975) and 9 October (1974); two records are for August, 15 for September, and one for October.

GARDEN WARBLER—*Sylvia borin*

Status.—Common summer visitor to breed; passage
migrant. Little recent change in status is apparent.

This species and the Blackcap have a very similar distribution, but the Woodland Survey (see page 17) found that Garden
Warblers were very scarce or absent in woodlands near the
coast and two or three times as numerous in woodlands on
clay soils as on sand or chalk. Altogether they were found to
be about half as numerous as Blackcaps, but on clay soils the
position was reversed.

The earliest date for Garden Warbler is 7 April (1965,
Darwell), but arrival is more usually first noted in late April
and the peak movement at Beachy Head occurs in the second
half of May. Numbers recorded there and elsewhere on spring
passage are small. Autumn passage is much larger. Peak numbers
at Beachy Head usually occur between 11 and 15 August,
and counts of 120 in a day have been made at this time,
although 40 to 75 is more usual. Quinn and Clement (1971)
compared the Beachy Head figures with Davis (1967), and
found that twice as many Garden Warblers passed through
Beachy Head in the autumn as the combined total at Davis'
seven sites (*see* Blackcap) and 10 times as many as at Dungeness
and Portland. The timing of the peak at Beachy Head is, like
that of Blackcap, much earlier than at other main British
observatories and it is likely that Beachy Head provides a
principal departure point for the British population of Garden
Warblers.

Passage continues until early October, with stragglers in
the second half of this month, and one was seen at Beachy
Head on 7 November 1968, the latest county record.

BLACKCAP—*Sylvia atricapilla*

Status.—Common summer visitor to breed; occasional in
winter; common passage migrant. Apart from a possible
increase in the number seen in winter, no recent change
in status is apparent.

The woodland survey showed this species to be widespread in Sussex woodlands and that it was most numerous in woods on the chalk and, perhaps surprising, near the coast. In these areas if formed three to four per cent. of the total populations recorded, compared to about 1.5 per cent. elsewhere. Although there was much variation between areas and years, Blackcaps were noted on average between once and twice an hour, except on the coastal plain where they were nearly twice as numerous. As there is possibly some competition between this species and Garden Warbler, this may reflect the latter species' virtual absence from the coastal plain.

Blackcaps probably now winter regularly in Sussex, and the number doing so is possibly increasing. Thus des Forges and Harber recorded four in December, three in January and six in February between 1947 and 1960, but birds were recorded annually in the December to February period between 1961 and 1976, except in 1964; monthly totals were:

Dec.	Jan.	Feb.
18	20	10

Unlike Chiffchaffs, Blackcaps are infrequently found in one area throughout the winter, but records for the winters of 1961/62 and 1962/63 showed them to be able to survive long periods of intense cold, and birds perhaps move about a good deal.

Considerable numbers pass through the county on migration. The Beachy Head records have shown an interesting pattern, which is discussed in detail by Quinn and Clement (1971). Spring passage is unexceptional, with first arrivals sometimes as early as late March, but more usually mid-April or early May. Numbers are unspectacular, with an average of about 50 birds a season, and this pattern agrees well with other south coast observatories.

Autumn passage, however, is markedly eccentric. Quinn and Clement compared the records with an analysis by Davis (1967) which discussed records from seven British bird observatories: Fair Isle, Spurn, Dungeness, Portland Bill, Lundy, Skokholm and Bardsey. This analysis showed that autumn passage peaked at these stations during October, except at Portland, where numbers were equally high in September and October, and Dungeness, where numbers tended to be higher in September. Davis considered that the October passage involved many continental birds and the September movements at Dungeness and Portland were of British birds emigrating. Quinn and Clement's figures, however, show that eight times as many Blackcaps are recorded at Beachy Head as the combined total for the seven sites discussed by Davis (and 50 times the Dungeness and Portland total), and that there is a marked peak between 16 and 25 September, when daily totals of 100 to 200 birds are regular; in 1976 a total of 1,000 or more was recorded in September, with 400 on the 14th. The conclusion that Beachy Head is one of the main departure points for the British breeding population seems valid.

Quinn and Clement record one other eccentricity. Davis found that, at his seven sites, males exceeded females by about nine per cent.; at Beachy Head ringing results in 1967 and 1970, the only years apparently checked, showed a two per cent. and nine per cent. predominance of females.

WHITETHROAT—*Sylvia communis*

Status.—Common summer visitor to breed and passage migrant. A marked decline has occurred since 1969.

The Whitethroat was probably the most widespread breeding warbler in Sussex, nesting commonly in all types of scrubby habitat, including hedgerows in farmland. In 1969, however, a very marked decline was noted and the species has not regained much ground since. Counts from farmland, down-land scrub, heathland, and the woodland survey all showed a decrease of between 40 and 75 per cent., and breeding numbers now appear to vary much more annually than they did before 1969. In fact the Woodland Survey (see page 17) suggested that the decline may have been under way as early as 1967, when the species comprised, on average, just over three per cent. of the bird populations recorded compared to 0.7 per cent. since.

Records of migration have shown a similar decline. Thus numbers at Beachy Head dropped by about 80 per cent. between 1968 and 1969 and have only partially recovered.

The earliest spring date is 19 March (1966, Southease), but arrival is not often noted before early to mid-April, and the Beachy Head records show the main arrival occurring in the first 10 days of May; movement may continue into June, including arrivals of our own breeding stock. Autumn passage is still extensive despite the considerable decline. Movement is noted throughout August and September and into the first half of October. Peak numbers at Beachy Head are noted in mid-August, when daily counts of 100 are still regular; in both 1967 and 1968 counts of 400 in a day were made at this time. Quinn and Clement (1971) found, as with other *Sylvia* warblers, a much larger autumn passage of Whitethroats through Beachy Head than other main British observatories (*see also under* Blackcap and Garden Warbler). A few stragglers are often noted in late October, and there are five November records, but the latest county record is of one at Darwell Reservoir on 17 December 1972.

LESSER WHITETHROAT—*Sylvia curruca*

Status.—**Common summer visitor to breed and passage· migrant. No recent change is apparent.**

Although distributed throughout Sussex, this species is always less numerous than the Whitethroat and occupies a rather different habitat, preferring taller and denser scrub. Counts for the Common Birds Census in Sussex between 1962 and 1968 showed Lesser Whitethroats to be about one-tenth as numerous as Whitethroats and present in only half the census plots. In the woodland survey they were found in only seven out of the 23 sites visited, compared with 21 for Whitethroats, and nowhere comprised more than 0.3 per cent. of the total bird populations recorded. Thus they were again about 10 times scarcer than Whitethroats.

The earliest spring date for Lesser Whitethroat in Sussex is 7 April (1973, Beachy Head). However, the Beachy Head records show little passage before the end of this month, and movement continues strongly until late May. Spring numbers are quite small, daily counts of more than 10 being unusual at Beachy Head, for example.

An exceptional autumn passage is recorded at Beachy Head, which Quinn and Clement (1971) noted as six to seven times greater than the combined total at the seven observatories considered by Davis (1967) (*see under* Blackcap and Garden Warbler). Movement lasts from early August, sometimes late July, until early, sometimes mid-, October. But the majority pass through between mid-August and early September, when peak counts of 50 to 100 in a day are noted annually at Beachy Head.

One trapped at Beachy Head on 28 October 1971 showed the characters of the race *blythi*. The only later date for Sussex is of one at Burgess Hill from 12 to 21 November 1957.

SARDINIAN WARBLER—*Sylvia melanocephala*

Status.—One record.

A male was present at Beachy Head from 23 August to at least 30 October 1976.

SUBALPINE WARBLER—*Sylvia cantillans*

Status.—One record.

One was seen at Pagham Harbour on 17 May 1961.

DARTFORD WARBLER—*Sylvia undata*

Status.—Rare breeding resident. Birds occasionally occur outside the breeding areas between autumn and spring. The breeding population has always fluctuated markedly.

The incidence of very severe winters has apparently always controlled the numbers of Dartford Warblers breeding in Sussex. The species was regarded as not uncommon in gorse brakes on the Downs from about 1852 until the winter of 1880, when exceptional snow and frost exterminated the population. Walpole-Bond noted that a recurrence of severe winters prevented a full recovery until 1920, but that from then until 1938 it was local, but not particularly rare on the Downs; he remarks that he knew 'places where as many as a dozen pairs live in a reasonably restricted range' as well as sites holding only single pairs, but gives no exact figures.

After 1939 a further series of severe winters combined with losses of habitat by agricultural improvements virtually eliminated the population once again, and none was found between 1947 and 1960, when one or two pairs were located. Surprisingly, this tiny population survived the severe winter of 1962/63, and by 1973 a total of about 23 pairs was known to be breeding in four localities. All these are very vulnerable, and accidental fires destroyed a site in 1968, and another in 1971. Unless steps are taken to try to prevent such carelessness, the species may not survive long as a Sussex breeding bird, irrespective of the incidence of severe winters.

Outside the breeding season Dartford Warblers are occasionally found in areas where they do not breed, particularly along the coast. For example, between 1962 and 1976 there were 14 such records, involving 15 birds, between 19 August and 16 April. Nine of these records were from coastal localities, and one was of a bird which wintered in a Lewes garden from 15 November 1971 to 22 February 1972; overwintering has also occurred along the coast. It is not known if these records represent dispersal of locally-bred birds, but this is possible, since there appears to be some connection between the frequency of such records and the presence of a Sussex breeding population.

WILLOW WARBLER—*Phylloscopus trochilus*

Status.—Abundant summer visitor to breed and passage
migrant. No recent change in status is apparent.

Counts for the Woodland Survey (see page 17) showed this
to be the fourth most numerous species breeding in Sussex
woodlands, and by far the most abundant and generally
distributed warbler. It comprised on average seven to 10 per
cent. of the total bird populations recorded, except near the
coast, where it comprised about five per cent. Numbers varied
widely between areas and years, but the species was most
numerous in rather scrubby woodland and plantations, where
it was encountered up to 25 times an hour, four times the
overall average. No overall change in status was recorded by the
survey. Little information about the Willow Warblers breeding
status is available outside this survey, but it is known to breed
quite commonly in scrub habitats on the Downs, for example,
25 to 40 pairs breed at Beachy Head, and it occasionally breeds
in hedgerows in farmland.

Willow Warblers have not yet been recorded as wintering
in Sussex, and the earliest definite date for spring arrival is
12 March (1967, Beachy Head), although des Forges and
Harber noted that arrival had been claimed as early as 4 March.
First arrivals are more usual at the end of March or early April,
however, and the peak spring movements occur in the second
half of April and early May. The difficulty of separating this
species from Chiffchaffs on migration without trapping is well
known, but the Beachy Head records suggest that many more
Willow Warblers than Chiffchaffs pass through Sussex in spring,
and that the bulk of the movements noted from mid-April
onwards comprise Willow Warblers; unfortunately it has not
yet been possible to demonstrate this satisfactorily by ringing
there, as has been done for the autumn. Counts of 200 to 300
Phylloscopi, mainly or entirely Willow Warblers, in a day are
not unusual at Beachy Head and elsewhere in the peak period,
and 800 were counted at Beachy Head on 15 April 1970. Some
movement of Willow Warblers continues to the end of May.

Autumn passage may start in late July (early date, 16th
1976), and peak numbers pass through in mid-August, when

counts of 200 or more in a day at Beachy Head are regular; 600 were counted there on 8 August 1968. Ringing results at Beachy Head show that the main passage occurs in the comparatively restricted period of August and the first week of September, although some movement continues until the end of the latter month. But these records show that only in the first week of September are there movements involving sizable numbers of both Willow Warblers and Chiffchaffs, and that the large movements of *Phylloscopi* later in September and early October are primarily of Chiffchaffs, which are rather more numerous overall on autumn passage than Willow Warblers. Thus there is an interesting reversal of the spring patterns of these two species.

The latest date for a Willow Warbler in Sussex is probably 9 December 1859, or 26 December 1892 (both said to have been obtained), but there are only two records for November, both for the 3rd, and it is not often identified in October. Thus only two have been recorded at Beachy Head after 30 September, for example.

Birds showing the characters of the northern race *acredula* were stated by des Forges and Harber to pass through the county between mid-April and the beginning of June, and Quinn and Clement (1971) remark that many late May migrants at Beachy Head appear to be of this form.

CHIFFCHAFF—*Phylloscopus collybita*

Status.—Common summer visitor to breed; a few winter; common passage migrant. Some increase in the numbers breeding and wintering has occurred in recent years.

Although widespread in woodland habitats throughout Sussex, Chiffchaffs are less uniformly distributed than Willow Warblers. Thus the Woodland Survey (see page 17) indicated that Chiffchaffs were comparatively scarce in some woods on the greensand and forest ridges, and suggested some competition between this species and Wood Warbler. Everywhere Chiffchaffs were on average two to five times scarcer than Willow Warblers and comprised about two to five per cent. of the total bird populations recorded. Nowhere were Chiffchaffs recorded more than six times an hour; usually less. The counts also indicate a small but consistent increase throughout the period 1963 to 1974. Outside this survey little breeding information is available.

A few winter, and the number doing so is increasing. Assuming that all December, January and February records refer to wintering birds rather than freak migrants, the first record of wintering was for 1875, and the first January record was in 1882, but by 1960 des Forges and Harber could still only list 14 records for December, 18 for January, and 18 for February. Between 1961 and 1976 monthly totals for these months were December, 59; January, 45; and February, thirty-six. Most winter records so far are for localities on or near the coast, and the most regular wintering site is Chichester gravel pits, where one or two are found annually. Single birds are most usual, but four were noted together at Shoreham on 13 January 1961. Although capable of surviving short spells of hard frost, this species seems less hardy than Blackcap, but, like that species, Chiffchaffs may not always stay in one locality throughout the winter.

Although extreme migration dates are confused by wintering birds, some Chiffchaffs often arrive in the first 10 days of March. The Beachy Head records show that the peak spring movements occur in the first half of April, and suggest that thereafter the great bulk of the spring movements of *Phylloscopi* comprise Willow Warblers (q.v.). On autumn passage, however, the pattern is reversed, with more protracted movements and higher overall numbers of Chiffchaffs. Ringing records at Beachy Head show that the main autumn movements of these two species barely overlap, and the peak movements of Chiffchaffs occur in mid-September, with sizable movements well into October. Daily counts of several hundred are not unusual at Beachy Head during the peak periods, and the largest fall there was of 450 on 16 September 1970. Some movements continue into November in most years.

Birds showing the plumage characters of one of the northern races, either *abietinus* or *tristis,* have been recorded as follows:

January (one), February (one), April (one), September (two), October (four), December (one). But on call notes birds of the Scandinavian race, *abietinus,* may, in fact, be regular and quite numerous autumn migrants through the county.

BONELLI'S WARBLER—*Phylloscopus bonelli*
Status.—Three records.

Single birds were seen at Beachy Head on 25 August 1970 and 9 April 1972, and at Alfriston on 7 August 1973.

WOOD WARBLER—*Phylloscopus sibilatrix*
Status.—Summer visitor to breed; scarce passage migrant.
No recent change in status is apparent.

The species' breeding distribution in Sussex is very similar to that of the Redstart, but Wood Warblers are considerably more numerous. Numbers have not been very accurately assessed but records indicating a total of about 150 pairs were obtained between 1965 and 1969, which showed that, as with Redstarts, most Wood Warblers nested in commons and woodlands from Midhurst north and west to the county boundary, with nearly 30 per cent. of this total, in the forests from Horsham to Worth Priory, with 20 per cent. of the total, and from Ashdown Forest east to the county boundary north of Wadhurst, with about 25 per cent. of the total. These figures should not be taken as complete counts, and the remaining records show a wide distribution through woodlands in much of the northern half of Sussex, although there is a clear correlation between breeding pairs and sandier soils, with very few in woods on the heavy clay soils; a few pairs breed on the Downs west of the river Arun.

Very few Wood Warblers are seen on migration. The earliest date is 11 April 1976, and between 1965 and 1976 a total of only about 30 was seen at the coast in the spring, up to 31 May, and 62 in the autumn between 20 July and 16 September; most autumn passage occurs in August, and Beachy Head is the locality which produces most records.

DUSKY WARBLER—*Phylloscopus fuscatus*
Status.—One record.

One was trapped at Beachy Head on 18 October 1974.

RADDE'S WARBLER—*Phylloscopus schwarzi*
Status.—One record.

One was trapped at Beachy Head on 18 October 1974.

YELLOW—BROWED WARBLER—*Phylloscopus inornatus*
Status.—Vagrant, usually in autumn.

Sixteen have been recorded. One was seen at Thorney Island from 10 January to 26 April 1975, and there are two spring records, of one with Goldcrests at Church Norton on 12 April 1971, and one at Westdean from 28 March to 20 April 1975. Otherwise there is one record for September (17th, 1961, at Selsey Bill, first county record), 10 for October, and two for November, up to the 30th. Further observations may show this species to be fairly regular in Sussex in the autumn.

PALLAS'S WARBLER—*Phylloscopus proregulus*

Status.—**Vagrant in autumn.**

There have been eight records comprising nine birds, all since 1968 and at Beachy Head. Birds have been seen between 11 October (1970) and 21 November (1974); five have been seen in October and four in November.

GREENISH WARBLER—*Phylloscopus trochiloides*

Status.—**Four records.**

One was seen at the Crumbles on 10 September 1959; one was seen at Selsey Bill on 27 September 1962; one was seen at the Crumbles on 19 October 1962; one was seen at the Crumbles on 17 September 1965.

GOLDCREST—*Regulus regulus*

Status.—**Common resident and passage migrant. Some recent increase in the breeding population is possible.**

Goldcrests breed widely throughout Sussex, including many suburban areas with suitable trees. Numbers were severely depleted by the 1962/63 winter, but had largely recovered by 1967 and the Woodland Survey (see page 17) suggested an increase of over 500 per cent. between 1963 and 1974, when the species may have been more numerous than ever before.

There is a marked passage in both spring and autumn. Spring passage may last from mid-February until mid-May, but is most usual from early March to mid-April. The numbers involved are comparatively small; for example, counts at Beachy Head rarely record more than 20 in a day; 60 on 29 March 1971 is the highest spring count there so far, although 100 were counted at Pagham Harbour on 26 March 1974. Much larger numbers are involved in autumn, when passage continues from early September to late November. The Beachy Head records show most movement in October, although large numbers are occasionally noted in late September and early November. Peak counts of up to 300 in a day have been recorded in October, and the average peak there from 1965 to 1976 was 130 birds.

FIRECREST—*Regulus ignicapillus*

Status.—Has bred; scarce winter visitor; passage migrant.
The number occurring has increased considerably in
recent years.

A pair was found breeding in 1973, which was the first breeding record for Sussex, and pairs were found in two areas in 1976. There have also been one or two other summer records recently and it seems likely that Firecrests have established a small summer population in the county, or will do so shortly.

Until 1960 des Forges and Harber recorded a total of about 220 Firecrests, mostly on migration, but there were six in winter (December to February) between 1946 and 1960. Wintering records are still scarce, but a total of about 15 to 20 birds was recorded as wintering between 1961 and 1976.

However, there has been a considerable increase of passage birds since 1960, with a total of about 820 recorded between 1961 and 1976, almost equally divided between spring and autumn. This itself is a marked change of pattern, as des Forges and Harber noted significantly more in spring.

Spring passage may start as early as 20 February, but most usually now extends from early March to early May and sometimes as late as 27 May. There is a fairly well-defined peak between late March and mid-April, and totals of about 50 birds were noted in 1968 and 1969, and 70 to 80 in 1974, although the average has been about 25 to thirty. Beachy Head has produced most records, and small parties are not particularly unusual there; 15 on 24 March and 11 on 20 April 1968 are the highest daily counts so far noted there in spring.

Autumn passage has been noted from mid-August to early December, but 65 per cent. of the records are for October. Totals of over 50 birds have been noted in several recent autumns, although the average is not much above twenty-five. As in the spring, most autumn Firecrests are seen at Beachy Head, where 12 on 27 October 1968 and 10 on 26 October 1974 are the highest daily counts so far recorded in autumn, although nearly 50 were ringed there in October 1974.

The increase in spring records appears to date from 1967 and correlated with an extension of the passage period into May; des Forges and Harber recorded none in May compared with a total of 26 between 1961 and 1976. The increase in autumn records was apparent as early as 1958, although it became more obvious after 1967 and has also coincided with a change in the passage period. Thus until 1958, 69 per cent. of all the autumn records were for November, about one per cent. for September and the rest evenly divided between October and December. But between 1959 and 1976 there were four August records, 16 per cent. of the records were for September, 54 per cent. for October, only 23 per cent. for November, and five per cent. for December.

PIED FLYCATCHER—*Ficedula hypoleuca*

Status.—Has bred. Regular passage migrant. Some recent increase in the number occurring is likely.

Single pairs bred near Chichester before 1900 and near the Ouse below Shortbridge about 1905, and a male was present in the interior of the county from 4 May to 8 June 1975, and 7 May to 5 June 1976.

Extreme dates for this species in Sussex are 8 April (1965, Angmering), and 1 November (1968, Beachy Head), but arrival is not usual before mid- to late April. Spring passage is slight, the annual average from 1947 to 1976 being less than 10 birds. The much larger autumn passage usually extends from early August to early October, although movement may start in

July (early date, 13 July 1957, Portslade). Most birds are seen at Beachy Head, where a fairly consistent peak between 21 August and 5 September often involves maximum counts of 15 to 30 birds in a day; 50 on 10 August 1968 is the highest count so far reported there.

Records from the whole county indicate a very marked increase in the numbers of Pied Flycatchers passing through in the autumn. Thus between 1947 and 1960 des Forges and Harber noted an annual average of about 13 birds, but between 1961 and 1976 the autumn average was about 100 birds and may have been higher at Beachy Head alone for some of the period; Quinn and Clement (1971) suggest an average of 140 passing through Beachy Head each autumn. Over 200 were recorded in Sussex in both 1968 and 1975. Since 75 per cent. of all the records come from Beachy Head, where regular watching did not start until 1960, it is very likely that more observation has contributed to this increase. But its scale and the absence of any change in the scale of the spring migration suggests that a change in the species' migration pattern is also involved.

RED-BREASTED FLYCATCHER—*Ficedula parva*
Status.—**Vagrant.**

One was seen at Handcross on 29 April 1948. In the autumn there have been seven records comprising eight birds at the coast between 4 September (1968, Seaford Head) and 21 October (1967, Crumbles). Two were seen together at Beachy Head on 20 October 1968. Otherwise all records have been of single birds.

SPOTTED FLYCATCHER—*Muscicapa striata*
Status.—**Summer visitor to breed: common passage migrant. No recent change in status is definitely known.**

Although this is a widely distributed breeding bird, it is not numerous. In the Woodland Survey (see page 17) it was recorded in 12 out of the 23 sites covered, but even in these it was only found in just over half the years the sites were visited, and usually comprised under 0.5 per cent. of the total bird populations recorded. Possibly Spotted Flycatchers are most numerous as breeding birds round towns and villages with well-established trees and gardens. Even there numbers are known to vary annually, and the records in total suggest much greater annual fluctuations than with other regular breeding summer visitors. Further investigation of breeding status would be worthwhile as some changes may have occurred recently. For example, Walpole-Bond noted Spotted Flycatchers as largely absent from the Downs, even wooded areas, which the woodland survey suggests is no longer true, with birds present in four out of seven such areas visited.

This is usually the last of our regular summer visitors to arrive. The earliest date for Sussex is 8 April (1909, Hastings), but arrival is unusual before the end of April, and most movement occurs in May and sometimes into early June. Some quite large spring arrivals have been noted. For example, Walpole-Bond recorded about 50 together near Portslade on 29 May 1921 and, in 1975, 50 were noted at Beachy Head and 62 at Sidlesham on 18 May; gatherings of up to 20 are quite common in mid-May. Autumn movements may start as early as the end of July, but the Beachy Head records show most movement between late August and mid-September. Fifty on 30 August 1968 is the highest daily count so far there in autumn, and peak counts of 15 to 25 are most usual. Few are seen after September, but stragglers may occur up to mid-October and the latest county record is of one at Beachy Head on 5 November 1975.

BEARDED TIT—*Panurus biarmicus*

Status.—A few pairs breed; scarce winter visitor and passage migrant. A marked increase has occurred in recent years.

The original breeding stock died out about the middle of the 19th century, because of reclamation of its nesting areas. Few details remain about the species' former distribution, but Walpole-Bond listed five probable breeding areas: Amberley Wildbrooks, the Adur Levels near Lancing, Lewes Brooks, Pevensey Levels, and near Winchelsea; it may have also bred at Fishbourne. After a series of irruptions in the 1960s a very small population, totalling less than 10 pairs, has again nested in two areas in the county. Nesting was first proved in 1972, but may have occurred in 1971; it is not yet established annually.

After the original breeding stock died out very few Bearded Tits were recorded until 1959, when the first of what became annual autumn irruptions occurred. The numbers involved have increased over the 18-year period from 1959 to 1976, with very marked peaks from 1964 to 1967 and from 1971 to 1974. The largest numbers recorded were in 1972, when about 120 were seen, but 50 to 80 were noted annually in both peak periods, while fewer than 20 were seen in other years. There seems no doubt that these records are connected with the marked increase in the English, and possibly the Dutch, populations in the same period, and Axell (1966) discussed the eruptive behaviour of this species in detail. There have been five ringing recoveries suggesting a source for our birds. Three, two of them juveniles, trapped at Minsmere in June, July and September 1967 were retrapped on 21 October at the Crumbles; one trapped at Chichester gravel pits on 30 January was retrapped at Minsmere on 23 September 1966, and one ringed at Filsham on 3 November 1973 was retrapped at Kleimeer, Koedjik, Holland, on 28 May 1975.

Well over half the Bearded Tits recorded in Sussex are seen in October and November, and irruptions usually start in early to mid-October, although there are records as early as the first week of September. Perhaps only 25 per cent. of the birds winter here, the records showing a continuous decrease from the end of November to March, and a few remaining into the first half of April.

Most records are for the coast, which simply reflects the distribution of the major Sussex reed-beds. But there are enough reports from the interior of the county to suggest a fairly general distribution within the county in good years. Not all records are from reed-beds, as the species has been recorded at Beachy Head on several occasions, and a wintering party at Chichester gravel pits in 1965/66 spent much time in a large area of rough swampy grassland overgrown with thistles, docks and other tall weeds.

LONG-TAILED TIT—*Aegithalos caudatus*
Status.—**Common resident. Numbers fluctuate considerably with the incidence of severe winters, but no overall change in status is apparent.**

Although the woodland survey recorded them as scarcer than Marsh Tits, Long-tailed Tits are quite generally distributed and probably breed in a greater variety of habitats in Sussex than any of our tits, except Great and Blue. The numbers of Long-tailed Tits fluctuate considerably with the incidence of severe winters, and the most recent, in 1962/63, caused much damage, from which this species probably did not fully recover for at least five years. This has undoubtedly strongly influenced the figures from the Woodland Survey (see page 17).

As with some other tit species considerable activity is noted at the coast in the autumn, although this behaviour is much less evident in the spring. To what extent long-distance movements are involved in unclear, but the absence of significant spring movement may mean that these movements are more in the nature of dispersal than true passage, and there appear to be no ringing recoveries from or in Sussex, although some Long-tailed Tits have been ringed there.

Overall the pattern of tit movements at the coast in Sussex is curious. Of the four species for which regular autumn and/or spring activity of this kind is recorded, only the Great Tit appears to indulge in significant spring movements here, and only this species has provided ringing evidence of overseas movement. Some investigation of these points seems indicated; *see also under* Great, Blue, and Coal Tit.

Birds showing characters of one of the white-headed races of Long-tailed Tit, either *caudatus* or *europaeus* have been recorded as follows: Hampden Park, Eastbourne, two or three on 22 December 1921, and one on 24 February 1922; Handcross, 22 January 1948; Peasmarsh, 19 to 23 November 1949; Iden, 20 March 1952; Bury Hill, 24 August 1958.

MARSH TIT—*Parus palustris*

Status.—Resident. No recent change in status is apparent.

The Woodland Survey (see page 17) suggested that this species might be less common than is sometimes indicated. It was absent from nine out of 23 sites visited, although four of these were near the coast where des Forges and Harber noted that it was scarce, and only in two sites did it regularly comprise more than about one per cent. of the total bird populations recorded. Otherwise Marsh Tits, where present, averaged about 0.8 per cent. of the populations present, and were not often recorded more frequently than once in two hours.

No significant variation in abundance was found between woods on sand, chalk or clay soils, and no marked population changes were noted.

Although the species may breed sometimes in well-treed suburban areas, where it is certainly present in the winter, there is virtually no other detailed information about it outside the woodland survey. Neither the Beachy Head nor Selsey Bill records provide any evidence of movement at the coast.

There is, however, an interesting record of longevity from Possingworth Park, where a juvenile ringed on 29 July 1961 was retrapped in 1962, 1966 (twice), 1969, and finally on 1 November 1970.

WILLOW TIT—*Parus montanus*

Status.—Scarce resident. A fairly marked change in distribution and possibly abundance may have occured in recent years.

In 1963 des Forges and Harber noted that Willow Tits were chiefly confined in the breeding season to wet or water-logged woodlands in the north of the county. This is certainly no longer true and the general records for the county show a fairly general distribution, and in particular that the species is well represented on the chalk, even breeding in scrubby areas (as opposed to woods) such as Beachy Head (where it first bred in 1965), and Lullington Heath. To what extent this just reflects a change in observer activity is unclear, and Walpole-Bond's account is of surprisingly little help. My assessment of the rather scanty information available, however, is that the species has expanded its range quite appreciably in Sussex in the past decade at least.

It is, however, still the scarcest of our breeding tits and in the Woodland Survey (see page 17) was found in only seven out of 23 sites; like Marsh Tit it was absent near the coast. Willow Tits nowhere comprised more than about 0.5 per cent. of the bird populations recorded, and, in fact, were only this abundant in woods on clay soils, where the counts suggested they were two or three times more numerous than elsewhere.

There is no evidence of any movement by this species in Sussex.

COAL TIT—*Parus ater*

Status.—Common resident; possibly winter visitor and passage migrant. No recent change in status is apparent.

The Woodland Survey (see page 17) showed a much more localised distribution for this species than either Great or Blue Tit, with about four times as many Coal Tits in woods on sand soils than those on chalk or clay or on the coastal plain.

With the species' known preference for coniferous woods, this suggests that its Sussex distribution is, in fact, related to some extent to the distribution of mature Scots Pine, which is a feature of many greensand areas particularly. On average Coal Tits comprised about 4.7 per cent. of the bird populations recorded in woods on sand soils, but there was a much greater variation between areas and years than for the other two species. In other woods the numbers of Coal Tits found fell to one per cent. or usually less of the populations recorded.

Outside woodland this species is much scarcer and, although a few breed fairly regularly in some suburban areas, it is probably not a regular breeding bird in farmland habitats. It is, however, more widely distributed in winter, when there is some evidence that in Sussex, as elsewhere, this species is increasingly supported by suburban bird tables.

As with the Blue Tit the Beachy Head records for Coal Tit suggest that movements at the coast are largely an autumn phenomenon; there have been very few spring records at Beachy Head. Thus the autumn records may well refer mainly to comparatively local movements and dispersal. Some longer movements or passage do occur, however, as several birds showing the characters of the continental race *ater* have been identified, including a total of 15 at Beachy Head on 18 September 1969.

GREAT TIT—*Parus major*

Status.—**Common resident; winter visitor and passage migrant. No recent change in status is apparent.**

Great Tits are common and widely-distributed breeding birds, occurring in all habitats with trees, including urban gardens. The Woodland Survey (see page 17) recorded them among the 10 most numerous birds in Sussex woodlands and as the second most numerous tit species. Blue Tits were more numerous, roughly in the proportion of five to three Great Tits, although the difference was greater in some areas. Great

Tits were distributed very evenly, but the counts suggested that they were significantly more numerous in Wealden woods than elsewhere. On average Great Tits comprised four to five per cent. of the bird populations recorded, but the proportion was as high as five to seven per cent. in some areas.

Elsewhere little detail of the species' abundance is available. Although a few counts on farmland indicate a density of about 105 pairs per 2,500 acres (10 sq. km.), this figure is probably meaningless as the species depends on the presence and distribution of mature trees in such open habitat.

Some passage occurs at the coast in most years. Records from Beachy Head have shown most such movement in early spring, particularly March, when westerly coasting movements, which have involved up to 50 birds in a day, are often noted. Curiously little visible passage has been seen in autumn there, in marked contrast to other tit species, but some passage certainly takes place; a pullus ringed at Authsheide Velzen, Germany, in late May 1971, was trapped at Beachy Head in October 1971.

Some Continental Great Tits may well winter in Sussex, in fact, as one showing the characters of the continental race *major* was trapped at Eastbourne on 29 January 1958, one ringed at Shoreham on 12 March 1960 was recovered at Bremerhaven, Germany, on 7 July 1960, and one ringed at Wilmington on 6 December 1963 was retrapped breeding at Brussegem, Belgium, on 15 April 1964. In addition one ringed at Beachy Head on 17 October 1969 and recovered at Brugge, Belgium, on 7 April 1974, and one ringed at Eprave, Belgium, on 31 May 1973 and retrapped at Fairlight on 3 March 1974 were presumably of this race.

BLUE TIT—*Parus caeruleus*

Status.—**Common resident; perhaps winter visitor and passage migrant. No recent change in status is apparent.**

Like the Great Tit this species breeds throughout the county where there are trees, including urban gardens. The Woodland

Survey (see page 17) recorded it as the most abundant tit species, but it was significantly scarcer in downland woods than in those on sand or clay soils or along the coastal plain; in downland woods Great and Blue Tits were thus almost equally numerous. Overall in the woodland survey Blue Tits comprised about five to eight per cent. of the populations recorded, with as much as 10 to 16 per cent. in some areas, making it one of the 10 most numerous woodland birds in Sussex. No evidence of any change of status was revealed by the survey.

In open habitats such as farmland the abundance of this species is, like that of Great Tits, directly related to the presence of suitable trees, and the few statistics available suggest little difference in the abundance of either species.

Some Blue Tit movement occurs at the coast in most years. The Beachy Head records show most movement in autumn, compared to the predominantly spring movements of the Great Tit. Flocks of *c.* 100 Blue Tits have been noted in several autumns at Beachy Head, and peak autumn counts of about this scale are frequent. With little evidence of any marked spring movement these autumn movements seem most likely to refer to fairly local populations. Ringing recoveries certainly indicate that most derive from no greater distance than Kent, Surrey, or Hampshire. But there are recoveries from Devon and Lancashire, and there are four records of birds showing the characters of the continental race *caeruleus,* at Littlehampton on 22 November 1944, found dead, the Rother estuary on 27 November 1957, trapped, Eastbourne on 18 April 1958, trapped, and the Crumbles on 7 October 1959, also trapped.

NUTHATCH—*Sitta europaea*

Status.—Resident. Paradoxically, although its range has apparently expanded in recent years some contemporary decline in numbers seems to have occurred.

The Woodland Survey (see page 17) indicated that this species was well distributed in Sussex woodlands, including those on the chalk. But it was scarce near the coast and very scarce in young plantations, although these often have a scattering of older trees left in their vicinity. Since little very marked difference in numbers was found between woods on sand, clay or chalk soils, des Forges and Harber's statement that it was scarce or absent on the Downs no longer appears true (*see also under* Treecreeper).

Despite much variation between individual areas and years, with figures of nearly six per cent. sometimes recorded, Nuthatches comprised on average about 0.5 to 1.5 per cent. of the total populations recorded. But the counts suggested very clearly that there has been a slow but consistent decline in numbers since 1965. No reason for this is known, and it has occurred at a time when some expansion in range, on the Downs, is also indicated.

This species is rarely seen outside woodlands, but occasionally occurs along the coast outside the breeding season.

WALLCREEPER—*Tichodroma muraria*
Status.—Two records.

One was shot at Winchelsea, apparently in late spring, about 1886; one was seen on Rottingdean undercliff at the beginning of June 1938.

TREECREEPER—*Certhia familiaris*
Status.—Resident. Some increase may have occured in recent years.

Up to 1961 des Forges and Harber noted that this species, like the Nuthatch, was generally distributed in suitable wooded localities in the interior, but scarcer near the coast, and almost absent on the Downs. The Woodland Survey (see page 17) confirmed this distribution, suggesting that woods on the sand or clay areas north of the Downs held about seven times as many Treecreepers as those on the chalk; very few were found near the coast. This is an inconspicuous species and may have been overlooked, but it was recorded as considerably less numerous than Nuthatch, comprising on average 0.6 per cent. or less of the total bird populations recorded, although numbers were up to four times higher in some areas.

In contrast to the Nuthatch (q.v.) a marked increase of Treecreepers may have occurred in the past five years, the counts suggesting a three-fold increase since about 1968. Thus the patterns indicated for this species and Nuthatch in the past 16 years make an interesting comparison. Treecreepers are, however, the more widely distributed birds outside woodlands proper.

There is little evidence of any marked movement by this species, although a few appear at Beachy Head, for example, in most autumns, and one showing the characters of the northern race *familiaris* was trapped at Holywell, Eastbourne, on 27 September 1958.

CORN BUNTING—*Emberiza calandra*

Status.—**Local resident; perhaps partial migrant. Some increase or extension of range by the breeding population has occurred in recent years.**

In Sussex Corn Buntings are primarily Downland birds and the breeding population is mainly concentrated along the whole length of the Downs and the coastal farmlands to their south. They are also now thinly distributed along the coast from Pevensey to Rye and the Kent boundary, an extension of the range in the eastern end of the county noted by des Forges and Harber. The species has always been scarce elsewhere in Sussex, but between 1965 and 1976 territorial males were recorded near Midhurst (four or five), Adversane, Furnace

Green, Chailey North Common, Plumpton, Ashdown Forest, and Hassocks where 15 males were counted in one square kilometre (250 acres) in 1973, an exceptional number north of the Downs. These records suggest some further extension of range, as Walpole-Bond knew of Corn Buntings north of the Downs only in the Parham/Pulborough area, near Billingshurst, and in Ashdown Forst. The present distribution north of the Downs would repay study.

Breeding densities on the Downs vary widely, a point also noted by Walpole-Bond, who described Corn Buntings as 'spottily' distributed. However, numerous counts have been recorded recently, particularly between the rivers Arun and Ouse. These have indicated an average density of 30 to 40 territorial males per 2,500 acres (10 sq. km.), but have ranged from 18 to seventy. Some counts have also been made along downland tracks, recording an average of about three to four territorial males per kilometre, but varying from 1.3 to 12.5. On the coastal plain Common Bird Census counts have suggested a density of about 60 males per 2,500 acres. Comparing modern records with Walpole-Bond's account suggests some westerly extension of range on the Downs since 1938, as he noted Corn Buntings as most abundant east of Shoreham, whereas they are now equally numerous as far west as the Arun.

Walpole-Bond noted that Corn Buntings were equally numerous in cultivated and uncultivated habitats, so that the vast increase of arable farming on the Downs may have had little influence on them. But change in the methods of arable farming may do so. I have noted a strong preference for clover leys as nesting sites on my own farm, and the acreage of such leys sown in Sussex declined by 23 per cent. between 1963 and 1974. Some examination of this point would be worthwhile.

As far as is known our breeding stock is resident and substantial flocks are found from September to April, often at communal roosts. Large roosts in reed-beds have been recorded at Arundel (up to 100), Steyning (up to 500), and Litlington (up to 200). Elsewhere flocks of 100 or more have been recorded recently at Selsey Bill (maximum 350), Beachy Head (maximum 350), Woodingdean (maximum 200), Camber (maximum 120), Rodmell (maximum 100), Shoreham and Pagham (maximum 250). Smaller flocks are regularly noted over the breeding range. Observations at roosts show that birds assemble from a wide area, coming down off the Downs to those at reed-beds, and counts there may provide a simple method of assessing the size of the breeding population.

There have been occasional records of movements at the coast in spring and autumn, but these have involved only a very few individuals.

YELLOWHAMMER—*Emberiza citrinella*

Status.—Common resident; perhaps passage migrant. No recent change in status is apparent.

This is a common species in scrub habitats and woodland edges. In the Woodland Survey (see page 17) it was present in 70 per cent. of the areas visited and was found to be very numerous in young forestry plantations, where it may comprise as much as 10 per cent. or more of the total bird populations recorded. Such plantations may now provide this bird's most important nesting habitat in Sussex, but numbers start to decline once these plantations reach about 10 feet in height, and after 15 years few remain.

Outside the woodland survey information on breeding status is limited. S. W. M. Hughes made counts in 2,320 acres of woodland habitats in north-central Sussex in 1969, and recorded 167 territorial males, indicating an average breeding density of 180 pairs per 2,500 acres (10 sq. km.). But densities varied from about 100 pairs per 2,500 acres to 750 in a conifer plantation about four to eight feet high. The few Common Bird Census counts available indicate much lower densities, of around 75 pairs per 2,500 acres, in farmland with hedges.

In winter Yellowhammers are found in open country in parties and quite large flocks. The records suggest that these are particularly attracted to places where cattle are fed in the open or other farming operations provide spilt or damaged grain as a food source. Flocks of up to 50 seem quite common, and there were eight records of flocks of over 100 between 1965 and 1976, nearly all from the Downs; the largest was of 400 at Ashcombe Farm in January 1975.

As far as is known our breeding birds are resident, but small coasting movements have been noted at Beachy Head in the autumn. Whether these birds are passing through the county or are local birds wandering about is not yet known.

ROCK BUNTING—*Emberiza cia*

Status.—One record comprising two birds.

Two were caught near Shoreham towards the end of October 1902.

ORTOLAN BUNTING—*Emberiza hortulana*

Status.—Rare passage migrant. No recent change in status is apparent.

Until 1961 des Forges and Harber gave about 15 records comprising 18 birds. Between 1962 and 1976 a further 17 were recorded. Altogether birds have been seen in April (three), May (three), June (one), August (four), September (20), October (three), and November (one). The earliest record was for 21 April (1896), and the November record was for the 3rd and 4th 1968 at Beachy Head. All records are for the coast and usually of single birds, but two have been recorded together several times, and a party of four was seen at Seaford Head on 17 September 1961.

CIRL BUNTING—*Emberiza cirlus*

Status.—Scarce resident. A marked decrease has occurred
in recent years.

A breeding survey of this species from 1971 to 1973
recorded a maximum total of 28 breeding pairs from 20 sites.
Most of this population was concentrated in the Cuckmere
valley, with 12 to 15 pairs, at Beachy Head, with five pairs,
and in the Eastbourne area, with four or five pairs. These results
showed a marked decline since the mid-1960s, when about
45 to 50 pairs were known and, in fact, the decline has probably been continuing since at least 1950. Formerly the species
was not uncommon in the coastal plain south of the Downs,
the lower river valleys, downland valleys and some areas at the
foot of the north scarp of the Downs.

Although the reasons for this decline may be partly climatic,
loss of habitat has undoubtedly contributed, with the removal
of overgrown hedges in farmland and the rapid growth of new
housing development around many towns such as Selsey,
Bognor, Steyning, and Alfriston, where the species once bred
in old-established and extensive gardens on the outskirts. A
full report of the survey was published in SxBR 1973, 57-60.

There was a remarkable ringing recovery in 1976 of a bird
ringed at Beachy Head on 22 July 1975, recovered at the
Isle of May in the Firth of Forth on 11 June.

LITTLE BUNTING—*Emberiza pusilla*

Status.—Three records.

One was caught near Brighton on 2 November 1864; one was
caught on the Crumbles in the autumn of 1906; one was seen at
Langney Point on 15 October 1964.

RUSTIC BUNTING.—*Emberiza rustica*
Status.—One record.

One was caught near Brighton on 23 October 1867.

BLACK-HEADED BUNTING—*Emberiza melanocephala*
Status.—One record.

An adult female was shot at Brighton about 3 November 1868.

REED BUNTING—*Emberiza schoeniclus*
Status.—Common breeding bird and passage migrant. Some recent increase of the breeding population is likely, with a spread into new nesting habitats.

Reed Buntings are most numerous in Sussex in the permanent grassland of the river valleys and levels and coastal marshes, where abundant rank marsh and waterside vegetation provides nesting sites. Breeding season counts covering much of the Amberley/Pulborough marshes, Pevensey Levels and Crowhurst marsh between 1969 and 1976, suggested breeding densities of between 40 and 70 pairs per 2,500 acres (10 sq. km.) at Pevensey and Crowhurst, and 105 at Amberley/Pulborough. These densities are probably fairly typical of such habitats. In addition there is a considerable, although scattered, population nesting round lakes and ponds, patches of marsh and damp heathland in the interior.

Recently observers in Sussex, as elsewhere in Britain, have noted a marked expansion into new habitat for nesting. Thus breeding pairs or territorial males have been found since 1965 in young conifer plantations, dry heathland, farmland hedges, standing barley and clover crops, and downland areas with gorse and long grass. Basically the species appears to be moving into more typical Yellowhammer and Corn Bunting habitats, and, at least in the farmland habitats noted, may be competing directly with Yellowhammers for nest sites and food. Not many figures have been recorded to indicate the numbers involved, but S. W. M. Hughes found nine Reed Bunting territories in 1,500 acres (600 hectares) of young conifers in north-west Sussex in 1970, and P. C. Bance recorded 23 singing males in Ashdown Forest in 1971, of which half were in dry localities, and 14 in the gorse areas there in 1974. An interesting point is that gorse figures quite largely as a component of these atypical nesting habitats in Sussex. Quite probably this extension of range has also involved an increase in numbers, but this is not established.

In winter in Sussex Reed Buntings are decidedly scarce and it seems likely that most of our breeding birds leave the county, as suggested by des Forges and Harber. Thus the county files hold only 13 records of winter (November to February) flocks of 20 to 50 birds between 1965 and 1976, and one of 120 on Ashdown Forest, near Fairwarp, on 20 November 1971. But there have been increasing numbers of records of single birds or small parties visiting bird-tables in suburban gardens, another extension of habitat which may prove advantageous to the species.

Despite the annual movements of our breeding stock, autumn passage at Beachy Head seems quite small, mainly comprising coasting movement. A much more marked passage, however, was noted at Selsey Bill between 1963 and 1969. Passage was recorded from mid-September until late November, with most in late September and October. Movements of up to about 50 in a day were noted most years. Coasting movement predominated, accounting for 82 per cent. of the records, and about twice as many moved east as west. But departures out to sea occurred every autumn, comprising 15 per cent. of the total birds noted; very few arrivals were seen. Little visible migration has been noted at the coast in spring, but quite large flocks may appear there in March and April, clearly indicating passage. One or two recent records also indicate that many breeding birds reappear in their nesting sites at the same time; males may arrive first.

LAPLAND BUNTING—*Calcarius lapponicus*

Status.—Rare winter visitor; scarce passage migrant.
The number wintering appears to have declined sharply
in recent years.

Until 1961 des Forges and Harber noted that most Lapland
Buntings were recorded in winter, particularly January and
February. This is no longer so, as the table, showing monthly
totals between 1962 and 1976 illustrates:

Sept.	Oct.	Nov.	Dec.	Jan.	Feb.	Mar.	Apr.
5	17	26	18	8	0	0	1

Apart from the April report, records in this period fell
between 10 September (earliest county record) and 18 January,
but all the January records were for a very cold spell in January
1966. Thus the species is now virtually only an autumn passage
migrant. Despite this change in status little overall change in
the numbers occurring is evident.

Except in 1956 des Forges and Harber recorded between one
and 15 annually between 1947 and 1961, with none in three
years. Between 1962 and 1975 70 were recorded, annual totals
ranging from one to 14, with none in two years. In 1956
exceptional numbers appeared, mainly in the autumn, when a
flock of *c.* 40 stayed at Beachy Head from 27 October to
early December, by far the largest party noted in recent years.

All records of this bird in Sussex are for the coast or nearby,
and all from Brighton to the Kent boundary, except for seven
from the vicinity of Chichester and Pagham Harbours.

SNOW BUNTING—*Plectrophenax nivalis*

Status.—Scarce but regular winter visitor and passage
migrant. No recent change in status is apparent.

Apart from two records for June and one for July, possibly
of injured birds, extreme dates for Snow Buntings in Sussex
are 13 September (1958, Midrips) and 6 May (1962, Pagham).
But comparatively few are recorded before November, and by

far the largest numbers are seen in December, when almost twice as many have been recorded recently as in any other month, and January. The table gives the monthly totals between 1962 and 1976 to illustrate the present pattern of occurrence:

									Average number
Sept.	Oct.	Nov.	Dec.	Jan.	Feb.	Mar.	Apr.	May	per year
2	30	172	535	350	233	68	11	1	81

The table suggests that rather less than half the Snow Buntings seen in Sussex stay for any length of time and that there is a marked passage in December. But I suspect that the pattern may be distorted by variations in observer activity in the winter. Some detailed investigation of the point may be worthwhile. There is no doubt, however, that the bulk of our wintering birds have left by March, and there is no evidence of any through passage in spring.

This is largely a bird of the shoreline in Sussex, and most are seen along the shore between Rye Harbour and the Midrips, where flocks of 100 have been recorded in several years, and flocks of about 30 to 50 are often found. Elsewhere along the coast single birds or parties of up to about 15 are most usual. Occasionally birds have been found along the Downs, including a party of nine at Harting Hill on 2 December 1965, and there are records further inland from the Amberley/Pulborough marshes, St. Leonard's Forest, Ashdown Forest, Darwell Reservoir and Arlington Reservoir.

WHITE-THROATED SPARROW—*Zonotrichia albicollis*

Status.—**One record.**

One was seen at Beachy Head from 19 to 30 October 1968.

BALTIMORE ORIOLE—*Icterus galbula*
Status.—One record.

An adult male was seen at Beachy Head on 5 and 6 October 1962.

CHAFFINCH—*Fringilla coelebs*

Status.—Abundant resident, winter visitor; passage migrant. Some decline in the number wintering is possible, otherwise no recent change in status is apparent.

The Woodland Survey (see page 17) recorded this species as one of the three most abundant and widely distributed woodland birds in Sussex. It was a dominant species in every area visited, which accounted, on average, for about nine per cent. of the total bird populations recorded and was contacted between four and eight times in every hour of counting. There was much variation between areas and years, but no clear trends or habitat preferences emerged, although individual sites held populations of as much as twice the average in some years. Chaffinches are also widespread in farmland, scrub and garden habitats throughout the county, and the few Common Bird Census counts for farmland indicate a breeding density of about 200 pairs per 2,500 acres (10 sq. km.). But this depends very largely on the presence of suitable cover.

As far as is known our breeding birds are resident and sizable flocks are recorded in winter. The records available on this subject are scanty but provide some evidence that winter flocks are more widely distributed than those of the other common wintering finches, with about 40 per cent. of the winter Chaffinch flocks of over 100 birds noted between 1965 and 1976 recorded north of the Downs, reflecting some habitat differences. In general flocks of this species also tend to be smaller than those of the other common species, and flocks of more than 200 are unusual. At least on the farmlands of the coastal plain Chaffinches have declined very much in winter, with the disappearance of the corn-rick and chaff-heap as a source of winter food. This has affected all finches, but Chaffinches have not adapted to other local habitats such as the sea-shore, as have, for example, Greenfinches.

Passage movements are also recorded. In the autumn evidence from regular watching at Selsey Bill and Beachy Head shows that des Forges and Harber's statement that large numbers of Chaffinches arrive in and pass through the county needs qualifying. Work at Selsey Bill between 1963 and 1969 showed that, in most years, movements were quite small, and the Beachy Head records from 1960 to 1970 suggested a similar pattern. But some large movements have been recorded. For example, 400 flew east at Beachy Head on 19 October 1969; 500 departed south from Selsey Bill on 18 October 1968; 4,000 arrived from the south at Beachy Head on 14 October 1971; and 1,000 did so on 8 October 1974. But these records stand out as exceptional. The Selsey Bill records also showed arrivals from the sea to predominate and that easterly movement was more pronounced than westerly. Most movement occurs from mid-October to mid-November.

There is very little recent evidence of any marked spring passage, apart from a movement of 610 east at Rye Harbour on 11 April 1971, although very small movements, including emigration and immigration, have been noted.

BRAMBLING—*Fringilla montifringilla*

Status.—Scarce winter visitor and passage migrant. No recent change in status is definitely known.

In most years the number wintering is very small unless there is a severe cold spell. Thus between 1965 and 1976 only 13 flocks of 50 or more were noted in the period December to February, of which four flocks in the second half of February may have been of birds on spring passage. The largest flocks were four totalling 1,500 birds flying north

over Possingworth Park, Blackboys, on 9 January 1975; 160 at
Little Common on 12 February 1969; 150 at Falmer on
9 February 1975 and 150 in Ashdown Forest in January 1976.
Otherwise records in winter refer to parties of 30 or less, and
frequently ones and twos. Winter distribution is similiar to that
of the Chaffinch.

More are seen in very cold weather. Thus flocks totalling 700
Bramblings were seen on the Selsey peninsular during a very
cold spell in early March 1965 and similar numbers were noted
along the coast in severe cold in January 1966. Cold weather
movements are also noted in these conditions.

The earliest date for autumn arrival is 24 September (1972,
Beachy Head), but autumn movement at the coast is usually
quite small. The Beachy Head records show most movement
in the second half of October or early November, but peak
movements of more than 30 to 50 in a day are rare; an arrival
of *c.* 500 on 10 November 1971 is a striking exception. Some
spring movements are noted in many years, inland as well as
at the coast, especially in March. These records include several
of flocks of 100 or so in the first half of March, and it is likely
that the main spring passage period is from mid-February to
mid-March. Usually very few are seen in April, but there are
old records for May. The latest spring date recently is 28 April
(1969, Beachy Head).

SERIN—*Serinus serinus*

Status.—Vagrant which has bred once. A marked
increase has occurred recently.

A pair bred in Ashdown Forest in 1969, which may possibly
have escaped from captivity. It seems remarkable that this
species should otherwise have bred first here rather than near
the coast, where all other recent birds have been seen and there
is plenty of suitable nesting habitat.

Apart from this record there have been 40 records comprising 53 birds altogether. Of these des Forges and Harber

gave about 13 records comprising 22 birds until 1961, although one at Langney Point on 2 November 1954 was the only report after 1932. One was seen at Selsey Bill on 30 August 1962, and since 1965 Serins have been seen every year except in 1971. Approximate monthly totals from 1965 to 1976 were:

Apr.	May	June	July	Aug.	Sept.	Oct.	Nov.	Dec.
7	10	6	3	1	0	5	3	1

Records fell between 15 April and 3 December and were all for the coast. Half the records were for 1972, when about 12 were seen; otherwise between one and three were noted annually.

GREENFINCH—*Carduelis chloris*

Status.—Common resident; passage migrant. No recent change in status is apparent.

As breeding birds Greenfinches are widespread, but they are probably most numerous in farmland with hedgerows, and gardens, particularly suburban gardens. In the Woodland Survey (see page 17) they were found in only half the sites visited and not always present in those every year. Very little information on numerical abundance is available, but densities of about 120 pairs per 2,500 acres (10 sq. km.) have been recorded on farmland. Our breeding birds appear to be resident.

In winter quite large flocks occur. These are nearly always found along the coast or the Downs; between 1965 and 1976 only four flocks of over 100 were noted north of the Downs, although ringing results suggest the bird is numerous. Flocks often winter on the seashore, where they feed on the seeds of such plants as sea beet, *Beta vulgaris maritima*. On the Downs and probably more widely inland than our records suggest, Greenfinches, in common with other common finches, are often found round kale and mustard fields; in the former they feed particularly on the seeds of knotgrass, *Polygonum aviculare*, and fat hen, *Chenopodium album*, which frequently infest kale. Modern herbicides may eliminate this food source.

Ringing results at Beachy Head have shown very clearly that such flocks are largely composed of local breeding birds and there is no evidence that birds from outside the county winter. Thus counts of winter flocks may give a useful measure of the breeding population.

There are, however, sizable and rather confusing movements at the coast in the autumn. These involve emigration, immigration, and coasting movements. Work at Selsey Bill between 1963 and 1969 showed most movement in October and November, with emigration predominating in October, and coasting movements, usually westerly, predominating in November. On average about 400 were noted emigrating each autumn and 300 coasting. Arrivals never involved more than 15 birds in any autumn. A very small return movement is noted in March and April.

GOLDFINCH—*Carduelis carduelis*

Status.—**Common summer visitor to breed; winter visitor; perhaps passage migrant. No recent change in status is very likely.**

Few data about the breeding status of this species have been recorded, but the Woodland Survey and Common Bird Census counts done in the county indicate a very similar distribution and abundance to the Greenfinch. Goldfinch numbers possibly fluctuate more, as most of the breeding population appears to be summer visitors.

In winter this species is comparatively scarce. Thus between 1965 and 1976 there were only six reports of winter flocks of more than 100 birds for the entire county. Observers have also particularly noted the comparative lack of Goldfinches in large mixed finch flocks on the Downs. Small parties are often present in winter, however, and several observers commented on an increase of such wintering parties in 1972 and 1973. In severe cold small westerly movements have also been noted along the coast. All these winter birds may come from outside Sussex. For example, I have consistently noted in my own area that the few wintering birds have usually left at least a month or more before the first breeding birds return in mid-April.

Without much doubt this bird is most numerous in Sussex in autumn, particularly September and October, when flocks of several hundreds are frequently reported. A substantial autumn passage occurs along the coast. Work at Selsey Bill from 1963 to 1969 showed most movement in October and early November, with a clear peak in the last 10 days of October. Emigration predominated, accounting for over 80 per cent. of the records, but coasting movements to east and west occurred annually, and a very few birds were noted arriving from the south. In the peak period movements of 500 to 1,000 in a day were noted annually; the largest autumn total noted was 4,500 birds in 1968.

Spring passage is much smaller. Our breeding birds start to reappear in early to mid-April, and passage continues through much of May, with a peak in the first half of that month. The Selsey Bill records showed an interesting pattern as, although arrivals were much more numerous than in the autumn, emigration still predominated, accounting for about 59 per cent. of the records. The source of this movement is obscure.

SISKIN—*Carduelis spinus*
Status.—**Common winter visitor and passage migrant. No recent change in status is likely.**

The winter distribution of this species in Sussex closely follows that of the Redpoll, with which Siskins often consort, with parties and flocks found in areas with birch and especially alder, and also coniferous woodlands and hornbeam (des Forges and Harber). Flocks are usually quite small, around 15 to 25 birds, or fewer, but parties of about 50 to 70 are not particularly rare, and four winter flocks of over 100, and three of over 200 were noted between 1965 and 1976; the largest was of 260 at Copthorne on 1 January 1972.

In recent winters there have also been records of Siskins feeding on peanuts at bird tables, including those in suburban gardens. In 1973 S. W. M. Hughes reported that this habit had been recorded from 81 gardens in the county between 1970 and 1973 and was clearly increasing. The birds turned to this food source from January to early April, with most records in March.

A small autumn passage is noted at coastal stations. At Selsey Bill between 1963 and 1969 movement was equally divided between October and November, with arrivals predominating in the latter month; the main trend of coasting movement was easterly. At Beachy Head, where a rather larger movement is noted, the dominant trend of movement is westerly, but arrivals from the sea, and departures out to sea, are noted. Siskins are seen there from mid-September to late November, and the largest numbers usually occur in late September or October. A very small spring arrival is noted between late March and early May.

REDPOLL—*Acanthis flammea*

Status.—**Probably resident; winter visitor; passage migrant. No recent overall change in status is likely.**

In 1938 Walpole-Bond noted that breeding was annual and pairs had been traced 'to many spots in the rough oblong bounded by Tunbridge Wells, Loxwood, Storrington and Heathfield'. Breeding was regular around Midhurst and St. Leonards-on-Sea, and single pairs had occasionally been found elsewhere. More recently comparatively few breeding data have been recorded. But Redpolls still breed in the Midhurst area, and, at least in some years, near St. Leonards-on-Sea. Otherwise the main breeding range appears to have shifted, as most recent breeding season reports have been from localities east of a line drawn from Newhaven to Ashdown Forest. Numbers are difficult to assess. Breeding season reports came from about 29 localities between 1965 and 1975, and included counts of 10 pairs in Brede High Wood in 1972, and a total of 15 to 20 pairs in Ashdown Forest between 1970 and 1973. In this locality numbers are increasing sharply and a minimum of 58 adults was present in the 1975 breeding season, when another 70 were found in the woods around Crowborough and Eridge nearby. A breeding census was started in 1976.

Comparing modern records with Walpole-Bond's account suggests that the species may have increased in the eastern end of the county, with some decline possible in central Sussex. Thus numbers overall may not have changed very much, but this bird is probably under-recorded and a survey of its present breeding status is in progress. It is not known if our breeding birds are resident.

But Redpolls are certainly more numerous and much more widespread in winter, when roving flocks and parties are found particularly in areas with birch or alders. These flocks are rarely very large, the largest usually comprising about 20 to 50 birds, but gatherings of up to 100 to 200 have been reported occasionally.

There is also a marked passage in autumn and spring, which is often noticed inland as well as at the coast. Work at Selsey Bill between 1963 and 1969 showed most autumn movement in October, with more emigration than coasting movement or arrival taking place. Arrivals, however, accounted for a much larger proportion (20 per cent.) of the total Redpoll passage than with Greenfinch, Goldfinch, or Linnet. But Redpoll numbers were quite small, usually totalling fewer than 100 birds in any autumn. Many more are now seen at Beachy Head, where the total numbers seen in most recent autumns has exceeded 500 birds; a total of 2,500 was recorded in 1970, and 2,220 in 1971. In fact, numbers may have remained at a much higher level since 1970 and peak counts of 200 to 300 in a day are made every autumn. Most of these birds are making coasting movements.

Spring passage is quite small, but arrivals or coasting movements may continue well into May, and the Beachy Head records show a consistent peak in the first week of that month.

Most Redpolls seen in Sussex are apparently of the race *cabaret,* but birds showing characters of the race *flammea,* Mealy Redpoll, are sometimes recorded. Thus between 1961 and 1976 there were two at Sidlesham on 19 October, and one at Washington in November 1964, and single birds at Marley on 27 February 1968 and 29 December 1972. At one time such birds were possibly more numerous.

TWITE—*Acanthis flavirostris*

Status.—Winter visitor and passage migrant. A marked increase in numbers has occurred recently.

Although Twite were regarded as regular winter visitors until 1937, des Forges and Harber noted that few were recorded between 1947 and 1956; some recovery was evident by 1961. This recovery has continued strongly and quite large flocks now winter along the coast, particularly around the Selsey/Pagham Harbour and Camber/Rye Harbour areas. In the former area flocks of 30 to 60 winter regularly, and flocks of 50 to 200 do so in the latter. Elsewhere numbers are usually smaller, although sizable flocks may build up anywhere along the coast, for example, there were 70 at the Cuckmere estuary on 24 October 1971, and 50 to 60 at Shoreham in both 1974/75 and 1975/76. Twite are largely confined to the coast in Sussex and in many places feed extensively on saltmarsh plants such as glassworts, *Salicornia sp.* Recently, however, there have been reports away from coastal habitats from Runcton, Mile Oak, Lewes Brooks, Bignor Hill, and Selsfield Common, near East Grinstead, but only the last two are any distance from the sea.

Extreme dates for Sussex are 22 September (1906, Eastbourne) and 19 April (1970, Beachy Head), and monthly totals between 1965 and 1976 show the present pattern of occurrence well. These were:

Sept.	Oct.	Nov.	Dec.	Jan.	Feb.	Mar.	Apr.
1	768	1158	1257	1095	563	188	6

Most arrival takes place in the second half of October, when numbers rapidly build up to the winter level; some through passage may occur in November. Winter visitors start to leave in February, and have virtually all gone before the end of March.

LINNET—*Acanthis cannabina*

Status.—Common resident and partial or passage migrant. No change in the breeding population is apparent recently, but some decline in the number wintering is possible.

Not many breeding data are recorded, but the few Common Bird Census counts available have indicated that this species is common in scrub habitats and farmland with hedges, with densities of about 130 to 140 pairs per 2,500 acres (10 sq. km.) recorded. Much higher densities have been noted in gorse brakes on the Downs, for example, 36 pairs bred on 155 acres of Lullington Heath in 1972. It is probably more abundant in this type of habitat than either Greenfinch or Goldfinch, but Linnets are less generally distributed as hardly any were recorded in the Woodland Survey.

In winter this is still a numerous bird, although the records suggest that, like the Greenfinch, large flocks are most usually found on the Downs or near the coast. Although finch flocks generally are probably under-recorded north of the Downs, they are usually found in arable farmland in winter, and their distribution thus coincides with the main arable areas of the county. In these areas winter flocks of 500 to 1,500 Linnets are not unusual, and kale, mustard, and maize fields appear, in common with other species, to be the most important habitats.

Without doubt, however, Linnets are most abundant in Sussex in the autumn, when there is an extensive passage and sizable flocks are widespread; over 2,000 have been recorded together near the coast. Autumn movements extend from late September to November, sometimes into December, but the main movement is in October with a peak usually in the second two weeks and thus a little earlier than Goldfinch. Work at Selsey Bill between 1963 and 1969 showed emigration to predominate, accounting for 75 per cent. of the Linnet passage; substantial numbers also moved both east and west along the coast, and a few arrived from the south.

The numbers involved are considerably larger than for any other finch and the largest single movement so far noted was of 4,350 leaving Selsey Bill on 15 and 16 October 1966.

Return movements start in March and there is an extensive immigration, accounting for over half the spring passage (*cf.* Goldfinch), in March and April, which peaks in the first two weeks of April. Some emigration is also noted at this time, and a few birds move along the coast.

SCARLET GROSBEAK—*Carpodacus erythrinus*

Status. — Three records.

One was caught near Brighton in the last week of September 1869; one was seen at Beachy Head on 1 October 1974; one was trapped at Beachy Head on 21 October 1976.

PARROT CROSSBILL—*Loxia pityopsittacus*

Status. — One record.

One was shot in St. Leonards Forest in March 1870.

CROSSBILL—*Loxia curvirostra*

Status.—Has bred; probably regular winter visitor, with large numbers in irruption years. No recent change is apparent.

Between 1926 and 1937 between one and eight pairs bred annually in one area. Otherwise breeding was proved in 13 years between 1840 and 1976. It has only been proved recently after a substantial irruption the previous autumn, in 1960, 1963 and 1967 (two pairs), but pairs may have nested in 1964 and 1973.

Crossbills may occur every year in Sussex, although they are not always observed. But outside irruption years the few recorded may well be visitors from neighbouring Hampshire and probably Surrey, where there are regular breeding populations.

Since 1947 the largest irruptions in Sussex were in 1962, when about 400 were recorded, and 1966, when about 800 were seen. After the 1962 invasion Crossbills remained quite widespread in the county for two years, and there was some evidence of fresh arrivals in both 1963 and 1964; only six were seen in 1965.

Most Crossbills are recorded from coniferous woodlands in the interior, in small parties or flocks up to 40 birds. In 1962 200 were recorded together in Friston Forest, the largest flock seen in recent years. In irruption years arrivals and movements are also noted at the coast, where arrivals may start as early as the third week of May, but more usually in late June. Most arrivals probably occur in July or August, but some movement may continue as late as September or October. In other years there is no particular pattern of occurrence except that nearly all records are for the period July to April.

BULLFINCH—*Pyrrhula pyrrhula*

Status.—Common resident. Perhaps also winter visitor and passage migrant. No recent change in status is definitely known.

This is another species for which comparatively few breeding data are recorded. In the Woodland Survey (see page 17) Bullfinches were found in all but three of the sites visited, although not always annually, and there is a clear indication in the counts that considerably fewer are present in woods on sandy soils than elsewhere. The species was nowhere abundant, most usually accounting for well under two per cent. of the total bird populations recorded. In farmland habitats the few Common Bird Census counts available suggest a breeding density of under 50 pairs per 2,500 acres (10 sq. km.).

Although some increase or spread on the downs is possible since 1938 there is little evidence from our counts of any very marked increase of breeding birds in recent years, despite the widely-held opinion to the contrary. Thus since 1963 these counts show no marked population trend at all, and a similar lack of any trend is shown by the ringing results from Beachy Head, where over 500 have been ringed. But there is evidence in the county records that quite large influxes sometimes occur in the autumn and winter. Notes referring to this were received in 1963, 1967, and 1971, and such influxes may easily be more regular than our records show. Newton (1972) shows that the damage Bullfinches do to fruit growing occurs from November to April. Thus any increase of this damage could be connected with an increase of the Bullfinch as a winter visitor, rather than any change of breeding status. Some exact examination of its winter status and movements is clearly needed.

Some autumn movement certainly occurs at the coast. The Beachy Head records show a small influx in late October, usually sufficient to double the resident population, which then remains at this higher level through the winter. Arrivals and coasting movements have also been recorded. An unusually large movement was noted in 1971, when 162 were ringed.

There are few indications of the source of these movements, the only recent ringing recovery being of one ringed at Beachy Head on 24 October 1970, recovered at Epping, Essex, on 8 June 1971.

Our breeding birds are of the form *pileata*. A bird of the northern race, *pyrrhula*, was obtained at Shornden, St. Leonards, on 7 January 1897, and others showing the characters of this race have been recorded from the eastern end of the county.

HAWFINCH—*Coccothraustes coccothraustes*

Status.—Resident; perhaps occasional passage migrant. No recent change in status is known.

The present status of this unobtrusive species in Sussex is not well documented and it is undoubtedly overlooked. However, the records leave little doubt that it is thinly distributed throughout the interior of the county and along much of the Downs. Occasionally small flocks are noted, the largest recently being of about 30 at Flimwell on 26 December 1972, and 20 near Horsted Kenyes on 15 April 1968; Walpole-Bond once saw a flock of two hundred.

Although our breeding birds appear to be resident there are records at the coast in the autumn, especially October, which suggest an occasional passage.

HOUSE SPARROW—*Passer domesticus*

Status.—Abundant resident. No recent change in status is known.

Very little information about this bird is ever received, but it is known to be very numerous around human habitation, particularly farmsteads. There is no very convincing evidence of migration by it in Sussex, although observations at Beachy Head and Selsey Bill suggest that a few get mildly excited about the idea in the autumn.

TREE SPARROW—*Passer montanus*

Status.—Resident; perhaps passage migrant. A marked
increase has occurred in recent years.

S. W. M. Hughes and F. W. Dougharty (1974) described the
changing breeding status of this species in detail up to 1973.
These notes are based on their account. As elsewhere in
southern England Tree Sparrows decreased markedly in Sussex
in the first 40 years of this century. By 1935 Walpole-Bond
knew of only two regular breeding colonies, at Angmering and
East Guldeford, and listed 21 other sites where breeding had
occurred sporadically. By 1961 des Forges and Harber recorded
an increase, with the main breeding population established
along the coast from Pevensey Levels to the Kent boundary.
This increase continued, and by 1973 Tree Sparrows had been
discovered breeding in 155 tetrads (2 x 2 km. squares) of the
county. The figure reproduced from Hughes and Dougharty
illustrates this expansion very clearly.

The size of the breeding population, however, is difficult
to assess. Between 1970 and 1975 there were breeding season
records from 30 to 40 places annually, but the records give
little clear idea of the numbers involved, and Hughes and
Dougharty remark that many observers have not followed
up their observations once the initial discovery of breeding has
been made. They noted, however, that Tree Sparrows apparently first colonised the main river valleys, spreading along them
in both directions once a successful colony was established.
Interestingly they also found that many new sites after 1969
were still associated with water, either ponds or streams.

Winter flocks occur in many places along the Downs and
coast, and rather less frequently north of the downs, although
winter flocks seem more widely distributed than with many
finches. Most Tree Sparrow flocks are of the order of 50 to
200 birds, but larger numbers sometimes occur and the largest
flocks noted between 1970 and 1976 were of 500 at Coney
Hill, Brighton on 17 February, and 400 on the Downs behind
Worthing in January and February 1972, and 400 at Sutton
on 2 November 1975.

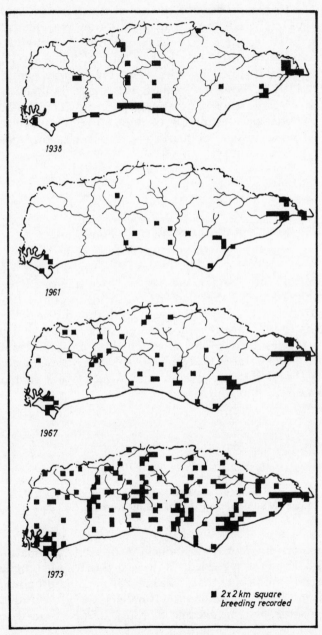

1938

1961

1967

1973

■ 2x2 km square
breeding recorded

Fig. 21.—Tree Sparrow breeding records for Sussex.

Quite extensive movements are noted at the coast in autumn, usually in October. These are mainly coasting movements, and at Beachy Head some very large westerly movements have been recorded recently, of which a total of 5,000 in October 1970, and 2,900 in 1971 have been the largest. Quinn and Clement (1971), however, remark that there is little ringing evidence of large-scale emigration by British Tree Sparrows, and the source and destination of these movements is puzzling. There is no evidence of marked spring movement there or elsewhere in the county.

ROSE-COLOURED STARLING—*Sturnus roseus*
Status.—Vagrant.

Until 1961 des Forges and Harber gave about 18 records comprising 19 birds, the most recent being of one at Pagham Harbour on 13 May 1954. One seen at Eastbourne on 1 December 1970 is the only record accepted since, although reports of this species tend to be disregarded as escapes. However, England (1974) states that this species does not deserve the category 'inevitably an escape' and suggests that immatures are less suspect than adults.

STARLING—*Sturnus vulgaris*
Status.—Abundant resident, winter visitor and passage migrant. Some recent decline in the numbers breeding is possible.

Comparatively few data about the breeding population of this bird are ever recorded. However, the Woodland Survey (see page 17) indicated that it was one of the 10 most abundant species in Sussex woodlands. Numbers varied considerably between areas, but on average Starlings formed from three to eight per cent. of the bird populations recorded. The survey suggested that many more were present in woods on the wealden clay and coastal plain than elsewhere, and also that numbers declined during the period. Thus in eight areas for which there are counts in three or more years total numbers were lower after 1965 than before. In addition very recently nesting numbers have declined in the Selsey peninsular, as many old elm trees have succumbed to Dutch elm disease and been felled. Wherever the elm is the dominant tree this may affect Starlings. Even so Starlings remain abundant and widespread outside woodlands, wherever there are suitable nest sites.

Outside the breeding season very large flocks occur. For example, massive autumn/winter roosts have been recorded recently at Cissbury Ring (up to 50,000), Chanctonbury and Ovingdean (up to 30,000), Lancing (up to 75,000), Pett Level (up to 10,000 in reeds), Upper Beeding (up to 40,000), Barcombe Mills (up to 15,000), Northiam area (up to 20,000), and Itchenor (up to 10,000). No doubt there are other similar very large roosts unrecorded as well as many smaller ones.

Much movement by Starlings is also noted at the coast. In winter severe frosts always cause coasting movements, sometimes involving phenomenal numbers: for example, 90,000 flew west along the coast in two hours at Southwick on 9 December 1967. There is much autumn passage along the whole coast, mainly in October and early November. Arrivals and departures are noted, but the former predominate and sometimes involve several thousand birds in a day. Spring passage is less marked, but also involves arrival and departure at the coast as well as an easterly coasting movement. Most spring passage is in March and April.

GOLDEN ORIOLE—*Oriolus oriolus*

Status.—**Has probably bred. Rare passage migrant, which has perhaps increased recently.**

Despite a number of records suggesting the possibility, there is no proven record of breeding. The most convincing report was of a pair in the north-west of the county in 1965, which almost certainly attempted to breed without success.

Walpole-Bond gave about 90 records between 1807 and 1937, nearly half of them for six years: 1833 (three), 1852 (five), 1853 (six at least), 1866 (10), 1891 (four at least), and 14 seen together by Borrer in an unspecified year. Only two more could be added by des Forges and Harber up to 1960, but since then there have been annual reports, except in 1961, 1972 and 1974, involving a total of 22 birds besides the pair already noted. Records for May (12), June (six), and July (two), and all records were of single birds except for two flying together across Pett Level on 7 July 1970. There are also old records for April, from the 12th, and three for August.

JAY—*Garrulus glandarius*

Status.—**Common resident; possibly winter visitor and passage migrant. No recent in status is apparent.**

The Woodland Survey (see page 17) indicated that this species is widely distributed in Sussex woodlands. It was present in nearly every area visited, but nowhere abundant, usually comprising under two per cent. of the bird populations recorded. The distribution found was remarkably even in the differing types of woodland visited, and there was no evidence of any change in abundance.

Although this is essentially a woodland bird it is quite often recorded in open country in autumn and winter, and sometimes in spring. Some of these are probably local birds wandering about, particularly if the acorn crop is poor, but marked irruptive movements have been noted. The largest such movement in recent years in Sussex was in the autumn of 1957, when parties of up to 20 were noted in several coastal localities in September and October; there was an obvious return movement in the following spring. Otherwise a few coastal records suggest some movement in most years, but there is no real evidence that Jays visit the county in winter on any scale as has been suggested.

MAGPIE—*Pica pica*
Status.—Common resident.

This is another species for which little information is generally received, although des Forges and Harber noted a marked increase as a result of the decline of game preserving in two world wars. Despite the present strong revival in game preservation in Sussex, there is no recent evidence of any change in numbers.

Outside the breeding season quite large flocks of Magpies are sometimes recorded. Thus des Forges and Harber noted flocks of up to 40, sometimes 100, in the spring, and I once recorded a flock of over 200 at Sidlesham in December. There have been no very recent records of such flocks.

NUTCRACKER—*Nucifraga caryocatactes*
Status.—Vagrant.

Until 1946 five were recorded, after which there were three in the autumn invasion into Britain of 1968, and one in 1970. Records have been for August (two), September (one), October (three), November (one), and December (two).

Of these records a bird obtained at Chilgrove on 21 December 1900 was assigned to the race *caryocatactes*, and three, obtained at Litlington on 26 September 1844, Pulborough on 19 October 1913, and Coldwaltham on 16 October 1968, were assigned to the race *macrorhynchos*.

JACKDAW—*Corvus monedula*
Status.—Common resident.

Little information about this species is usually recorded. Walpole-Bond noted that about half of the county population was concentrated on the chalk cliffs up to 1938. Although it is still common there today; for example about 50 pairs breed at Beachy Head, it is not known if this still applies, although I am extremely doubtful. Otherwise the species is numerous wherever there are suitable nesting sites.

Some indication of the size of local populations may be given by counts of roosting flights. Thus flocks of up to 1,000 are regular at roosts in the Eastbourne area, and counts at Watersfield have recorded as many as 2,000, but more usually up to 500, going to a roost in Amberley Wildbrooks. A roost of 1,000 to 2,000 is also regularly noted in Possingworth Park, and roosts of 400 to 500 have been found recently at Ashurstwood and at Coates, near Bignor. Unfortunately, we do not know from how large an area these roosting flocks are derived.

ROOK—*Corvus frugilegus*
*Status.—***Common resident, which has probably declined recently. At present evidence of passage or winter arrival is unconvincing.**

Until 1960 des Forges and Harber noted this as a common and possibly increasing species. They noted that most colonies were of well under 500 pairs, but a few exceeded this number. The only colony of this size for which a record still exists, however, was at Beauport Park, Hastings, and this colony is extinct.

A survey of Sussex rookeries was made between 1972 and 1975 and, in 1975 when well over 90 per cent. of the county was covered, a total of 726 was recorded, containing at least 17,904 occupied nests. W. Merritt, who organised the survey, noted that observers tended slightly to under-count colonies, and estimated the total county population at not more than 19,000 pairs. Most rookeries were of less than 50 nests, but 20 of more than 100 were found, of which two held over 200 nests, and five over 150; the largest rookery found was of 226 nests at Chilgrove. Merritt estimated that the most important nesting trees were oaks (*c.* 35 per cent. of nests), Scots pine (*c.* 30 per cent. of nests), elm (*c.* 15 per cent. of nests), and beech (*c.* 10 per cent. of nests). In parts of the coastal plain the percentage in elms is very much higher, and the high incidence of elm disease there gives cause for concern.

Although the species is widespread in Sussex the survey showed most pairs concentrated in areas with a good mixture of arable farmland and permanent pasture, such as the coastal plain or the river valleys where they breach the chalk, and fewest in heathland or heavily-wooded areas. Thus for example, the 10 km. squares SU 80, SU 90, and TQ 40, each of which is substantially mixed farmlands, each held over 1,000 pairs (total 3,480), while TQ 33 and TQ 62, with substantial areas of woodland, each held less than 120 pairs (total 225); the extreme north-west of the county also holds comparatively few Rooks.

Few comparative data are available to assess population changes, but a census over a substantial part of the Downs between the Adur and Cuckmere rivers in 1945 recorded 4,969 pairs, compared with about 2,895 in the same area in 1975, and 2,900 in 1974. This suggests that some decline has taken place over the past 15 years, which seems to be the national pattern (Parslow 1973). A full report of this survey is to be published in the SxBR.

Although des Forges and Harber noted regular autumn arrivals on the East Sussex coast there have been few convincing records more recently of migration or movements by winter visitors.

CARRION CROW—*Corvus corone corone*
Status.—Common resident.

Very little information about the present status of this species is available, although des Forges and Harber noted a considerable increase during the 1939 to 1945 war. This was apparently connected with the decline in game preserving, an activity which is once again very evident in Sussex. No effect on the numbers of Carrion Crows has been recently recorded as a result, however, and the species is widespread throughout the county.

Although a solitary nesting species, quite large flocks, sometimes of up to 50 or more, are noted in winter, when the tendency to move to the coast noted by des Forges and Harber is still apparent.

HOODED CROW—*Corvus corone cornix*
Status.—Has bred. Scarce winter visitor; probably scarce passage migrant.

A pair bred in Tilgate Forest in 1906, and a Hooded Crow mated with a Carrion Crow in St. Leonard's Forest in 1908.

In winter des Forges and Harber recorded a marked decline of Hooded Crows compared with the late 19th century. About 86 were recorded between 1947 and 1960, with up to five usually noted annually; 30 were recorded in the winter of 1952/53. Between 1961 and 1976 numbers were very similar, a total of about 63 being noted, with an annual average of three or four; eight were recorded in late 1969, including a party of seven at Pebsham, near Bexhill, and again in 1976, and a total of 10 in 1971.

Apart from breeding birds and one which may have summered at Birling Gap in 1948, extreme dates were 24 September (year unknown), and 31 May (1971, Sidlesham and Patcham). Most birds were recorded in November, December and January, and most winter visitors apparently depart in February and March. Since 1961 a total of 13 have been seen in April and May, most of which appear to have been on migration.

RAVEN—*Corvus corax*
Status.—Vagrant, which was formerly a resident.

Walpole-Bond listed all the breeding sites he was able to trace, which covered 18 localities inland and 10 along the cliffs. The inland localities indicated a general distribution in the county, but breeding had ceased inland by about 1880, and by about 1895 along the coast, almost certainly because of constant persecution. Subsequently a pair bred at Seaford Head, and then Beachy Head, between 1938 and 1945, but at least one of these birds had escaped from captivity; a survivor of this pair remained until 1950.

Otherwise Ravens have always been scarce autumn and winter visitors and, since 1946, there have only been nine records, including one which remained at Beachy Head from 10 April to 31 December 1976.

RECENT CHANGES IN THE STATUS OF SUSSEX BIRDS

ANY DESCRIPTION of changes in bird populations in the last 20 or so years must attempt to isolate the effects of a massive contemporary increase in bird-watching activity. In Sussex this has been encouraged by the county Society formed in 1962, which pursues an active programme of field survey work and has significantly influenced patterns of observation.

Thus this increase in activity has two parts, the straightforward rise in the number of observers, and a possibly greater .rise in the volume of systematic observation. The rise in the number of observers may be simply measured by the numbers contributing to the *Sussex Bird Report,* which rose from 63 in 1948 to 149 in 1960, and to 380 in 1976, an increase of 504 per cent. in 28 years. The exact significance of this increase is difficult to assess, but a feature of the more general observations available to us is the amount of duplication involved, with many more repetitive records of the same birds from popular areas such as Pagham Harbour, than original material on numbers and distribution elsewhere.

Thus I have no doubt that in Sussex the increase in systematic observation is far more important. This started in 1959 and 1960, with the Selsey Bill Observatory, and the Beachy Head Ringing Station. Work at these stations has amassed much more detailed information on the migration along the county coastline than was previously available. There has also been a marked increase in the systematic study of habitats and the status and distribution of particular species and groups of species, which has led to a more general study of birds inland in Sussex, which had been neglected in what has proved to be a very important period after 1945 in favour of migration study.

It is possible for some species to measure the effects of these changes on the number of records we receive. Thus at both

Selsey Bill and Beachy Head a record of the time spent watching has been kept which helps to eliminate distortions. And reports of declines are less affected than those of increases, because if the numbers of records received declines as observers increase, then presumably the decline of the species is genuine. Inevitably, however, statements that a species' status has changed are sometimes based on a subjective assessment of the records. Here it is of interest that patterns common to a number of species may emerge, for example a sharp increase in the occurrence of some northern birds since 1967/68.

Despite these difficulties, however, no-one who has watched birds in Sussex continuously over the past 20 years has any doubt that many striking changes have occurred and continue. In the tables I have set out those changes which are well supported by numerical evidence from our records or for which I think there is sufficient information recorded to make them reasonable assumptions, together with the known or assumed causes of change. These lists are not exhaustive and I have excluded some species, such as Little Grebe, Nightjar and Wood Warbler, for which changes are suspected, but for which too few comparative data exist to form an opinion. The Sussex Ornithological Society's survey programme is slowly filling many of these gaps in our information. The tables are divided into residents, winter visitors, summer visitors and passage migrants, although these are rather arbitrary, if convenient, divisions and many species fall into several categories. These notes are also deliberately parochial in character since this is a county avifauna and changes in a species' abundance are not always uniform over its range.

TABLE IX

RESIDENTS.—Total species primarily resident in Sussex in 1975: 83. Changes recorded for 41 = 49 per cent., of which 19 (23 per cent.) have increased and 22 (26 per cent.) have decreased.

Species	Increase or Decrease	Reason
Gt. Cr. Grebe	Increase	New breeding water available.
Heron	Decrease	Long-term pattern; loss of wetlands

continued—

Table IX—*continued*

Species	Increase or Decrease	Reason
Canada Goose	Increase	Continued introductions
Tufted Duck	Increase	Long-term pattern; new breeding waters available
Sparrowhawk	Decrease	Pesticides; possibly increased game preserving
Kestrel	Decrease	Habitat changes on chalk cliffs and arising from changes in agricultural practice, particularly loss of grassland; possibly pesticides
Peregrine	Decrease	Pesticides; possibly also loss of suitable nesting ledges through cliff falls
R. L. Partridge	Decrease	Unclear, perhaps agricultural changes
Partridge	Decrease	Changes in agricultural practice; possibly climatic, damper summers
Water Rail	Decrease	Drainage of fresh marshes
Lapwing	Decrease	Long-term decline; and, recently, changes in agricultural practice
Ringed Plover (breeding population)	Decrease	Increased coastal development and disturbance
Redshank (breeding population)	Decrease	Drainage of wet grasslands
Snipe	Decrease	Drainage of wet grasslands
Woodcock	Increase	Extension of range into new habitat on Downs
Herring Gull (breeding population)	Decrease	Perhaps chalk cliff falls leaving fewer nest ledges
Blk. Hd. Gull (breeding population)	Increase	New colony established in Chichester Harbour
Collared Dove	Increase	Continuing colonisation
Little Owl	Decrease	Not fully known, but changes in habitat possible
Long-eared Owl	Decrease	Not known
Kingfisher	Decrease	Modern river management and pollution
Gt. Sp. Woodpecker	Increase	Not fully known; possibly part of national trend
Woodlark	Decrease	Part of national trend
Grey Wagtail	Increase	Part of national trend; possibly also exploitation of sewage farms for winter feeding
Pied Wagtail	Decrease	Not known
Wren	Increase	Fewer cold winters?
Robin	Increase	Fewer cold winters?
Stonechat	Decrease	Loss of habitat to forestry and farming
Blackbird	Increase	Fewer cold winters?
Song Thrush	Increase	Fewer cold winters?

continued—

Table IX—*continued*

Species	Increase or Decrease	Reason
Goldcrest	Increase	Fewer cold winters?
Willow Tit	Increase	Spread into new habitats
Nuthatch	Decrease	Not known
Treecreeper	Increase	Not known
Corn Bunting	Increase	Continued spread into new areas
Cirl Bunting	Decrease	Loss of habitat to building; climatic change?
Reed Bunting	Increase	Spread into new habitat
Redpoll	Increase	Part of national trend
Tree Sparrow	Increase	Part of national trend
Starling (breeding population)	Decrease	In S.W. Sussex due to elm disease
Rook	Decrease	Agricultural changes; possibly elm disease

In addition the winter status of Teal, Shoveler, Shelduck, Blackcap and Chiffchaff, which all have resident populations, has altered markedly as shown in Table X.

TABLE X

WINTER VISITORS.—Total species primarily occurring as winter visitors in Sussex in 1975: 59. Changes recorded for 26 (44 per cent.), of which 20 (34 per cent.) have increased, and six (10 per cent.) have decreased.

Species	Increase or Decrease	Reason
Rd. T. Diver	Decrease	Perhaps oil pollution
Bl. N Grebe	Decrease	Not known
Slav. Grebe	Increase	Not known
Bewick's Swan	Increase	Perhaps improved summer climate in breeding area
Brent Goose	Increase	Improved summer climate in breeding area
Shelduck	Increase	Not known
Gadwall	Increase	Continued long-term trend; introductions
Teal	Decrease	Drainage of fresh marshes
Shoveler	Decrease	Drainage of fresh marshes
Eider	Increase	Continuing long-term trend
Long-tail Duck	Increase	Possibly as Brent Goose, but numbers may fluctuate more than at present shown
C. Scoter	Decrease	Perhaps oil pollution
Hen Harrier	Increase	Increase in British breeding population

continued—

Table X—*continued*

Species	Increase or Decrease	Reason
R. L. Buzzard	Increase	Not known; perhaps simply fluctuates widely
Grey Plover	Increase	Probably as Brent Goose
Avocet	Increase	? Increase in British Population (*see* Table XII)
Knot	Increase	Probably as Brent Goose, Grey Plover, etc.
Sanderling	Increase	Probably as Brent Goose, etc.
Ruff	Increase	? Re-established British breeding population; possibly as Brent Goose, etc. (*see* Table XII)
Med. Gull	Increase	Continued long-term trend
Great Grey Shrike	Increase	As Brent Goose, etc.
Blackcap	Increase	Continued long-term trend; perhaps feeding at bird tables
Chiffchaff	Increase	Continued long-term trend
Bearded Tit (has bred)	Increase	Increasing and spreading British population
Lapland Bunting	Decrease	Not known, but never numerous
Twite	Increase	Not known

There seems little reason to doubt that the climatic improvement on the breeding grounds, which has so benefited the Brent Geese, has also benefited most other arctic breeding species, so that more than the 10 or so listed here have perhaps increased, although our records are to incomplete to show this.

TABLE XI

SUMMER VISITORS.—Total species primarily summer visitors to Sussex in 1975: 37. Changes recorded for 20 = 54 per cent. of which six (16 per cent.) have increased, and 14 (38 per cent.) have decreased.

Species	Increase or Decrease	Reason
Fulmar	Increase	Part of general increase
Shag	Increase	Not known
Garganey	Decrease	Partly at least due to drainage of fresh marshes
Hobby	Increase	Not known
Little R. Plover	Increase	New colonist
Stone Curlew	Decrease	Habitat loss due to agriculture
Common Tern	Decrease	Human disturbance and predation; coastal development
Roseate Tern	Increase	Not known
Sand Martin	Decrease	Perhaps changes in management of sand-pits

continued—

TABLE XI—*continued*

Species	Increase or Decrease	Reason
Yellow Wagtail	Decrease	Loss of grassland and pasture improvement
Blue-head Wagtail ..	Decrease	Loss of grassland and pasture improvement
Red-backed Shrike ..	Decrease	Climatic; damper summers?
Wheatear	Decrease	Habitat loss due to agriculture
Whinchat	Decrease	Always a marginal Sussex breeding bird
Redstart	Decrease	Climatic change in wintering area; possibly loss of breeding habitat
Nightingale	Decrease	Probably loss of breeding habitat
Whitethroat	Decrease	Climatic change in wintering area; perhaps recovering
Reed Warbler	Decrease	Loss of habitat in main areas of fresh marsh
Sedge Warbler	Decrease	Loss of habitat in main areas of fresh marsh
Chiffchaff	Increase	Not known

Perhaps more of our breeding summer visitors have been affected to some extent by the climatic changes noted under Red-backed Shrike and Whitethroat. Declines are suspected for Nightjars and Wood Warblers, for example, but our records are too incomplete to confirm them. Most of the species listed in Table XI also occur as numerous passage migrants and the changes listed have also similarly affected their status on passage.

TABLE XII

PASSAGE MIGRANTS, VAGRANTS AND RARITIES.—Total species primarily occurring as passage migrants, vagrants or rarities in Sussex in 1975: 164, of which 23 first recorded since 1961. Ignoring these changes recorded for 19 (11 per cent.) of which 14 (8 per cent.) have increased, and five (3 per cent.) have decreased.

Species	Increase or Decrease	Reason
Storm Petrel	Decrease	Not known
White Stork	Increase	Not known
Osprey	Increase	British population increase
Honey Buzzard	Increase	British population increase?
Montagu's Harrier ..	Decrease	Change in British status
Oystercatcher (passage only)	Decrease	*See* note
Avocet (spring passage only)	Increase	*See* note; unlikely to be connected with changes in British population

continued—

Table XII—*continued*

Species	Increase or Decrease	Reason
Ruff (particularly spring)	Increase	*See* note
Grey Phalarope	Decrease	Not known
Great Skua	Increase	Increasing British population
Pomarine Skua	Increase	*See* note; possibly climatic on breeding grounds
Iceland Gull	Decrease	Not known
Mediterranean Gull ..	Increase	Continuing long-term trend
Little Gull	Increase	Increase of Dutch population
Wryneck	Increase	Perhaps re-colonisation of N. Britain and therefore shift in range
Cetti's Warbler	Increase	Extension of range, now breeding
Firecrest	Increase	Extension of range, now breeding
Pied Flycatcher	Increase	Not known
Serin	Increase	Extension of range, has bred

Note.—The changes noted here for Oystercatcher, Avocet, Ruff, and Pomarine Skua seem to be most probably connected with changes in their migration patterns rather than populations.

Thus out of the total county list of 343 species the status of 106, almost a third, has certainly or most probably changed in the past 20 years or so. In addition, other species have shown marked fluctuations over the same period. For example, the Sussex breeding populations of Stock Doves and Greenfinches, among other species, dipped sharply in the late 1950s and early 1960s following the use of some agricultural pesticides; Dartford Warblers re-colonised the county in 1959 after being eliminated for the second time in 70 years by a series of severe winters in the 1940s; Little Terns declined sharply in the 1950s with increasing disturbance of their coastal nesting sites, recovering when nature reserves were created for their benefit, and similar changes are suspected for other species such as Barn Owl.

Marked changes in the distribution of some species have also occurred within the county, without their overall status changing. The Wigeon is a typical example, and when this pattern increases a species' dependence on a restricted habitat, such as estuaries or man-made waters for many wildfowl, it must be considered a potentially damaging change.

I have suggested a total of 19 causes, not all proven, for 87 of the changes listed. Of these four are particularly significant. Eighteen species appear to have been affected by climatic changes here or elsewhere, 19 by changes in agricultural practice including the use of pesticides and the draining of wet grassland, 13 are either new colonists, re-colonists, or have increased British populations, and, for another 13, the recent changes appear to be the continuation of an existing trend, which I have not tried to break down further. Of the remaining 24 species 15 have been affected by man's activities.

Overall the marked changes which have occurred in the appearance of Sussex in the past quarter century have had surprisingly little effect on our birds. Losses by 47 species have been balanced by gains in 59, and 23 new species have been recorded. But there has been a marked change in the structure of the county's avifauna. Increases and declines among resident species are certainly almost equal, but it is mainly the common and more adaptable garden, woodland and farmland birds which have achieved gains, while the more specialised species, particularly those of wetland and coastal habitats, have declined. Together with the decline of 38 per cent., probably more, of our breeding summer visitors, this suggests to me that our breeding avifauna has been considerably impoverished. The marked gains we have seen of winter and passage visitors hardly compensate for this loss, since these have tended to occur in rather limited areas such as our estuaries and favoured coastal sites for migrants.

Furthermore, I am quite sure that the milder winter weather we have experienced since 1963 and particularly 1967 has tended to reduce the impact on birds of the changes in the vegetational structure of our farmlands. The extent to which I, as a farmer, can and do modify this with modern herbicides and changed techniques has yet to be fully appreciated by most bird-watchers. I have long believed that these changes, which must affect birds' food supply, are most likely to reduce their chance to breed successfully. If this is so these changes do not yet appear to have reduced populations largely, I suspect, because of improved survival in the recent run of milder winters. A return to the more frequent severe winters typical of the 1940s and 1950s could see severe and long-lasting reductions in the populations of many common species.

*   *   *   *   *

BIBLIOGRAPHY AND REFERENCES

Regular reference to the basic sources of information about Sussex birds are abbreviated as follows:

Walpole-Bond.

A History of Sussex Birds, J. Walpole-Bond. 1938. Witherby, London.

Walpole-Bond made an extensive literature survey for his book, covering all the main previous sources. Records are discussed fully and even ones the author doubts are included. It is thus a very complete record of Sussex ornithology until 1940 and is a particularly valuable reference for breeding biology.

des Forges and Harber.

A Guide to the Birds of Sussex, G. des Forges and D. D. Harber. 1963. Oliver and Boyd, Edinburgh and London.

Summarises records and status until 1960/61, and thoroughly and carefully edits Walpole-Bond's records. I have used this work as a definitive basic list of Sussex birds.

SxBR.

Sussex Bird Report. Published annually since 1948, first by G. des Forges (1948), then by G. des Forges and D. D. Harber (1949–1955), then by D. D. Harber (1956–1961), then by the Sussex Ornithological Society (1962–). Since 1962 the responsibility for writing these *Reports* rested with D. D. Harber until 1964, M. Shrubb from 1965 to 1971, and C. M. James up to 1976.

The Sussex Ornithological Society maintains a comprehensive filing system to store all the records sent to it for these Reports and gathered during surveys. This is stored at Woods Mill, Henfield, by permission of the Sussex Trust for Nature Conservation. These files now provide a detailed basic source of reference on Sussex birds and may be consulted with the permission of the Society. Since 1963 the *Sussex Bird Report* has included a series of papers on the status of species selected as subjects for survey. These provide the best source of information for these species and are as follows: (the dates given are the year which the *Report* covers.)

Cooper, J. F. 1974. *Bird population trends as shown by ringing.*

Cooper J. F. 1975. *An analysis of spring sea-watches at Beachy Head in Sussex.*

Hollings, M. 1963. *Survey of Sussex woodland birds, a preliminary note.*

Hughes, S. W. M. 1969. *The decline of the Woodlark as a Sussex breeding species.*

Hughes, S. W. M. 1970. *Surveying a breeding population of Swifts.*

Hughes, S. W. M. 1971. *The breeding distribution and status of the Tree Pipit in Sussex.*

Hughes, S. W. M. 1972. *The Canada Goose in Sussex.*

Hughes, S. W. M. 1973a. *An additional note on the Canada Goose in Sussex.* 1973b. *Siskins feeding on peanuts.*

Hughes, S. W. M. 1974. *The distribution of the Stonechat in Sussex outside the breeding season.*

Hughes, S. W. M. 1975a. *The Woodcock in Sussex.* 1975b. *The 1975 census of the Great Crested Grebe in Sussex.*

Hughes, S. W. M. and M. A. Hughes. 1970. *A note on the ecological expansion of the Reed Bunting in N.W. Sussex.*

Hughes, S. W. M. and F. W. Dougharty. 1974. *The recolonisation of Sussex by the Tree Sparrow.*

Hughes, S. W. M. and M. Shrubb. 1973. *The breeding distribution and status of the Stonechat in Sussex.*

Merritt, W., R. R. Greenhalf, and P. F. Bonham. 1969. *A survey of the Grey Wagtail in Sussex.*

Porter, R. F. 1965. *A breeding survey of the Sussex cliffs in 1965.* Counts of breeding populations of Herring Gulls and Rock Pipits.

Porter, R. F. 1966. *The spread of the Collared Dove in Sussex.*

Porter, R. F. 1969. *The continued spread of the Collared Dove in Sussex.*

Shrubb, M. 1964. *Report on breeding bird surveys*. Includes summaries of the final results of surveys of Great Crested Grebe, Stone Curlew and Wheatear.

Shrubb, M. 1967. *The status and distribution of Snipe, Redshank and Yellow Wagtail as breeding birds in Sussex*.

Shrubb, M. 1968. *The present status of the Kestrel in Sussex*.

Wilson, P. J. 1973. *A survey of the Cirl Bunting in Sussex*.

The Hastings Rarities. As noted in the introduction the following references, listed chronologically, probably provide the best available source of information on this subject. Walpole-Bond also includes all these records and much incidental information about them in *History of Sussex Birds*.

Nelder, J. A. 1962. *A statistical examination of the Hastings Rarities*. British Birds, 55, p. 283.

Nicholson, E. M. and I. J. Ferguson-Lees. 1962. *The Hastings Rarities*. British Birds, 55, p. 299.

Harrison, J. M. 1968. *Bristow and the Hastings Rarities Affair*. A. H. Butler, Ltd., St. Leonards-on-Sea.

Nicholson, E. M., I. J. Ferguson-Lees and J. A. Nelder. 1969. *The Hastings Rarities again*. British Birds, 62, p. 364.

Harrison, J. M. 1971. *The Hastings Rarities; further comments*. British Birds, 64, p. 61.

Other sources and references used

Alexander, H. G. 1974. *Seventy years of bird-watching*. T. and A. D. Poyser, Berkhamsted.

Alexander, W. B. 1945. *The Woodcock in the British Isles*. Ibis, 87, p. 512. 1946a. *The Woodcock in the British Isles*. Ibis, 88, p. 1. 1946b. *The Woodcock in the British Isles*. Ibis, 88, p. 159. 1946c. *The Woodcock in the British Isles*. Ibis, 88, p. 271.

Arnold, E. C. 1940. *Bird Reserves*. H. F. and G. Witherby, London.

Atkinson-Willes, G. L. 1963. *Wildfowl in Great Britain*. H.M.S.O., London.

Axell, H. E. 1966. *Eruptions of Bearded Tits during 1959–1965*. British Birds, 59, p. 513.

Brandon, P. 1974. *The Sussex Landscape.* Hodder and Stoughton, London.

Burrows, G. S. 1973. *Ecological Appraisal of West Sussex.* West Sussex County Council.

Campbell, J. W. 1946. *The food of Wigeon and Brent Geese.* British Birds, 39, pp. 194 and 226.

Christian, Garth. 1967. *Ashdown Forest.* Society of Friends of Ashdown Forest, Sussex.

Cohen, E. 1963. *Birds of Hampshire and the Isle of Wight.* Oliver and Boyd, Edinburgh and London.

Davis, P. 1967. *The migration seasons of Sylvia Warblers at British Bird Observatories.* Bird Study, 14.2, p. 65.

England, M. D. 1974. *A further review of the problem of 'escapes'.* British Birds, 67, p. 177.

Friedlander, C. P. 1970. *Heathland Ecology.* Heinemann, London.

Hampshire Bird Report. Published by the Ornithological Section of the Hampshire Field Club. This report includes material from the Hayling shore of Chichester Harbour, which is in Hampshire, not Sussex. Since 1971 these records have also been included in SxBR.

Hastings and East Sussex Naturalist. The journal of the Hastings and East Sussex Naturalists Society. This provides a useful source of information about birds in the eastern end of Sussex. A series is available at Woods Mill.

Hudson, R. 1973. *Early and late dates of summer migrants.* British Trust for Ornithology Guide, No. 15.

Jesse, R. H. B. 1960. *A Survey of the Agriculture of Sussex.* R.A.S.E., London.

Kent Bird Report. Published by the Kent Ornithological Society. This *Report* includes material from the Midrips area and certain reservoirs on the Kent/Sussex boundary. By arrangement most of this material should be duplicated in SxBr.

Ministry of Agriculture, Fisheries and Food. *Agricultural and Horticultural Returns.* Annual Census, 1963–1974.

Newton, I. 1972. *Finches.* Collins, London.

Nolan, M. E. 1971. *Variations in yearly abundance of selected species at Beachy Head as shown by ringing.* The Beachy Head Bird Report. 1960 to 1970.

Offices of Population Census and Surveys. 1949-74. H.M.S.O. London.

Parslow, J. L. F. 1973. *Breeding Birds of Britain and Ireland: a historical survey.* T. and A. D. Poyser, Berkhamsted. Most of the material in this book was originally published as a series of papers in British Birds, 60 and 61.

Prestt, I. 1965. *An enquiry into the recent breeding status of some of the smaller birds of prey and crows in Britain.* Bird Study, 12.3, p. 196.

Quinn A. 1971. *The genus Sylvia at Beachy Head.* The Beachy Head Bird Report. 1960 to 1970.

Quinn A. and P. Clement. 1971. *The Beachy Head Bird Report 1960 to 1970.* Published by the Beachy Head Ringing Group.

Ratcliffe, D. A. 1963. *The present status of the Peregrine in Great Britain.* Bird Study, 10.2, p. 56.

Sharrock, J. T. R. 1976. *The Atlas of Breeding Birds in Britain and Ireland.* T. and A. D. Poyser, Berkhamsted.

Simms, E. 1971. *Woodland birds.* Collins, London.

Southwood, T. R. E. 1961. *The number of species of insects associated with various trees.* J. Anim. Ecol., 30: 1-8.

Tubbs, C. R. 1977. *Wildfowl and Waders in Langstone Harbour.* British Birds, 70, pp. 177-199.

Wooldridge, S. W. and Goldring, F. 1953. *The Weald.* Collins, London.

INDEX OF ENGLISH NAMES

*Those marked * excepted, records of subspecies
are given at the end of the species account.*

INDEX OF SCIENTIFIC NAMES OF GENERA